• HBJ READING PROGRAM •

CROSSROADS

 LAUREATE EDITION

LEVEL 10

Bernice E. Cullinan
Roger C. Farr
W. Dorsey Hammond
Nancy L. Roser
Dorothy S. Strickland

HBJ **HARCOURT BRACE JOVANOVICH, PUBLISHERS**
Orlando   San Diego   Chicago   Dallas

Acknowledgments

For permission to reprint copyrighted material, grateful acknowledgment is made to the following sources:

Atheneum Publishers, an imprint of Macmillan Publishing Company: Adapted text and illustrations from *Making Music* by Arthur K. Paxton and Helen Sive Paxton. Copyright © 1986 by Arthur K. Paxton.

Jeanne Bendick: From *Putting the Sun to Work* by Jeanne Bendick. Copyright © 1979 by Jeanne Bendick.

Bradbury Press, an affiliate of Macmillan, Inc.: From *The Year of the Comet* by Roberta Wiegand. Copyright © 1984 by Roberta Wiegand.

Curtis Brown, Ltd.: Adapted from *How Juan Got Home* by Peggy Mann. © 1972 by Peggy Mann. Published by Coward, McCann & Geoghegan, Inc.

Children's Better Health Institute, Indianapolis, IN: Adapted from "Laugh Yourself Healthy" by Elizabeth Terry in *Jack and Jill* Magazine, June/July 1987. Copyright © 1987 by Children's Better Health Institute, Benjamin Franklin Literary & Medical Society, Inc.

Childrens Press: From *The Mystery of the Rolltop Desk* by Evelyn Witter. Copyright © 1977 by Regensteiner Publishing Enterprises, Inc.

Coward, McCann & Geoghegan, Inc.: Adapted from *And Then What Happened, Paul Revere?* by Jean Fritz. Text copyright © 1973 by Jean Fritz.

Dial Books for Young Readers: Adapted from *The Patchwork Quilt* by Valerie Flournoy, pictures by Jerry Pinkney. Text copyright © 1985 by Valerie Flournoy; pictures copyright © 1985 by Jerry Pinkney.

Aileen Fisher: "Until We Built a Cabin" from *That's Why* by Aileen Fisher.

Harcourt Brace Jovanovich, Inc.: From pp. 15–16 in *HBJ Health,* Revised Edition, Level Orange. Copyright © 1987 by Harcourt Brace Jovanovich, Inc. From pp. 18–19 and 252–254 in *HBJ SOCIAL STUDIES: States and Regions,* Landmark Edition. Copyright © 1988 by Harcourt Brace Jovanovich, Inc.

Harcourt Brace Jovanovich, Inc. and Scott Meredith Literary Agency, on behalf of Arthur C. Clarke: From "Who's There?" in *Tales of Ten Worlds* by Arthur C. Clarke. Copyright © 1958 by United Newspapers Magazine Corporation.

Harper & Row, Publishers, Inc.: "Wind Circles" from *Out in the Dark and Daylight* by Aileen Fisher. Copyright © 1980 by Aileen Fisher. Abridged and adapted from pp. 15–47 in *Childtimes* by Eloise Greenfield and Lessie Jones Little. Copyright © 1979 by Eloise Greenfield and Lessie Jones Little; copyright © 1971 by Pattie Ridley Jones. Published by Thomas Y. Crowell. Complete text, abridged and adapted, and illustrations from *SELF-PORTRAIT: Trina Schart Hyman,* written and illustrated by Trina Schart Hyman. Copyright © 1981 by Trina Schart Hyman. "Lewis Has a Trumpet" from *Dogs & Dragons, Trees & Dreams* by Karla Kuskin. Copyright © 1958 by Karla Kuskin. Abridged and adapted from Chapters 3–10 in *From Anna* (Retitled: "Anna's New Beginning") by Jean Little. Copyright © 1972 by Jean Little. Abridged and adapted from pp. 14–33 in *Me and My Family Tree* by Paul Showers. Copyright © 1978 by Paul Showers. Published by Thomas Y. Crowell. Slightly adapted from *My Robot Buddy* by Alfred Slote. Text copyright © 1975 by Alfred Slote. Published by J.B. Lippincott.

Harper & Row, Publishers, Inc. and Virginia Kidd Literary Agency: Adapted from Chapters 1 and 3 in *The Fallen Spaceman* by Lee Harding. Copyright © 1973, 1980 by Lee Harding.

Highlights for Children, Inc., Columbus, OH: "Just Because I'm Left-Handed" by Linda McCollum Brown from *Highlights for Children,* April 1984. Copyright © 1984 by Highlights for Children, Inc. "Ballet Is for Everyone" by Susanne Banta Harper from *Highlights for Children,* March 1985. Copyright © 1985 by Highlights for Children, Inc. "Jennie's Horse, Jennie's Pony" by Deborah Ellison Hocking from *Highlights for Children,* July–August 1986. Copyright © 1986 by Highlights for Children, Inc.

Houghton Mifflin Company: Abridged from *Help! I'm a Prisoner in the Library* by Eth Clifford. Copyright © 1979 by Ethel Clifford Rosenberg.

James Houston: From *Songs of the Dream People* (Titled: "A Central Eskimo Chant"), selected and edited by James Houston. Copyright © 1972 by James Houston.

Barbara A. Huff: "The Library" by Barbara A. Huff. Copyright © 1972 by Barbara A. Huff.

Alfred A. Knopf, Inc.: From *The Queen Who Couldn't Bake Gingerbread: An Adaptation of a German Folk Tale* (Titled: "The Queen Who Couldn't Bake Gingerbread") by Dorothy Van Woerkom. Copyright © 1975 by Dorothy Van Woerkom.

Little, Brown and Company, in association with The Atlantic Monthly Press: From pp. 15–48 in *McBroom Tells the Truth* by Sid Fleischman. Copyright © 1966 by Sid Fleischman.

Macmillan Publishing Company: "Roads" from *Poems* by Rachel Field. Published by Macmillan, New York, 1957. From pp. 114–115 in *Good Health for You,* 4, by John T. Fodor, Lennin H. Glass, and Ben C. Gmur. Copyright © 1983 by Laidlaw Brothers, Publishers.

McIntosh and Otis, Inc.: From *Dvora's Journey* by Marge Blaine. Copyright © 1979 by Marge Blaine. Published by Holt, Rinehart and Winston.

Merrill Publishing Company: From pp. 88–89 in *Accent on Science* by Dr. Robert B. Sund et al. Copyright 1985, 1983, 1980 by Bell & Howell Company.

Monday Morning Books, Inc.: "The Talking Computer" by Murray Suid in *The Teacher-Friendly Computer Book.* Published by Monday Morning Books, Inc., 1984.

William Morrow & Company, Inc.: Abridged text, and illustrations from pp. 13, 83, and 118, in *Dear Mr. Henshaw* by Beverly Cleary, illustrated by Paul O. Zelinsky. Copyright © 1983 by Beverly Cleary.

National Wildlife Federation: From "Those Weird Wagners" by Bonnie Bisbee in *Ranger Rick* Magazine, December 1984, Vol. 18, No. 12. Copyright © 1984 by the National Wildlife Federation.

G. P. Putnam's Sons: "The Snow Has Come at Last," a Navaho poem, from *The Turquoise Horse, Prose & Poetry of the American Indian,* selected by Flora Hood. Text © 1972 by Flora Hood.

Random House, Inc.: Adapted from pp. 37–47 in *The Black Stallion* by Walter Farley. Copyright 1941, renewed 1969 by Walter Farley.

Marian Reiner, on behalf of Eve Merriam: "Which Washington?" from *There Is No Rhyme for Silver* by Eve Merriam. Copyright © 1962 by Eve Merriam. All rights reserved.

Marian Reiner, on behalf of Lilian Moore: "Telling Time" from *Think of Shadows* by Lilian Moore. Text copyright © 1975, 1980 by Lilian Moore. All rights reserved.

Scholastic Inc.: Adapted from *The Riddle of the Drum* by Verna Aardema. Text copyright © 1979 by Verna Aardema.

Charles Scribner's Sons, a division of Macmillan, Inc.: Adapted from *The Best Town in the World* by Byrd Baylor. Copyright © 1982 by Byrd Baylor.

Viking Penguin Inc.: Adapted from *The Midnight Fox* by Betsy Byars. Copyright © 1968 by Betsy Byars. Adapted from *Trouble River* by Betsy Byars. Copyright © 1969 by Betsy Byars. From *The Boy Who Loved Music* (Retitled: "A Farewell to Music") by David Lasker, illustrated by Joe Lasker. Copyright © 1979 by David Lasker and Joe Lasker. Adapted from "The Night Sky" (Retitled: "Einstein Anderson and the Night Sky") in *Einstein Anderson Makes Up for Lost Time* by Seymour Simon. Copyright © 1981 by Seymour Simon.

Albert Whitman & Company: From *Making Room for Uncle Joe* by Ada B. Litchfield. Text © 1984 by Ada B. Litchfield.

(continued on page 577)

Printed in the United States of America
ISBN 0–15–330011–6

Contents

Unit 1

Detours 2

Unit 2
Skylights 144

Unit 3
Symphonies

Unit 4
Memories

Awards

The authors and illustrators of selections in this book have received the following awards either for their work in this book or for another of their works. The specific award is indicated under the medallion on the opening page of each award-winning selection.

American Institute of Graphic Arts Award
American Library Association Notable Books for Children
Australian Children's Book of the Year Award
Boston Globe–Horn Book Award
Randolph Caldecott Medal
Canada Council Children's Literature Prize
Canadian Children's Book Award
Lewis Carroll Shelf Award
Child Study Children's Book Committee of Bank Street College Award
Children's Book Showcase
Children's Choices
Christopher Award
CRABberry Award
Drama League of America Prize
Eagle Award
Dorothy Canfield Fisher Award
Friends of Children and Literature (FOCAL) Award
Eva L. Gordon Award
International Board on Books for Young People Honor Award
Junior Literary Guild Selection
Ezra Jack Keats New Writer Award
Vicky Metcalf Award
National Council of Teachers of English Award for Excellence in Poetry
John Newbery Medal
New Jersey Institute of Technology Award
New York Times Best Illustrated Children's Books
One Hundred Best Books
Pacific Northwest Library Association
Edgar Allan Poe Award
Special Jury Prize from the Marberg Film Festival
Western Writers of America Spur Award
Laura Ingalls Wilder Award
Young Reader's Choice Award

Unit 1

Detours

What do we do when we want to go somewhere but the way is blocked? We probably take a detour, a different way around. Most often, we think of detours when we think of traveling and roads. During our travels, we may suddenly see a "detour" sign with an arrow that points us in a new direction. Despite the trouble, we may find that the detour is really an interesting road to take.

Some detours have nothing to do with real travel. We may take a detour when our plans do not work quite the way we expect. When that happens, we have to make new plans and work around the problem. The new way may be hard, but it may also be exciting and lead to adventure.

In this unit, you will read about many characters who have to make some kind of detour when faced with problems that block their way. As you read the selections, look for the different kinds of detours the characters take, and see where these detours lead them.

Twenty and Ten *by Claire Huchet Bishop. Penguin.* During World War II, twenty French children live safely in a mountain school where a nun hides ten Jewish refugee children from the Nazis despite great danger, sacrifice, and fear.

King of the Wind *by Marguerite Henry. Macmillan.* This award-winning story is about an Arabian stallion that overcomes bad fortune to become one of the most famous horses of all time.

The Dastardly Murder of Dirty Pete *by Eth Clifford. Houghton.* In this follow-up to *Help! I'm a Prisoner in the Library,* Jo-Beth and Mary Rose travel with their father to the West Coast, where they get lost. They end up in a deserted town.

The Good Luck Dog *by Lilo Hess. Scribner.* A pampered house dog is stolen and luckily, after some danger, finds an owner who loves him and needs him as a hearing ear dog.

Louis Braille *by Stephen Keeler. Bookwright.* This is the story of the life of Louis Braille, a blind man who invented a language that can be read by people who cannot see.

One of Us *by Nikki Amdur. Dial.* Nora is sad and
friendless in her new home. Then she befriends a
blind boy ignored by his classmates. When Nora
makes other friends, she includes him.

Much Ado About Aldo *by Johanna Hurwitz. Morrow.* Aldo
loves animals, so he stops eating meat. When his
class studies chameleons, he saves the crickets meant
to feed the chameleons.

Smoke Above the Lane *by Meindert DeJong. Harper.* Two
unlikely friends, a tramp and a little skunk, arrive in
town just in time for the Labor Day Parade.

Carnival and Kopeck and More About Hannah *by
Mindy W. Skolsky. Harper.* After Hannah's grandmother tells about her childhood (when she was
naughty to her own grandmother), Hannah finds
that history repeats itself.

There Are Two Kinds of Terrible *by Peggy Mann. Avon.*
When Robbie breaks his arm on the last day of
school, he thinks it is the most terrible thing that
could happen to him. Then something terrible
happens to his mother, and he realizes that there are
"two kinds of terrible."

*In this selection, a detour into a library
leads to adventure. Read to find out how two
sisters try to get out of the library.*

Help! I'm a Prisoner in the Library

by Eth Clifford

Mary Rose and her sister Jo-Beth came to Indianapolis from Fort Wayne with their father. In the middle of the city, during a snowstorm, the car ran out of gas. Their father walked to a nearby gas station for help while Mary Rose and Jo-Beth waited in the car. Then Jo-Beth decided she needed to find a rest room—right away!

The two sisters walked quickly to a nearby library, which looked like a big old house. They meant to stay there for only a few minutes, but they saw a large display in a back room and went to look at it.

While they were standing behind the display, the librarian prepared to close up the library. She checked all the rooms but did not see the two girls. After she locked the doors, she turned off the main lights and turned on the blue night lights. Then she went upstairs.

When the lights went out so suddenly, the two girls were so shocked they couldn't speak. Jo-Beth gave a small gasp. Mary Rose realized almost at once that they had forgotten about the time.

"The librarian's gone home. I'll bet she locked us in!" Mary Rose nodded her head. "And Daddy doesn't even know where we are."

Jo-Beth shivered. "I don't like these spooky blue lights. They make everything so weird." Mary Rose agreed.

Jo-Beth came out from behind the display and crept along to the front door, with Mary Rose right behind her. At the door, she pulled and tugged at the knob.

"What good is that? The doors are locked."

"I know they're locked," Jo-Beth snapped. She was so angry she kicked the door. "Whoever heard of locking a door *inside* with a key?"

Jo-Beth turned and stood with her back up against the door. The blue lights were even worse in here because the room was so big. Shadows crouched down from the walls and moved closer and closer. Jo-Beth swallowed hard, but the hollow sensation in her stomach refused to go away.

"Oh, Mary Rose," she sobbed. "We're never going to get out of here. The librarian's gone, and nobody knows where we are."

Mary Rose started to walk away from the door.

Jo-Beth promptly followed. "I don't want to stay here by myself. Where are you going?"

"I'm going to find the phone. You said at least one sensible thing. Nobody knows we're here. So I guess it would be a good idea to call somebody on the phone and tell them where we are."

"Who are you going to call?" Jo-Beth asked when Mary Rose found the phone. It was hidden on a shelf below the sign that read "Check Books Out Here."

Mary Rose didn't pay any attention. She dialed the operator, and a voice spoke to her at the other end. Mary Rose said, "I want to call Fort Wayne collect." She gave the operator her home number and her mother's name.

She listened to the voice on the phone, and then she hung up.

"The operator says the phones are down in Fort Wayne. On account of the blizzard."

"What's a blizzard?" Jo-Beth asked.

"It's a terrible snowstorm. *Mountains* of snow. And gusty winds." That's what they always said on TV in the weather reports. "Gusty winds."

"The operator said the blizzard was everywhere. Come on over to the window so we can look out and see it," Mary Rose said.

At one of the front windows facing out on the porch, the two girls rubbed the wet panes and tried to peer out. It was night—darkness came early in the winter. Still, the falling snow brightened the world outside, especially when the street lights gleamed on the twirling flakes.

"I know," Jo-Beth cried. "I'll make a sign and put it up on the window."

"You can if you want to. I'm going to call the police."

Jo-Beth ran back to the librarian's desk. She pulled drawers open until she found what she was looking for—a big sheet of paper, a thick black marking pen, and some tape. Meanwhile, Mary Rose picked up the phone.

"Operator," she said, "I want the police."

"H-e-l-p-!" Jo-Beth started to print.

"Are you in trouble?" the operator asked. She sounded suspicious.

"Yes, we are. Please. I want the police."

"How do you spell *prisoner*?" Jo-Beth asked.

A voice in Mary Rose's ear came on at the same time. The man spoke just as Mary Rose was saying to her sister, "Put down p-r-i-s-o-n . . ."

"Who is this?" the voice asked.

". . . e-r," Mary Rose finished quickly. "Is this the police?"

Jo-Beth shouted into the phone. "We're prisoners! We're prisoners in the library!"

"You kids stop playing with your phone," the officer scolded. "We have to keep all these lines open for emergencies." He slammed the receiver down so hard it made Mary Rose's ear tingle.

"Are they coming to get us?"

"He hung up on me. He didn't even want to *listen*."

Mary Rose wasn't a girl to give up easily. She lifted the receiver again.

"Hello, operator? I want the fire department."

Jo-Beth, meanwhile, was finishing her sign. It looked fine to her. In big letters, she had printed "Help! I'm a Prisoner in the Liberry."

"Now to hang it up in the window," Jo-Beth thought. A sign was better than a phone call. People believed in signs.

Mary Rose was having a problem.

"Aren't you the same little girl who just asked for the police?"

"Yes, but they hung up on me."

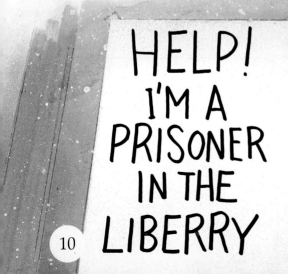

HELP! I'M A PRISONER IN THE LIBERRY

"Is your mother or father there?" the operator asked. When Mary Rose said no, the operator wanted to know, "Is there any grownup in the house at all?"

"That's what I'm trying to tell you." Why didn't people *listen*? "Nobody's here except me and my little sister. We're locked up in the . . ."

Without warning, the phone went dead. No sound came from it at all, not even a hum or a dial tone. At the same time, the lights went out and the room was swallowed up in darkness.

Jo-Beth called from the window in panic, "The lights just went off in the street." She started to run toward her sister. Mary Rose could hear her banging into things as she tried to find her way back to the librarian's desk and Mary Rose.

"I wish the blue lights would come back on," Jo-Beth whispered. "They were spooky, but they were better than nothing."

"The power line must be down." Mary Rose didn't feel nearly as brave as she sounded. "Stop shaking, Jo-Beth. Just think of it this way. We can't get out. But nobody can get in, either. So we're perfectly safe."

Jo-Beth relaxed a little. "I wouldn't mind it so much if it wasn't so dark."

"Maybe I can find a flashlight in one of these drawers." Mary Rose ran her fingers across the desk and down one side. In the very last drawer, she found a key ring with a tiny flashlight attached to it.

At that exact moment, there was a heavy thud over their heads, as if someone had fallen down.

The moaning started almost at once.

Jo-Beth grabbed her sister so hard that Mary Rose dropped the flashlight.

"Don't do that!" Mary Rose exclaimed. She dropped to her knees and started to fumble about on the floor for the flashlight.

"You said we were safe because the door was locked. You said nobody could get in. Well, *something* got in."

"There is no use arguing," Mary Rose thought. She had a big decision to make, and her sister was no help at all. The question was—should they hide downstairs, or should they go upstairs and see who, or what, was there?

Jo-Beth whispered, "I hate this place. I'm never going to come back. If we ever get out."

Mary Rose told her sister to be quiet. She listened hard, turning her head from side to side. The moaning had stopped, but that didn't mean that whatever was up there was gone.

She took a deep breath. "Jo-Beth, you can stay here if you want to, but I'm going upstairs and see what's up there."

Jo-Beth put out her hand as if to stop Mary Rose. She wanted to plead with Mary Rose not to leave her. But she knew what Mary Rose was like once she made up her mind about something.

"I'm going to sit right here on the floor," Jo-Beth said. Mary Rose shrugged. She began to walk away, toward the steps. "Wait," Jo-Beth cried. "You've got the light."

Mary Rose shrugged again. She beamed the light up at the stairway. She took another deep breath, closing her eyes for a moment. Then she put one hand on the banister and held on to the flashlight with the other. She didn't say a word when Jo-Beth raced after her, breathing hard.

"Let me walk in front of you. Please, Mary Rose. I'd rather have you right in back of me than . . ."

Her voice trailed off, but Mary Rose knew exactly what her sister meant because she could feel the awful quiet dark emptiness pressing in behind her.

Halfway up the stairs there was a broad landing. Jo-Beth stopped abruptly, so abruptly that Mary Rose ran into her and cracked her jaw on Jo-Beth's head.

"Don't ever do that again," Mary Rose said angrily. "I think you broke my jaw."

"I'll tell you one thing, Mary Rose. I'm not going up any more steps. If we do, it will be to our certain death." Jo-Beth liked the sound of that. She repeated it with joyful gloom. "Certain death."

"Great. Just great. That's what I love about you, Jo-Beth. You really know how to cheer a person up. Come on!"

Jo-Beth would have settled for staying on the landing, but Mary Rose was determined to complete the journey to the second floor.

Before long, the girls reached the head of the stairway and another wide landing, which turned around on both sides into two spacious hallways. In each hallway were a number of doors. At the farthest end on the left, a door was open. A light flickered from somewhere inside the room.

"Come on," Mary Rose said.

Jo-Beth held back. "You go first. You're older than I am. And bigger. And you have the flashlight. You can use it as a weapon if you have to."

Mary Rose looked down at the key ring and the tiny flashlight attached. She didn't bother answering. She just sighed and began to walk along the hallway.

Mary Rose peered in through the open doorway. She saw a large room, comfortably furnished, with a fire glowing in a large fireplace. That was the flickering light they had seen.

The two girls walked into the room, looking about curiously.

"Somebody lives here," Jo-Beth said finally. "I didn't know anybody ever lived in a library."

"That's what we must have heard, Jo-Beth. We must have heard the librarian. She must have knocked something over." Mary Rose's eyes began to shine with excitement. "Do you realize what this means?"

"We can get something to eat!" Jo-Beth felt relaxed enough now to remember that she was starved.

"No," Mary Rose said. "It means we can get out!"

1. How did Mary Rose and Jo-Beth get locked in the library?

2. What important things did Mary Rose and Jo-Beth do when they found out they were locked in the library?

3. Was Mary Rose's decision to go upstairs a good one? Explain your answer.

4. What clue on page 6 tells you that the librarian might live in the building?

5. How do you think the girls will get out of the library?

6. Why was it important for the girls to know when to be serious?

Prewrite

Pretend you are either Mary Rose or Jo-Beth. Imagine how you felt when you were locked in the library. How did the library look? What sounds did you hear? How did you feel? What would you have done if you had had to stay there all night? How would you try to get out of the library? If you can, work with a classmate to act out what happened.

Draft

Now, imagine that you have been accidentally locked in the library. You have your diary with you, and you have decided to write about what is happening. When you get out of the library, your experience might make a good story for the newspaper. In the meantime, write something in your diary about one of the following:
- What you see and hear.
- How you feel.
- How you plan to get out of the library.

Revise

Read what you have written. Is it scary? Is it exciting? What other details would help someone else know what you saw? What you felt? What you planned to do? Add or change whatever you can to make your diary entry more interesting.

The Library
by Barbara A. Huff

It looks like any building
When you pass it on the street,
Made of stone and glass and marble,
Made of iron and concrete.

But once inside you can ride
A camel or a train,
Visit Rome, Siam, or Nome,
Feel a hurricane,
Meet a king, learn to sing,
How to bake a pie,
Go to sea, plant a tree,
Find how airplanes fly,
Train a horse, and of course
Have all the dogs you'd like,
See the moon, a sandy dune,
Or catch a whopping pike.
Everything that books can bring
You'll find inside those walls.
A world is there for you to share
When adventure calls.

You cannot tell its magic
By the way the building looks,
But there's wonderment within it,
The wonderment of books.

Realistic Fiction

Some stories we read seem to tell about real characters and events. Yet the stories are not true. We call these stories **realistic fiction.**

Realistic fiction is not the same as fantasy. In realistic fiction there are no characters with magical powers, and there are no talking animals. Everything in the story seems real, even though it never actually happened.

The characters in realistic fiction do the same kinds of things real people do. They laugh and cry about the same kinds of things that make real people laugh and cry. A reader can easily imagine that he or she is one of the characters in the story. When a story reminds us of things real people do or ways they feel, we say that the story is "believable." Realistic stories are believable.

Think of the story about Mary Rose and Jo-Beth, who were locked in the library. Why is their story considered realistic fiction? The story of these girls could actually have happened, and it is believable. It is about two girls who could be real and who experience a real-life situation.

Read the following paragraphs. Decide which one is realistic fiction and why.

A. The library was dark and still that night. A small animal moved slowly among the books. It looked everywhere. When the mouse was sure nothing was around, it changed into WONDER MOUSE!

B. The library was dark and still that night. A small animal moved slowly out from among the books. It sniffed the air and looked everywhere. When the mouse saw no danger, it jumped to the floor.

Paragraph B is an example of realistic fiction because what happened could really take place in our world. Paragraph A is not realistic. It describes something from fantasy, where animals can talk or act like humans.

Read and think about the characteristics of realistic fiction.

- The characters and events seem real, but the story is not true.
- The story is believable.
- The story seems to take place in the real world.
- The story reminds us of things real people do or ways real people feel and act.

Think about these characteristics as you read from now on. Are the stories realistic fiction, or are they fantasy? What clues help you decide?

Uncle Joe must leave his special school to go live with his sister's family for a while. Read to see how this detour changes the family.

Making Room for Uncle Joe

by Ada B. Litchfield

Mom looked really serious as she read us the letter from Uncle Joe's social worker.

Uncle Joe is Mom's younger brother. He has Down's syndrome. People with Down's syndrome are mentally retarded and need help taking care of themselves. After Uncle Joe was born, his mother died, and no one else in the family could give him the care he needed. That's why he had been in a state hospital school for such a long time.

Uncle Joe had been happy at his school. But now it was closing, the letter said, and the people who lived there had to find other homes. Uncle Joe would have to live with us for a while. We were his only family.

"The social worker says she's looking for an apartment for Uncle Joe, but they are hard to find," Mom explained. "So your dad and I think Joe should stay with us until —"

"He'd better find an apartment fast," my older sister, Beth, shouted. "We can't have a retarded person living here forever!"

"He won't be here forever, Beth," I said. "It's just until he finds another place."

"Good grief," Beth said. "Doesn't anyone see how embarrassing this will be for all of us?" She burst into tears and ran out of the room.

"Let her go," Dad said when Mom tried to call Beth back. "She needs to think things over."

I had to think things over, too. Suppose Uncle Joe was a nuisance? Suppose he hung around me all the time? Suppose he messed with my baseball cards?

"Dan, helping Uncle Joe is something our family has to do together," Dad said, as if he were reading my thoughts. "Your mother and I will appreciate any help you and Beth and Amy can give us."

"I'll help Uncle Joe," Amy said.

Amy is only five and a half. What kind of help could she be?

"I'll help, too," I said, trying to sound cheerful. To tell the truth, I didn't feel cheerful at all.

I felt worse when I talked to my friend Ben the next day.

"Down's syndrome, eh?" Ben said with a know-it-all look on his face. "You should be upset. I saw a TV program about people with Down's syndrome. Their eyes slant and their noses look squashed in." He showed me with his fingers what he meant. "Does your uncle look like that?"

"I don't remember," I said. "I only saw him once when I was little."

I didn't know if what Ben said was true or not, but I didn't think it was a very helpful thing for a friend to say.

When I got home, I found Mom and Dad moving furniture around. They had moved the TV from the family room into the living room and the record player into Beth's room.

"We're making room for Uncle Joe," Mom said when she saw me. "You're just in time to help."

Dad and I brought an extra bed up from the basement into the family room. Uncle Joe would sleep there.

Early the next day, Mom and Dad drove to the state school to bring Uncle Joe home. All morning, Amy and Beth and I waited at the front window, watching for them to return. Finally, about noon, we saw our car turn into the driveway. In a few minutes, Mom and Dad came up the walk. Behind them came a short man carrying a suitcase and a small blue bag.

As soon as Beth saw them, she left the window and went into her bedroom.

Uncle Joe came into the house very slowly. His cap was on crooked. He was wearing a jacket with sleeves too short for his arms. His pants were too long for his legs. His eyes did slant a little, and his nose did look a little squashed in.

He looked around at everything in the room and at Amy and me. Then he smiled.

"Hi," he said. "My name's Joe. What's . . . uh . . . yours?"

"This is Dan," my father said. "And here's Amy."

Amy made a little bow, and I bobbed my head.

"And, oh, yes," Dad said, "there's one more." He left the room and came back holding Beth by the arm.

"This is Beth," Dad said.

"Hello, Beth," Uncle Joe said. "You're pretty."

"Thank you," said Beth. She looked surprised.

Dad took Uncle Joe's suitcase into the family room. Uncle Joe wouldn't let him take the blue bag. Instead, he brought it over to me.

"This is my bowling ball," he said, holding the bag up almost in my face. "My friend Ace gave it to me."

Soon after that we all sat down for lunch. All except Uncle Joe, that is. He sat in a chair by the china cabinet, holding his bowling ball on his lap.

"Come sit here, Joe," Mom said, pointing to the empty chair beside Amy. "Put that bowling ball down somewhere and come eat."

"No," Uncle Joe said, shaking his head. "I miss Ace. I need a friend with me . . . uh . . . when I eat lunch."

He hung his head and looked sad. Nobody seemed to know what to do, except Amy. She slid out of her chair, went to Uncle Joe, and put her hand in his.

"I'll be your friend, Uncle Joe," she said. "You can eat with me." She pulled him to the table.

That was the beginning of Amy's friendship with Uncle Joe. As soon as we finished lunch, she showed him her library book. Every day after that, Uncle Joe and Amy spent a lot of time together with their heads bent over Amy's books. I don't think he always knew if she read the right words or not, but he listened carefully anyway, nodding his head. Showing off for someone made Amy very happy.

Yes, Amy and Uncle Joe got along fine right away, but for the rest of us, having Uncle Joe around wasn't easy.

He had to be reminded to wear his glasses, comb his hair, take a shower, and things like that. Somebody had to see that he put on matching socks.

Uncle Joe offered to help around the house, but he often seemed to get directions mixed up. Usually he was more trouble than help.

We didn't know what to do. Finally Mom got the idea that I should take him bowling. I didn't want to go, but before I knew what was happening, Uncle Joe had come out of his room wearing his bowling jacket and carrying his blue bag.

All the way to Bowl-a-rama, I hoped none of my friends would see us. I hadn't seen any of them—even Ben—for a few weeks. But we didn't see anyone I knew, and as soon as we started bowling, I forgot about everything else.

Uncle Joe was a good bowler. Sometimes he got a spare. Sometimes he got a strike.

Me? I was lucky if I knocked down any pins at all.

"It's okay, Danny," Uncle Joe kept saying in his slow way. "I . . . uh . . . know you can do it. You'll get a strike. Just . . . uh . . . keep trying."

And I did. I got a strike. On the very last frame, all the pins went down—whack, whack, whack—just like that!

We both shouted and jumped up and down.

Everyone around us looked, but I didn't care. I didn't even care when I saw Ben and two other guys from my school watching us.

At first, they just stared and nudged each other. I could tell they were looking for something to laugh at. When they finally came over to us, I introduced them to Uncle Joe.

"I'm glad to meet you . . . Ben . . . and John . . . and Eli," Uncle Joe said. He shook each of their hands and smiled at them. They looked down at the floor and shuffled their feet, but Uncle Joe didn't seem to notice.

"Would you like to bowl with us?" he asked.

They all nodded yes. Ben and Eli had bowled before, but John hadn't. Uncle Joe showed him how to hold the ball and encouraged him the way he had encouraged me.

In no time at all, everybody seemed to forget that Uncle Joe had Down's syndrome. We were all just trying to knock down bowling pins. We were all just having fun.

After that, Ben and my other friends started coming over to the house again. They were always kind to Uncle Joe, and he loved to talk with them.

After a while, things seemed to go better at home. Mom and Dad took more time showing Uncle Joe how to do simple jobs. Uncle Joe began to be a real help around the house. He could carry in groceries and help put them away. He liked to peel carrots and potatoes for dinner. He helped wash and polish the car. He helped Amy put the new bell on her tricycle, and he helped me paint a display rack for my baseball cards.

But what about Beth?

For a long time, Beth acted almost as if Uncle Joe didn't exist. He never bothered her, but sometimes he would sit quietly in the living room and listen while she practiced her piano lesson. Once he clapped, but that startled her so much he never did it again.

Then one day, when he thought no one was around, Uncle Joe sat down at the piano and played "Chopsticks."

Everyone in the family came running, and we clapped so loudly for him that he played it again.

"My friend Ace showed me how to do that," Uncle Joe said, grinning.

Beth went over to the piano. "I know how to play another part of that piece," she said. She sat down next to Uncle Joe and taught him how to play "Chopsticks" as a duet.

Later, Beth showed Uncle Joe how to play other tunes. Sometimes he played them over and over so many times we all got tired of listening, but we felt good because Beth was being kind to Uncle Joe.

By the time spring came, things had settled down into what Mom called a "comfortable routine."

Then another letter came from Uncle Joe's social worker.

Mom read the letter to us. It said that Uncle Joe would be leaving. Everything had finally been arranged. Uncle Joe would share an apartment with two other men in the city. He would work at a sheltered workshop close to where he lived.

A sheltered workshop is a place where some handicapped people are taught to do special jobs. They sort nuts and bolts, put together small motors, package things to send through the mail, or do other simple tasks. The work is easy, and they are paid for doing it.

At first, Uncle Joe seemed pleased. He had Mom read the letter again and again.

I was sure he felt good about having a place of his own and a job of his own. He wanted to take care of himself.

I was sure my parents felt good about not having to be responsible for Uncle Joe anymore.

We would all be glad to have the family room back again so we could entertain our friends there.

We'd always known that Uncle Joe would be leaving sometime. So why did everyone look so sad that night at dinner?

"I'm going to miss you, Uncle Joe," Amy said. She burst into tears.

"I'll miss you, too," said Uncle Joe. He began to look very unhappy.

"Who will listen to me practice for my recital now?" Beth said. Tears were running down her cheeks, too.

"Hey, I'm not going to cry about this," I said to myself, taking a drink of water. But there was a lump in my throat, and I choked so badly I had to leave the table.

I knew I was going to miss Uncle Joe something awful.

When I came back, even my father looked as if he'd been crying. He cleared his throat and blew his nose.

"Listen," he said at last, "your mother and I have been talking this over for quite a while. We thought you all might be pretty upset if Joe leaves. We don't see why Uncle Joe has to live somewhere else if he doesn't want to. We are his family. I can drive him to that workshop every day on my way to the office, and he can take the bus back. What do you say, Joe? Would you like to stay with us?"

Uncle Joe looked thoughtful for a long time. He pulled at his hair. Then he started to grin. "I want to stay here. Yes, I do . . . I can work hard and . . . uh . . . pay for my food. I want to stay here all the time forever with my family."

"Then it's settled," Mom said. "I'll call the social worker right away and tell her we'd all like Uncle Joe to stay with us."

"Yippee!" shouted Amy. She climbed into Uncle Joe's lap and gave him a big hug.

And Uncle Joe? He looked so happy, nobody cared that he had forgotten to comb his hair. Or that there was a mess of crumbs around his plate and more on the floor. We all knew that in many ways Uncle Joe is a neat guy.

We were glad he had come to stay with us . . . all the time, forever.

1. How did knowing Uncle Joe change Dan's family?

2. What were three things that Uncle Joe did that made him important to the family?

3. Was Mom's idea that Dan take Uncle Joe bowling a good one? Explain your answer.

4. How do you know that Dan's friends learned to accept Uncle Joe?

5. Why did the family decide that Uncle Joe should stay with them instead of going to the new apartment?

6. How does this selection show that it is not a good idea to judge people before getting to know them?

Prewrite

Think about the ways life changed when Uncle Joe came to live with Dan's family. Some of the changes were good, and some were not. Copy and complete the chart on the next page. List each change as an advantage (good change) or disadvantage (bad change).

Advantages
1. Uncle Joe got to know his family.
2.
3.

Disadvantages
1. The family had to be responsible for Uncle Joe.
2.
3.

Draft

Write a letter to Dan's family. Explain why you think it was or was not a good idea for Uncle Joe to come live with them. Use the reasons you have listed in your chart.

Revise

Read your letter. Does it say what you want it to say? Is it convincing? Are your reasons clear? Make any changes that are needed to have the letter say exactly what you want it to say.

A detour is "a new path." In this selection Juan has taken a detour. How do you think Juan will finally get "home"?

How Juan Got Home

by Peggy Mann

Juan came from Puerto Rico to live with his uncle in New York City. When he arrived, he tried to make new friends. However, he spoke very little English, and the families in his uncle's neighborhood did not speak Spanish. Soon Juan wished that he could go back home.

One day Juan went to a Spanish neighborhood to buy food for a special meal. There Juan met Carlos, a boy about his age. Carlos invited Juan to play stickball, a street game that is a lot like baseball. Carlos was amazed when Juan hit the ball so far that it went past the third sewer cover, way up the street. A three-sewer hit was a very long hit. Juan's new friend asked him to play for the neighborhood team in the big game on Saturday.

When he got home, Juan burst into his uncle's apartment and announced the news. He was going to play on the team against the Young Princes!

Uncle Esteban seemed mightily pleased. He gave Juan a resounding thwack on the back and raised the boy's arm in the manner of a winning boxer. Then he asked, "Where are the *plátanos*[1] and the *gandules*[2] and the *ajíes*[3]?"

Juan gasped and clapped his hand over his mouth. He had left the groceries somewhere. But where?

"I'll go back," he told his uncle. "I'll find them!"

Uncle Esteban laughed. "Never mind," he said. "You've already found something a lot better."

The next afternoon, which was Saturday, Uncle Esteban made plans to go and watch his nephew in the big game. "Also," said Uncle Esteban, "I may find a few friends myself. Who knows?"

They arrived early. Carlos was sitting on the stoop of his house, waiting. But as soon as he caught sight of Juan he raced down the street to welcome him.

---

[1] plátanos [plä′tä•nōs]: Bananalike fruits.
[2] gandules [gän•doo′lās]: Pigeon peas.
[3] ajíes [ä•hē′ās]: Chili peppers.

"Man!" he said to Juan, breathless. "Am I glad to see you! I've been telling the team all about you. How a little kid—what are you, seven, eight years old?—can hit three sewers!"

Juan understood some of the sentences. He drew himself up with dignity. "I am ten years old."

"Oh," Carlos said. "So you're little for your age, that's all. But no matter how old you are—or how little—you're the first kid on this street that's hit three sewers all summer long." Then he looked at Juan and frowned. "What I'm wondering now is, was it just a lucky accident? Do you think you could ever do such a thing again?"

Since Juan did not understand, he merely grinned and nodded.

The game was scheduled for four o'clock. By three-thirty the entire neighborhood, it seemed, was out on the street. The steps of the brownstone stoops were as crowded as bleachers. The box seats set out by the areaways and the alleyways were all taken. Some people had even brought camp chairs and stools to sit out on the sidewalk. And the windows facing the street were filled with spectators gathered to watch the big game. Voices rose like a wall of sound.

Juan had never in his life felt so nervous. It was one thing to hit a stone with a stick across the Piñonas River with only his friends, Ricardo and Eduardo and Julio and Ramon, watching. It was quite something else to try to get a three-sewer hit under the eyes of all these staring strangers. Fervently he wished he had never ventured forth from his uncle's apartment to buy the things they needed for the special Spanish supper.

Uncle Esteban was chatting with some men who were setting out a card table on the sidewalk. He seemed to have forgotten all about Juan.

"C'mon," Carlos said. "I gotta be sure you know the rules of the game." He took Juan by the arm and brought him over to a very tall boy called Pee-Wee. This boy spoke good Spanish, and carefully explained to Juan about the pitcher, the catcher, the first, second, and third bases, and how to run from one to the next. "¿Alguna pregunta?"[4] said Pee-Wee then. "Any questions?"

The only question Juan had was how had he gotten into this mess. And how could he get himself out of it, and go back home to his uncle's house. But he managed to grin as though everything was fine and calm inside and he said, "I onnerstan'."

When it came his turn to stand up and bat, he felt faint with fear. All the eyes on the street seemed to be boring into him. As he stood at home plate holding the sawed-off mop handle, silence spread down the block. It was an exploding silence. Pee-Wee had told him that the word had gone around. This little kid had hit three sewers. Could he do it again? They all were watching; all were waiting.

---

[4] ¿Alguna pregunta [äl•gōō'nä prä•gōōn'tä]: Any questions?

The pitcher was a tall black boy. "Batter up, champ," he called. "You the midget miracle man they been crowing about?"

Laughter rose from the Young Princes and from the people watching the game. Hooting, derisive laughter.

Anger clenched inside Juan's chest like a hard fist. Why were they making fun of him? Because he was a stranger? Because he was little for his age?

When the ball came flying toward him he slammed at it with all his strength, and watched then with stunned satisfaction as the ball sped down the street.

Everyone was screaming at him. "Run. . . . Run!" But he did not know what the word meant. Some kind of English *Bravo!*[5] maybe. He smiled at the standing, screaming sidewalk crowd and raised one hand over his head in a victory sign, as his uncle had done at home.

Pee-Wee ran up, and he began shaking him. "*¡Corre! ¡Corre!*"[6]

Suddenly Juan remembered the rules and started racing toward first base: the fender of a parked car. The screams of the crowd grew louder. He made it to second base, a chalked circle in the middle of the street. Pee-Wee was racing along beside him. "Keep going!" Pee-Wee shouted in Spanish. "The ball went under a truck. Keep running!"

He reached third base: the fire hydrant. And then came the sprint back. He slid onto home plate, his breath coming in hard gasps.

Carlos and Pee-Wee and the rest of his teammates were all around him, slapping him on the back and shouting, "Man, you got home! You made a home run! You got home!"

Pride swelling inside him, he sat on the curb, Carlos on one side of him, Pee-Wee on the other. Carlos instructed Pee-Wee to ask whether Juan would come over again and

---

[5] Bravo! [brä'vō]: Well done!

[6] ¡Corre! ¡Corre! [côr'rä côr'rä]: Run! Run!

play on their team. And Juan instructed Pee-Wee to say sure, he would come! He'd come over here every day to play. Even when school started in September, he'd keep coming.

Pee-Wee translated this, and Carlos clapped Juan on the knee. "Man," he said. "You're in!"

Juan was up at bat four more times that afternoon. He hit no more home runs, but that didn't seem to matter. He had done it once, so there was always the hope he might do it again. Each time he stood up at bat an expected hush of anticipation spread down the street. They were with him, he knew. Even those on the other team. He was in! He belonged.

Between his times at bat he sat on the curbstone, Carlos on one side, Pee-Wee on the other. At first he spoke only to Pee-Wee, spoke only in Spanish. But by the end of the afternoon he was shouting and cheering like all the others as one of his teammates hit the ball and raced down the street.

"Come on, man! Move it!" Loud and proud he yelled the words—words of the English language.

1. How did Juan get "home"?

2. List three important things that happened in the story that helped Juan to get "home."

3. What parts of the story did you think were funny? Why?

4. Did you think that Juan would make a three-sewer hit in the big game? Why or why not?

5. What clues in the story made you think that Juan might stop wishing he could return to Puerto Rico?

6. How does the saying "Actions speak louder than words" apply to this story?

Prewrite

Think about the ways in which you and Juan are alike and how you are different. Have you ever moved to a new place and had to make friends? Have you ever had to learn a new language? Are you good at sports? Are you small for your age? Draw two idea bursts like the ones on the next page. Fill in as many examples as you can of how you and Juan are alike and how you are different.

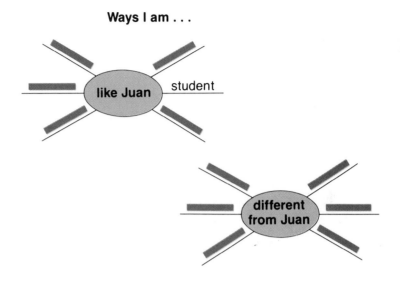

Ways I am . . .

like Juan

student

different
from Juan

Draft

Write a paragraph describing yourself. Explain
the ways in which you are like Juan and the
ways in which you are different from Juan. Use
examples from your idea bursts.

Revise

Read your paragraph. Could someone who did
not know you get an idea of what you are like?
Does the paragraph give a good description of
you? What else could you add to make this
paragraph come to life? Make the necessary
changes in your paragraph.

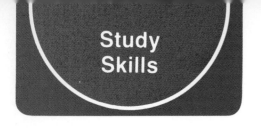

Study
Skills

Schedules

A **schedule** is a plan of things to be done or a list telling at what times things will happen. Using a schedule can help you plan what you need to do.

Perhaps you follow a schedule in school. You may have art, math, or lunch at certain times during the day.

Juan's Uncle Esteban keeps a schedule for his work. He must plan with whom he needs to meet each day. When Juan wanted to come to the office on Thursday, Uncle Esteban checked his schedule. At what time could Juan meet with him on Thursday? Look at Uncle Esteban's schedule below.

THURSDAY		October **21**
A.M.	10:00	Lois Blake
	10:30	Tom Gomez
	11:00	Mary Trout
	11:30	Carol Beach
P.M.	1:00	David Cox
	1:30	Paul Mixon
	2:00	Rachel Wong
	2:30	Pat Day
	3:00	
	3:30	Rose Green

Juan could meet with his uncle at 3:00 P.M. on Thursday. His uncle will write Juan's name in the schedule for that time.

Train, Plane, and Bus Schedules

Trains, planes, and buses follow schedules, too. People who want to plan a trip must know where the train, plane, or bus goes and when it leaves one place and arrives at the next. They find this information on a schedule. By looking at the schedule, people know when the train, plane, or bus will leave and when it will arrive. They can then plan to get to the train station or airport or bus stop in plenty of time.

Juan may use a bus schedule to help him get to his uncle's office at the right time on Thursday afternoon. The bus schedule shown on the next page is the bus schedule Juan will use. A look at the top tells him that this is a schedule for Monday through Friday. It also tells him that these times are P.M., or afternoon times.

The first column of the schedule lists the stops the bus makes. The next columns list the time that each bus arrives at each stop. Juan can use the schedule to plan which bus he will take.

RED LINE BUS COMPANY

Monday - Friday
P.M. Schedule

	Bus A	Bus B	Bus C	Bus D
Fifth Avenue	12:30	1:00	1:30	2:00
Cook Street	12:45	1:15	1:45	2:15
Lake Street	1:00	1:30	2:00	2:30
Flower Lane	1:15	1:45	2:15	2:45
Main Street	1:30	2:00	2:30	3:00
Palm Drive	——	2:15	2:45	3:15

Juan lives on Cook Street, near the bus stop. His uncle's office is on Palm Drive, across the street from the bus stop. So Juan knows he must go from the Cook Street stop to the Palm Drive stop.

When Juan uses this schedule, he starts at the bottom of the schedule. There he sees that the Palm Drive stop is the last stop on the bus route. He can also see that bus A does not go to Palm Drive.

The schedule shows Juan that bus B gets to Palm Drive at 2:15 P.M. If he uses bus B, he will have to wait forty-five minutes to see his uncle at 3:00 P.M. Next, Juan checks bus C. If he takes bus C, he will get to Palm Drive at 2:45 P.M., which would be fifteen minutes early. Juan sees that bus D arrives at Palm Drive at 3:15 P.M., which is too late. Juan plans to take bus C.

Now Juan works from the bottom up to find out when he must be at the bus stop. He uses his finger to follow the column for bus C up to the time it arrives at the Cook Street stop. The bus he wants to take arrives at Cook Street at 1:45 P.M. Juan plans to leave his home no later than 1:35 P.M. to be sure he is at the stop when the bus arrives.

Juan and Uncle Esteban use a bus schedule together. On Saturday they plan to make a special trip. They are going to a stickball game near Jackson Road. The trip is an easy one, because the game will be played close to the Jackson Road stop.

Juan and Uncle Esteban will get on the bus at Clove Street. The stickball game is at 9:30 A.M., and they don't want to be late. Their trip can be planned using the following bus schedule. What bus should they take? Why?

WEEKENDS AND HOLIDAYS				
A.M.	BUS 1	BUS 2	BUS 3	BUS 4
Clove Street	—	8:35	8:51	9:10
Jewell Avenue	8:25	8:42	8:58	9:17
King Street	8:44	9:01	9:17	9:36
Queen Street	8:58	9:15	9:31	—
Jackson Road	9:06	9:23	9:39	9:48

Remember that a schedule is a plan of things to be done or a list of times telling when things will happen. Using a schedule can help you plan your time wisely and make your travels more enjoyable.

John Newbery Medal
Author

In this selection, Tom goes to live on a farm for the summer. This detour leads him to an adventure with a black fox. Read to see how Tom helps the black fox.

The Midnight Fox

by Betsy Byars

Five summers ago, Tom discovered a beautiful black fox in the woods near his aunt and uncle's farm. The more Tom watched the fox, the more the fox became special to him.

The trouble began when the black fox killed a turkey and a hen that belonged to Aunt Millie. Uncle Fred wanted to stop the black fox from killing any more animals. So one day he caught the black fox's baby and put it in a cage. He planned to use the baby fox as bait to trap the mother.

In this story Tom thinks back to that day and to the night that followed, when he was forced to make an important decision.

Sometimes at night when the rain is beating against the windows of my room, I think about that summer on the farm. It has been five years, but when I close my eyes I am once again by the creek watching the black fox come leaping over the green, green grass. She is as light and free as the wind, exactly as she was the first time I saw her.

Or sometimes it is that last terrible night, and I am standing beneath the oak tree with the rain beating against me. The lightning flashes, the world is turned white for a moment, and I see everything as it was—the broken lock, the empty cage, the small tracks disappearing into the rain. Then it seems to me that I can hear, as plainly as I heard it that August night, above the rain, beyond the years, the high, clear bark of the midnight fox.

"Are you getting sick?" Aunt Millie asked at supper that night.

"I guess I'm a little tired."

"Well, I should think so! Helping with the pump out in the broiling sun all morning and then tracking that fox all afternoon. It's a wonder you don't have heat stroke. You eat something though, hear? You have to keep up your strength."

I finished my supper and went up to my room. I did not even look out the window, because I knew I could see the rabbit hutch by the garage and I never again wanted to see that baby fox cowering against the wall.

It seemed to get dark quickly that night. Uncle Fred was already out on the back porch. He had brought out a chair and was sitting with his gun beside him, pointing to the floor. I never saw anyone sit any quieter. You wouldn't have noticed him at all, he was so still.

I stood behind him inside the screen door. Through the screen I could see the tiny fox lift his black nose and cry again. Now, for the first time, there was an answer—the bark of his mother.

I looked toward the garden, because that's where the sound had come from, but Uncle Fred did not even turn his head. In a frenzy now that he had heard his mother, the baby fox moved about the cage, pulling at the wire and crying again and again.

Just then there was the sound of thunder from the west, a long rolling sound. Aunt Millie came to the door beside me and said, "Bless me, is that thunder?" She looked out at the sky. "Was that thunder, Fred?"

"Could be," he said without moving.

We stood in the doorway, feeling the breeze, forgetting for a moment the baby fox.

Then I saw Uncle Fred's gun rise ever so slightly in the direction of the fence behind the garage. I could not see any sign of the fox, but I knew that she must be there. Uncle Fred would not be wrong.

The breeze quickened, and abruptly the dishpan which Aunt Millie had left on the porch railing clattered to the floor. For the first time Uncle Fred turned his head and looked in annoyance at the pan and then at Aunt Millie.

"Did it scare your fox off?" she asked.

He nodded, then shifted in the chair and said, "She'll be back."

In just this short time the sky to the west had gotten black as ink. Low on the horizon, forks of lightning streaked the sky.

"Now, Fred, don't you sit out here while it's thundering and lightning. I mean it. No fox is worth getting struck by lightning for."

He nodded, and she turned to me and said, "You come on and help me shut the windows."

I started up the stairs, and she said again, "Fred, come on in when it starts storming. That fox'll be back tomorrow night, too."

I went upstairs and started closing the windows. I had just gotten one window down when I heard the gunshot. I had never heard any worse sound in my life. It was a very final sound, like the most enormous period in the world. Bam. Period. The end.

I ran out of my room and down the steps. I went out the back door, opening it so fast I hit the back of Uncle Fred's chair. I looked toward the rabbit hutch, said "Where?" and then looked at the back fence. Then I looked down at Uncle Fred, who was doing something with his gun.

"Missed," he said.

Suddenly I felt weak. My legs were like two pieces of rope, like that trick that magicians do when they make rope come straight up out of a basket and then say a magic word and make the rope collapse. My legs felt like they were going to collapse at any second. I managed to force these two pieces of rope to carry me up the stairs and into the room.

I closed two windows, and the third one, in sympathy perhaps, just banged down all by itself. Then I sank to the bed.

I lay in bed for a long time, still in my clothes, and then I got up very carefully. I walked over to the window and looked out at the tree that Aunt Millie's sons used to just run up and down all the time like monkeys. I opened the window, pushed out the screen, reached out into the rain, and felt for the smooth spot Aunt Millie had told me was worn into the bark of the tree.

I took off my shoes and knelt on the window sill. There was an enormous flash of lightning that turned the whole world white for a moment. Then I climbed out onto the nearest branch and circled the trunk round with my arms.

I thought that I could never get one step farther. I thought that I could never move even one muscle or I would fall.

After a while, though, I began to sort of slip down the tree. I never let go of the main trunk for a second. I just moved my arms downward in very small movements.

If there were smooth spots on those branches, my feet never found them. They only touched one rough limb after another. Slowly, I kept inching down the tree, feeling my way, never looking at the ground. Finally, my foot reached out for another limb and felt the cold wet grass. It shocked me for a moment. Then I jumped down, landing on my hands and knees.

I got up and ran to the rabbit hutch. The baby fox was huddled in one corner of the pen. The lightning flashed and I saw him watching me.

"I'm going to get you out," I said.

There were bricks stacked in a neat pile under the hutch and I took one and began to bang it against the lock. I was prepared to do this all night if necessary, but the lock was an old one and it opened right away.

I unhooked the broken lock, opened the cage, and stepped back against the tree.

The baby fox did not move for a moment. He cried sharply. From the bushes there was an answering bark.

The lightning flashed again, and in that second he jumped and ran toward the bushes. He barked as he ran. There was an immediate answer, and then only the sound of the rain. I waited against the tree, thinking about them. Then I heard the black fox bark once more as she ran through the orchard with her baby.

Suddenly the rain began to slacken, and I walked around the house. I had never been so wet in my life. Now that it was over I was cold, too, and tired. I looked up at the tree and there didn't seem to be any point in climbing back up. In just a few hours everyone would know what I had done anyway. I went up on the porch and rang the doorbell.

It was Aunt Millie in her cotton robe who turned on the porch light and peered out through the side windows at me.

I must have been an awful sight, for she flung open the door at once and drew me in.

"What are you doing out there? What are you doing?"

"Who is it?" Uncle Fred asked as he came into the hall.

"It's Tom," Aunt Millie said.

They both turned and looked at me, waiting for an explanation. I cleared my throat and said, "Uncle Fred and Aunt Millie, I am awfully sorry but I have let the baby fox out of the rabbit hutch." I sounded very stiff and formal, and I thought the voice was a terrible thing to have to depend on, because I really did want them to know that I was sorry, and I didn't sound it the least bit. I knew how much Uncle Fred had looked forward to the hunt and how important getting rid of the fox was to Aunt Millie, and I hated for them to be disappointed now.

There was a moment of silence. Then Aunt Millie said, "Why, that's perfectly all right, isn't it, Fred?

Don't you think another thing about that. You just come on to bed. You're going to get pneumonia standing there in that puddle. I'll get you some towels.''

Uncle Fred and I were left in the hall alone, and I looked up at him.

"I'm sorry," I said again.

He looked at me. I knew he was seeing through all the very casual questions I had been asking all summer about foxes, and seeing through the long days I had spent in the woods. I think those pieces just snapped into place right then in Uncle Fred's mind. I knew that if there was one person in the world who understood me, it was this man.

He cleared his throat. "I never liked to see wild things in a pen myself," he said.

Aunt Millie came down the hall and threw a towel over my head and started rubbing. "Now get upstairs. I am not going to have you lying in bed with pneumonia when your mother arrives."

We went into my room. Then she turned down my bed, went out, and came back with a glass of milk.

"I'm sorry about your turkey and hen," I said.

"Oh, that! It was more the heat than anything else. Just don't think about it anymore. The fox and her baby are miles away from here now, and they'll never come back to bother my birds. That's one thing about a fox. It learns."

She turned out the light and said, "It is starting to rain again. I declare we are going to be flooded out." Then she went downstairs.

The rest of the summer went by quickly. Pretty soon my visit to the farm began to seem hazy.

But then sometimes at night, when the rain is beating against the windows of my room, I think about that summer and everything is crystal-clear. I am once again beside the creek. The air is clean and the grass is deep and very green. I look up and see the black fox leaping over the crest of the hill, and she is exactly as she was the first time I saw her.

Or I am beneath that tree again. The cold rain is beating down upon me, and my heart is in my throat. And I hear, just as plainly as I heard it that August night, above the rain, beyond the years, the high, clear bark of the midnight fox.

1. Why did Uncle Fred want to kill the black fox?

2. How did Tom save the fox?

3. Describe Tom's actions that led up to the release of the baby fox.

4. Do you think that Tom acted bravely? Why or why not?

5. When Tom described the fox, what words did he use to help you know that he wanted the fox to be free?

6. What did Uncle Fred say to Tom to show him that he understood why Tom set the baby fox free?

7. Many times the way people think about something is influenced by their background and interests. How does this idea apply to the story?

Prewrite

The sound of rain against the windows in his room sometimes reminded Tom of the summer he spent on his aunt and uncle's farm. Think about what each of the sounds on the next page makes you remember.

Sound	Reminds me of . . .
a baby crying	
a dog barking	
a siren wailing	
a door slamming	

Are there other sounds that make you remember special places or events?

Draft

Choose one of the sounds you thought about and carefully write a short description of the place or the event that the sound helps you to remember. Be sure to include all the details that will make the place or event seem real to another reader.

Revise

Read your description. Could someone else see what the place or event you remembered was like? Could he or she feel what you felt? What else do you need to add? Do you want to change any words in order to make your description more real? Think about it, and then make the changes necessary to improve your description.

As you read this biography, think about the story you just read by this author. Recall details from that story that reflect the author's own experiences in life.

Betsy Byars

by Arlene Pillar

When Betsy Byars's four children were young, they read early drafts of their mother's books. They would draw small arrows pointing down next to parts they thought were boring. Next to parts they thought were interesting, they drew arrows pointing up. The children were Mrs. Byars's greatest critics. Today, many books later, we know that children reading Betsy Byars's books would draw arrows pointing up on nearly every page. Children enjoy reading what she writes.

Betsy Comer Byars was born on August 7, 1928, in Charlotte, North Carolina. She grew up there. Her family lived part of the time in the city and part of the time in the country. As a child, Betsy had rabbits, a goat, a rooster, and a dog. She loves animals, and this love is obvious in her book *The Midnight Fox* when she describes the black fox. Mrs. Byars writes that the fox's "black fur was tipped with white . . . as if the moon were shining on her fur, frosting it."

Betsy studied English at Queens College in North Carolina. When she graduated, Betsy was not thinking of becoming a writer. She says, "I thought writers spent their time in front of a typewriter, and that seemed boring." Writing became important only after she married Edward Byars and was at home raising three daughters and a son. She began by writing for magazines that adults read. Today, Mrs. Byars is one of the best-loved writers of books for young people.

"When I first started writing," Betsy Byars says, "I wrote daily, beginning when my kids left for school in the morning and ending at three o'clock when they got home." She is sure that she would never have written anything without putting in all those long days. Mrs. Byars adds, "Writing is something that has to be learned, like playing the piano, and a writer has to put in many, many hours."

Betsy Byars has been a writer for more than twenty years. One of the things she has learned from her job is that making up stories about young people is very interesting. She is never bored. This certainly shows how much her thinking has changed since her college days.

The ideas for Betsy Byars's stories tend to come from things that really happened. For example, she once really saw a fox in the woods, as Tom did in *The Midnight Fox*. The idea, however, is only the beginning. It may take Mrs. Byars a full year to write a book. Then she may spend another year "thinking about it, polishing it, and making improvements."

Mrs. Byars puts facts about herself, her friends, and her family in her stories. The dog in *Trouble River* is a lot like her own dog. Sara in *The Summer of the Swans* has big feet. Betsy did, too, at that age. The idea for *The Night Swimmers* came from friends, who told her a true story about some nighttime visitors to their swimming pool. *The 18th Emergency,* about a bully, shows the fear that Betsy had as a child. There was a bully in her own school.

Many things interest Betsy Byars. These interests lead to ideas. For example, the idea for *The Summer of the Swans* came from a story in her college magazine. At the university there were swans that kept leaving their beautiful lake for less pleasing ponds. In her mind, she moved the swans to West Virginia, and the story began.

Mrs. Byars's stories tell of the problems some boys and girls face. She is skilled at showing how young people feel, think, and act, so her characters make young readers feel a part of what is happening. Some of the subjects she writes about are fears, growing pains, and taking chances. Many young people have experienced these things for themselves, and they are pleased when Mrs. Byars explores them on the printed page.

Betsy Byars believes in showing life the way it is. Sometimes life is not very nice. Endings are not always happy. Problems are not always solved. Mrs. Byars believes that her readers can understand life's hard truths. As Roy says in *The Night Swimmers,* it is like swallowing spinach: the "experience makes you stronger."

Betsy Byars's books have been translated into many languages. Some have been made into movies for television. Also, they bring in lots of fan mail. Mrs. Byars gets about two hundred letters a week from young people. However, adults also think she is a wonderful writer. In 1971, she won the Newbery Medal for *The Summer of the Swans*. Many of her other books have won important prizes, too.

Betsy Byars lives with her husband in South Carolina. They have a cat named Tiger and a dog named Harvey. She does most of her writing in the winter months. In the summer, she and Mr. Byars spend a lot of time gliding in their sailplane. They put the plane together and take it apart themselves. The Byarses enjoy flying, and they enjoy traveling around the United States to do it. Of course, as she travels, Betsy Byars is always looking for ideas. She wants to be sure to keep those arrows pointing up.

1. How does the story "The Midnight Fox" reflect Betsy Byars's childhood?

2. What three things that really happened to her did Betsy Byars use for story ideas?

3. How do you think that Betsy Byars's children helped their mother write better stories?

4. Which kind of story do you like better, one that shows life the way it is or one that ends happily with all problems solved? Why?

5. What words did Betsy Byars use to tell you that writers need to practice writing?

6. Many people like to read stories in which the characters do things that the people themselves have also experienced. How does this apply to Betsy Byars's writing?

Think and Write

Prewrite

Betsy Byars gets ideas for stories from things that really happen. Think of some things that have happened to you and discuss them. What ideas for stories do they give you? Make some drawings, or cut pictures from magazines or newspapers, that tell your story ideas. Next to each picture, write a sentence that tells the main idea for your story. For example, next to a picture of a dog and a kitten, you might write, "A dog takes care of a lost kitten."

Draft

Choose one of your story ideas. Then copy and complete the following plan to show how you would develop the story.

Main Characters: _____

How the Story Begins: _____

The Middle of the Story: _____

How the Story Ends: _____

Revise

Look at your story plan. Think about the main characters — what are they like? Add a description of the main characters to your story plan. What details would you include to tell the story? At the bottom of the plan, make note of these details. Make necessary changes so that your plan tells the whole story.

John Newbery Medal Author

In this selection, a boy and his grandma escape down a river on a raft. Read to find out why Trouble River is a good name for the river.

Trouble River

by Betsy Byars

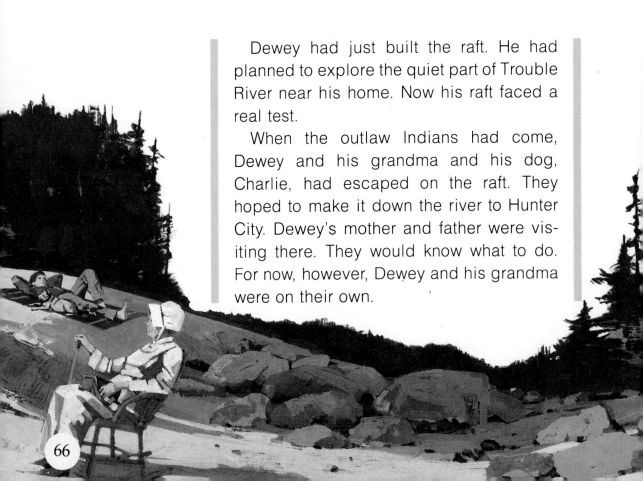

Dewey had just built the raft. He had planned to explore the quiet part of Trouble River near his home. Now his raft faced a real test.

When the outlaw Indians had come, Dewey and his grandma and his dog, Charlie, had escaped on the raft. They hoped to make it down the river to Hunter City. Dewey's mother and father were visiting there. They would know what to do. For now, however, Dewey and his grandma were on their own.

At dusk they stopped in the shelter of an old, dry creek bed. There was a widened sandy place where a pool had once formed. Dewey set his grandma's rocker on the sand. Then he spread his blanket on the rise above it.

They ate what was left of the cornmeal cakes. They also ate some fresh berries that Dewey had gathered.

"Try to get some sleep," Dewey's grandma said.

"Yes'm."

He had been sitting on the edge of the blanket, drawing a stick through the sand. Now he turned. Charlie was curled up in the center of the blanket, so Dewey lay beside him. He was so tired that his body ached, but he could not sleep. He lay with his hands locked behind his head.

"Push that dog off the blanket," his grandma said. "I swear that worthless thing'll be up in my chair next."

"He's all right, Grandma." Dewey hugged the dog to him. He had the lonely feeling that he and Grandma and Charlie were the only living creatures left in the world. He buried his face in the dog's fur and waited until the tears in his eyes had dried.

"Grandma," he said after a while.

"What is it now? I thought you were asleep."

"I was wondering, Grandma, what's going to happen to us." The thought had been troubling him all afternoon.

She paused and then she said, "There is something inside a person—I don't know how to give it a name exactly—but when something bad happens to you, well, a person thinks, This here's the end. I've thought it. I thought it when I had to come live out here on the prairie. I crawled up in that wagon and I said to myself, 'This here's the end.' I reckon you'll think it more than once in your life. Then a little time passes, a week or maybe a year. This something inside a person—whatever you'd call it—makes you come alive again."

"I wonder if I could be like that," Dewey said.

"You could if there was anything to you at all," she said. "Now get some sleep. You can't be steering us into Hunter City tomorrow if you don't get some sleep."

Dewey lay on his back for a long time, looking up at the sky. When sleep finally came, it was troubled.

He awoke, wet with sweat in the chilly air. Then he realized that it was not a dream that had awakened him. Charlie had risen on the blanket and was looking up into the darkness, a low growl deep in his throat. His teeth showed white beneath his raised upper lip.

This had seemed the ideal spot to camp when Dewey had first seen it. It was sheltered and protected. Now he realized that it would be easy for an enemy to slip up on them.

Dewey waited. He could see nothing. Then, from the bushes above, he heard a snarl and the rising howl of a wolf. He said in a low voice, "Grandma, wake up."

"What? What?" she said. She awakened so suddenly that her cane jabbed deep into the soft sand.

"Grandma, I think there are wolves up there."

"Wolves!" she said. She was fully awake now, for she feared them. "They'll eat us alive."

Her voice was helpless and old. Her hands clutched the arms of her rocker so tightly that the veins stood out.

In the shadows, a wolf, snarling and threatening, crossed to the edge of the creek bed.

Dewey said quickly, "Let's go."

He took his grandma by the arm, and with the other lifted the heavy rocker. "Charlie," he said firmly, "come."

Reluctantly, Charlie followed the boy as he stumbled toward the raft under his load.

"Help me, boy," his grandma gasped. "Help me!"

"I am, Grandma. I am."

He threw the chair on the raft. Before she was seated, he began to push the raft away from the shore with his oar.

"I'm not set yet," she said. Then, "But go on, boy, go on."

On the shore a wolf howled, a high, lonely sound. Then the other wolves took up the chorus. They ran in a pack to the bank and started for the raft, reaching out over the water with open jaws.

Charlie barked sharply. He stood on the edge of the raft, crouched as if he were about to jump into the water.

"Oh!" said Dewey's grandma with a sigh. She rose slightly and moved her chair to the center of the raft. "Oh! don't stop no more, boy," she said. "Whatever happens, don't stop no more. Those awful wolves."

"I can keep going if you can, Grandma."

Trouble River wound through the prairie like an animal on the scent of its prey. It hurried, then slowed. It twisted, then straightened. Then, at last, after its long and twisted journey, it began to gain speed before it rushed right into Big River. There, at the joining of the two rivers, would be Hunter City.

"Seems like we're picking up a little speed, doesn't it, boy?" she said, and her voice was lighter. "Maybe we'll get there by morning."

"Yes'm."

Dewey smiled. He dipped his paddle into the water and again began to feel the glow of confidence. He felt that the worst of the journey was over. Surely by morning they would be in Hunter City. He had no way of knowing about the stretch of treacherous water that lay ahead.

Dewey kept his eyes on the shores of the river. In the moonlight he occasionally saw the wolves slinking on the shore, but it did not trouble him. As long as he kept the raft in the center of the river, he and his grandma would be safe from them.

He poled the raft closer to the far bank.

"Keep it steady, boy," his grandma said. "This is no time to be upsetting now that we're almost there."

"No'm."

Charlie had given up growling at the wolves and now sat uneasily by Grandma's feet. The blanket had been lost in the rush for the raft. Now he had nothing to lie on. The water licking between the logs made him uneasy. He stuck his cold nose up into Grandma's hand.

"You worthless critter," she said. "You think I got nothing better to do than to hold your nose?" Still, she patted his head before she withdrew her hand. "I reckon we'll all be glad to see friendly faces, the dog, too."

Now they fell silent. Only the sound of Dewey's oar dipping into the water broke the silence. Dewey had no idea of the time. He knew daylight was still hours away.

He bent to reach under the raft, feeling the strips of hide. Some of them had begun to fray because of the constant rubbing of the logs, but he thought there was no danger. The raft would see them through.

He changed position and began to rub some of the stiffness out of his arms. His bare feet were cold against the wet logs. Suddenly he wanted to be in Hunter City so badly that his knees began to shake. He dipped his oar deep into the water to speed their progress.

By dawn they were gaining speed again. The river had straightened, and now the water rushed toward its goal, Big River.

"Maybe you better slow us down, boy," Grandma said. It was the first she had spoken in hours, though she had not been asleep. "It's not that I don't want to get there fast as you do."

"Yes'm, I will."

"It's just that I don't want to get upset."

"I'll slow her down."

He plunged his oar into the water, bracing himself, and waited for the raft to slow, but this seemed to have no effect.

"Slow her down." Grandma jabbed her cane into the air. "Now, boy."

"I am," he said. Again he swept the oar against the current, then added in a low voice, "Much as I can."

"Perhaps the raft will slow itself when we round that bend," Grandma said. She took her cane, set it across her lap, and held it along with the handle of her satchel in both hands.

"We're really moving," he said.

"What, boy?" she shouted over the noise of the water.

"I said we're really moving."

"Well, you don't need to tell me that." She looked uneasily at the wild river.

The river had narrowed. The shore was close on either side, but try as he would, Dewey could not move the raft from the rush of the current. All his paddling did nothing.

"Are we slowing any, boy?" she asked.

"No'm." He gasped as the raft tipped in the rough current. The water was now white with foam.

Grandma in her chair leaned forward tensely. Dewey gripped his oar. Charlie, on his feet now, whined and moved about unsteadily behind Grandma's chair. They listened closely, without moving.

So it was that they heard the rapids before they saw them. It was a wild noise that filled the air like the hum of a million insects.

"What *is* that, boy?" his grandma shouted.

He did not answer, for both of them knew. Dewey watched wide-eyed as the little raft swept around the bend in the river. Then Dewey gasped, and he heard his grandma scream.

There, stretching below them, were the rapids. Through a treacherous crack in the bluffs, the water ran, dashing against rocks, throwing spray high into the air.

"Get down, boy," Grandma cried.

He heard her when he was already on his knees, thrown by the force of the first waterfall. He slung one arm about Charlie and then crouched under his grandma's rocker. His other arm held the chair to the raft.

Water washed over Dewey, drenching him.

They plunged, turned twice, and fell as if they were dropping to the center of the earth. Dewey was in the air for a moment, and then they struck the water. The rocking chair hit Dewey on the shoulder.

"Grandma," he cried. Water was in his mouth, his eyes. He thought they had plunged under the water and were lost. He swallowed the icy water and sucked it into his nose as he gasped for breath.

Then, suddenly, it was over. It was like coming out of a nightmare, for they came through the dark shadows of the bluffs into the early morning sunlight. The sun turned the rippling water golden, and then the river widened to fill the broad valley beyond.

Dewey lifted his head. The dog, his fur flattened over his body, strained to be free. Dewey let him go. Charlie looked around, ready to leap for safety, then found to his surprise that he was safe. The water was smooth now, unhurried, with only the faint sound of the rapids behind to remind them of their recent danger.

"Grandma?" Dewey said.

There was no answer.

"Grandma!" He straightened and raised himself to one knee. "Grandma!"

"I'm still here, boy," she said in a voice that sounded small and far away.

"Are you all right?"

He looked at her. Her clothes were stuck against her thin body. Her hair, always so neatly bound behind her head, now hung in wet wisps. The bonnet she had guarded so carefully hung like a limp rag behind her. But her satchel, wet and flattened over the objects it contained, was still held safely in her lap.

Suddenly Dewey got to his feet. He put one hand up to his eyes to shield them from the sun.

"Grandma, Grandma!" He covered her thin shoulder with his hand. "Grandma, yonder's Hunter City!"

1. Why was Trouble River a good name for the river in this story?

2. What troubles did Dewey and his grandma have on their way to Hunter City?

3. What part of the story did you think was the scariest? Why?

4. What words did the author use on page 72 to help you hear the sound of the rapids?

5. How do you know that Dewey's raft survived the "real test" of Trouble River?

6. How does the expression "He who hesitates is lost" apply to this selection?

Prewrite

Dewey's grandmother says that something inside people makes them come alive, even when they think they cannot go on. Discuss this idea. Is Dewey the sort of person who can keep going no matter what? What makes you think that? Consider the times in the story when Dewey might have felt, "This is the end." List those instances on a piece of paper. What happened each time? What did Dewey do?

Draft

Write a paragraph explaining why you think Dewey is the kind of person who does not give up easily. Use the examples you listed to show what you mean.

Revise

Read your paragraph. Is your explanation clear? Do your examples show why you think Dewey can keep going in the face of trouble? Add or change whatever you can to make your paragraph clear.

Description

An author uses **description** to paint word pictures in a reader's mind. Read the paragraphs below:

A. The river was not always the same. In some places it curved. In other places it was straight. Sometimes the water flowed fast. At other times, it was slow.

B. Trouble River wound through the prairie like an animal on the scent of its prey. It hurried, then slowed. It twisted, then straightened.

Both paragraphs describe rivers. Paragraph A simply gives information about the river. But in paragraph B, Betsy Byars describes Trouble River in a way that helps you really see it in your mind. She compares the river to an animal that rushes and then slows down, that moves in one direction and then in another.

Read the passages that follow.

C. Grandma in her chair leaned forward tensely. Dewey gripped his oar. Charlie whined and moved about unsteadily. They listened closely, without moving. So it was that they heard the rapids before they saw them. It was a wild noise that filled the air like the hum of a million insects.

D. Grandma looked ahead. Dewey held onto the oar. The dog moved and whined. They listened hard and heard the noise of the rapids. The noise was loud.

How are the passages alike? Both passages give the information about hearing the rapids. In passage C, Betsy Byars helps you feel how Dewey and Grandma must have felt as they listened. She compares the sound they heard to the hum of a million insects. This helps you to hear what the sound was like.

Passage D does not have words that help you share the feelings that Grandma and Dewey had on the river.

Authors use "sensory" words in descriptions. Sensory words ask you to use your five senses: touch, taste, hearing, sight, and smell to share the experiences described by the author.

Now read the following passage from "The Midnight Fox." Use the sidenotes to help you find the sensory words that the author uses.

I lay in bed for a long time, still in my clothes, and then I got up very carefully. I walked over to the window and looked out at the tree that Aunt Millie's sons used to just run up and down all the time like monkeys. I opened the window, pushed out the screen, reached out into the rain, and felt for the smooth spot Aunt Millie had told me was worn into the bark of the tree.

This description lets you follow Tom's actions step by step.

The author is appealing to your sense of touch as she tells you about the smooth spot on the tree that Tom was reaching for in the rain.

I took off my shoes and knelt on the window sill. There was an enormous flash of lightning that turned the whole world white for a moment. Then I climbed out onto the nearest branch and circled the trunk round with my arms.

I thought that I could never get one step farther. I thought that I could never move even one muscle or I would fall.

After a while, though, I began to sort of slip down the tree. I never let go of the main trunk for a second. I just moved my arms downward in very small movements.

If there were smooth spots on those branches, my feet never found them. They only touched one rough limb after another. Slowly, I kept inching down the tree, feeling my way, never looking at the ground. Finally, my foot reached out for another limb and felt the cold wet grass. It shocked me for a moment. Then I jumped down, landing on my hands and knees.

from *The Midnight Fox*
by Betsy Byars

Now read the following from "Trouble River." Look for the descriptive words the author uses to help you visualize the scene and feel what is happening to Grandma and Dewey.

There, stretching below them, were the rapids. Through a treacherous crack in the bluffs, the water ran, dashing against rocks, throwing spray high into the air.

"Get down, boy," Grandma cried.

He heard her when he was already on his knees, thrown by the force of the first waterfall. He slung one arm about Charlie and then crouched under his grandma's rocker. His other arm held the chair to the raft. Water washed over Dewey, drenching him.

They plunged, turned twice, and fell as if they were dropping to the center of the earth. Dewey was in the air for a moment, and then they struck the water. The rocking chair hit Dewey on the shoulder.

"Grandma," he cried. Water was in his mouth, his eyes. He thought they had plunged under the water and were lost. He swallowed the icy water and sucked it into his nose as he gasped for breath.

from *Trouble River*
by Betsy Byars

What words does the author use to create a picture of this scene in your mind?

What words in this paragraph lets you know how powerful the water was?

What words in this paragraph involve your senses of touch and taste?

In "Trouble River," the author compares leaving the rapids with "coming out of a nightmare." As she describes the change from the "dark shadows of the bluffs into the early morning sunlight," she helps you to visualize a more pleasant scene.

Authors sometimes make comparisons to help you visualize what is being described. Authors use description when they write to make the reader almost hear, see, touch, taste, or smell what is happening in their stories.

Read the following descriptions. To what senses do they appeal?

1. He heard the high, clear bark of the midnight fox.
2. Grandma's hair hung in wet wisps.
3. One bite made her think of the sharp, nippy, green apples she had eaten years before.
4. The faint, puzzling traces of spices reached him.
5. Try as he would, Sam could not put his hand on the slippery, wiggly animal.

In sentence 1, the words *high* and *clear* help you "hear" the bark of the midnight fox. In sentence 2, *in wet wisps* helps you "see" how Grandma's hair looked. *Sharp* and *nippy* help you "taste" the green apple in sentence 3. The words *faint* and *puzzling* help you "smell" the spices in sentence 4. *Slippery* and *wiggly* give you the "feel" of the animal in the last sentence.

As you read, look for the descriptive language an author uses to draw you into the story. When you write, try to use descriptive language, too. This will help your readers become a part of your stories.

In this selection, a girl and her family set out for America from their home in Russia. As you read, think about how this family feels as they travel toward their new life.

Dvora's Journey

by Marge Blaine

In 1904, a feeling of unrest and dissatisfaction existed among many people in Russia. They were unhappy with the conditions under which they were forced to live. Life was especially hard for Russian Jews.

Dvora, a Jewish girl, and her family made plans to escape from Russia into Poland. From there they hoped to travel all the way to America to start a new life. They thought that they would have more opportunities and more freedom in America.

The family faced many dangers and hardships on their journey. Perhaps the most dangerous time came when they arrived at the river.

We drew closer and closer to the river. Papa stopped the cart near the edge. Tall grass grew along the bank. Behind the grass were bushes and a few trees. I could see the other side, far across the water.

"Everyone out!" Papa called. "All the bundles, too!"

"But where are we going?" I asked. "There's nothing here."

Papa pointed. "Look," he said. "In the grass. Can you see the little house? That's where we'll stay."

I followed Papa's finger. Almost hidden by the grass was a straw hut. Did Papa mean we'd stay there? I guess he did, because he carried our belongings inside. Then Papa climbed back on the wagon.

"Where are you going, Papa?" Saul asked.

"To the village. I have to find the man who's going to guide us across."

I thought being indoors after three days in the cart would be a relief, but the hut was terrible. It was dark and it smelled.

"Can we go outside?" Minnie asked as soon as Papa left. "We can play near the river."

"No, children," Mama told us. "You'll have to stay inside. We don't want anyone to find us here."

Papa didn't come back until late. Although he was tired, he was smiling.

"Is everything all right, Jacob?" Mama asked.

Papa nodded. "I found Peter, the man I wanted. He'll get us across the river and into Poland."

"What took you so long, Papa?" Yossel asked.

"Well, it was hard to find Peter. I just couldn't walk around the village asking, 'Where's the man who smuggles Jews into Poland?' could I?"

We laughed. "I guess not," Saul said. "How *did* you find him?"

"Don't ask! It was some job. And then I had to find someone to buy the cart and the horse, too. But we're all set now."

We stayed in the hut for five days and nights. It

was awful, cooped up in the darkness with nothing to do. We took turns peeking through the door, watching the birds that hid in the grass or the changing shape of the clouds.

One afternoon I heard Saul ask Papa, "What if Peter doesn't come?"

"He'll come. Don't worry," Papa said.

"But what if he took your money and doesn't take us across?" Saul sounded worried.

My father shook his head. "I'm not so foolish," he explained. "I gave him half. Half here and half when we're safe in Poland. My friend Sol told me that's the way to do it."

Finally Papa left for town. When he came back, he had good news. "Tonight's the night," he told us. "Tonight we're leaving Russia." He looked around the hut. "Make sure everything's ready. Peter will be here after dark."

We waited in the darkness in front of the hut. No one said a word. Other families stood in groups along the bank.

It was chilly and I pulled my shawl tight. I heard a rustling in the bushes behind us. "I hope it's Peter," I whispered to Rivkeh, "and not the border guards."

"Sshhh! No talking," Papa reminded us.

Overhead I saw the stars and the moon, the last time I'd see the stars of Russia. "Are the same stars in Poland? And do they have stars in America?" I wondered. Before I had a chance to ask Saul, a man stepped out of the woods.

He began walking toward the water, motioning for us to follow. We stopped at the edge of the river. "Not a sound now," Peter warned. "The guards have guns and we don't want anyone shot!"

Stealing the border suddenly seemed real, not a game we were playing. If we made it, we'd be free, free from soldiers who took what they wanted without paying, free from the army, free to go to America. And if we didn't make it? I tried not to think about that.

"How are we going to get across?" I heard Minnie ask. "There aren't any boats."

"Walk!" my father told her, settling the heavy bundle holding his tools more securely on his back. "We're going to walk."

All around were gasps and splashing sounds as people began making their way into the water. The group that had been nearest to us, three men, two women, and a girl about my age, was already quite far out. I could see their outline in the moonlight: the strangely shaped mass of their bundles, small circles for their heads, and the longer shapes of their bodies, cut in half by the water. It looked pretty deep to me.

"Come on. Let's go," Papa repeated. "And don't let anything drop. If it falls into the river, we won't get it back."

Rivkeh and I stepped forward. My foot touched the water. "Aaiii!" I almost screamed. It was icy. How would I be able to walk through it?

I had no choice. In went my other foot. With each step I took I felt the water climb higher. It seemed even colder than it had at first. I pulled my shawl tighter in an effort to keep at least some of me warm. The river got deeper as we went farther in.

"What about our dresses?" I hissed to Rivkeh. "If it gets any deeper, they'll be soaked!"

"Try to hold your skirt up with your free hand."

"Free hand! I don't have any. One's keeping my bundle from falling into the water, and the other's holding my shawl."

"Well, just do the best you can."

I felt the current at my legs, trying to pull me downstream. I kept going, one foot after another, trying to keep from falling, trying to stay straight ahead, hoping the guards were busy along another part of the river.

We were almost halfway across by now and no one had tried to stop us. I began to think we'd make it, but my feet were getting worse. They felt as though they were turning to ice. At least the river wasn't getting any deeper now. I kept my skirts up as well as I could, hoping they'd stay dry.

Just then I heard a smothered cry from up ahead.

The girl I'd noticed before grabbed wildly at her bundle. I saw her arm reach out, trying to save it. She leaned over as far as she could, but it was gone. The current had taken it.

Far off I heard another splash and a cry, only it was too far away to see what had happened.

We kept walking. The water was shallower by now and somehow less cold. I saw trees and bushes along the bank and hurried to reach it. At last we were on the other side.

I looked to make sure we were all safe. I saw Papa, Mama, and Minnie. Minnie's skirts must have fallen into the water, because they clung to her legs. Mine were just a little wet along the bottom, but my legs felt clammy anyway.

Saul and Yossel were the last ones out. "Oh, Yossel!" Mama cried. "What happened?"

Yossel was soaked. Water dripped from his hair, down his shoulders, and onto the ground. "I slipped," he said. "Saul grabbed my hand and pulled me out."

Saul had one wet arm across Yossel's back, but the rest of him was dry. "It's a good thing I was right there," Saul told us.

"Let me change you," Mama said. "There's dry clothing right here."

"We can't stop, Esther," Papa ordered. "We're not out of Russia yet."

Mama wrapped her shawl around Yossel and we started off, following the others along a small path in the woods. Soon we came out into a field. It stretched far out in the distance. Stubble from corn scraped my legs.

There must have been forty or fifty people walking across the field. We looked like a strange market procession, lines of men and women, boys and girls, all of us with heavy bundles on our shoulders or backs, making our way together.

I saw the girl who'd lost her possessions walking slowly ahead of me. I went more quickly to catch up. When I reached her side, I could see she was crying.

"I saw what happened," I said softly. "I'm sorry you lost your things."

She nodded to show she'd heard, but didn't answer.

"What's your name?" I asked.

"Naomi."

"I'm Dvora," I told her. "Are all those people in your family?" I asked, pointing to the men and women in front of us.

"No."

"Where are your parents?" I asked. "Are they in America?"

Naomi shook her head. "They're dead," she told me. "My father was in the army. He was killed before I was born."

"I'm sorry," I said. "What about your mother?"

"My mother and I lived with my uncle. Then she died when I was about five or six. I've been living with my uncle ever since. Now he's sending me to another uncle in New York."

I couldn't think of anything to say. "I'm sorry," I finally told her again.

"That's all right." Naomi had stopped crying by this time. "I was scared at first," she said, "but I think it'll be better for me there. My uncle wrote that there are lots of jobs. He's in a factory where they make dresses and coats. He says they can always use a good seamstress."

I thought of Rivkeh. She sewed beautifully.

"What about you?" Naomi asked. "Are you going to get a job in America?"

I shook my head. "No. I don't think so. My father promised I could go to school. I'd like to be a teacher, only I don't know if girls can be teachers there."

"Girls can be teachers there."

"How do you know?"

"My uncle sent all his children through school. They've had women teachers—even the boys!"

"Oh, Naomi," I said. "That makes me feel so much better about going." She smiled. "What was in your bundle?" I asked her.

"My other skirt—I was saving it to wear when I met my uncle—my good shawl—it used to be my mother's—and a gift, a cloth I'd embroidered for my uncle."

"It's too bad you lost it."

"I know. It's a good thing the money for my ticket was sewn inside my dress." Naomi looked up. "At first I thought I couldn't live without those things, especially Mama's shawl, but I guess I can."

We didn't talk for a while. I guess we were both thinking about America and what we'd find there. We walked through the field all night. Finally Peter stopped.

"What's the matter?" one of the men asked.

"Nothing," he said. "You'll be all right now. You're inside Poland."

People began to cheer and hug one another. The men crowded around Peter and shook his hand. They seemed almost happy to pay him their money.

"Town's that way," Peter told them, pointing the way we were going. "And the station's right on the main street."

Mama took out dry clothing for Yossel and food for all of us before we started off again. We were in Poland. The first part of the journey to America was over; the next part was about to begin.

1. How did the people feel about leaving Russia? What detail in the story told you this?

2. Name three of the hardships Dvora's family faced on their journey.

3. Why do you think having more freedom was so important to Dvora's family that they would undertake such a dangerous journey?

4. What did you read that let you know that the people were happy to be inside Poland?

5. What important information did Peter give the people once they were inside Poland to help them continue on their journey to America?

6. How does the statement "Give me liberty or give me death" apply to this selection?

Think and Write

Prewrite

Think about how Dvora and her family felt when they crossed the river into Poland. What dangers were there? What happened while they were crossing the river? What kept them from giving up? Work with other classmates to act out the river crossing, discussing how you think

Dvora felt. Think of three questions you could ask Dvora about her river crossing.

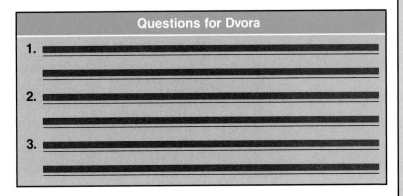

Draft

Pretend you are a television reporter. Make up answers to the questions you would ask Dvora and include them in a paragraph about her adventure. As you write, remember how you thought Dvora felt about crossing the river.

Revise

Read your paragraph. Remember, you are supposed to be a television reporter. Does your paragraph include details that make crossing the river seem real? Will the answers to the questions you ask Dvora help the viewers see and feel what Dvora and her family saw and felt? Make changes where needed.

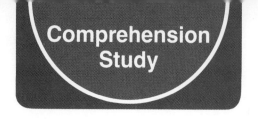

Sequence

Many stories and articles contain a series of events that happen in a certain order. If the order of the events is not clear, readers may become confused and may not understand what they read. To make the order of events clear, writers tell about events in sequence and give readers time-order clues.

Read the following paragraphs. Decide what is missing.

Betsy Byars was born in Charlotte, North Carolina. She had many pets. Her love for animals is obvious in her book *The Midnight Fox*.

Betsy studied English at Queens College in North Carolina. She was not thinking of becoming a writer. Mrs. Byars is one of the best-loved writers for young people.

The paragraphs mention several events, but they do not tell you when these events took place. Because there is no order in the writing, you have no clues to the sequence, or time order, of the events.

Now read the same paragraphs rewritten with time-order clues. Notice how the clues connect the events.

Betsy Byars was born on August 7, 1928, in Charlotte, North Carolina. As a child, Betsy had many pets. Her love for animals is obvious in her book *The Midnight Fox.*

Betsy studied English at Queens College in North Carolina. When she graduated from college, Betsy was not thinking of becoming a writer. Writing became important only after she married Edward Byars and was at home raising her children. Today, Mrs. Byars is one of the best-loved writers for young people.

The time-order clues in this paragraph include dates and time words. Both kinds of clues help explain how events are connected.

Clues to Time Order: Dates and Time Words

Writers often use dates to show time order. A date may be general, such as *Wednesday*, or *1492*, which could mean any Wednesday or anytime in the year 1492, or a date may be specific, such as Friday, July 22, 1988.

You know that in addition to dates, writers use time words to show how events are related. Among the time-order words are: *before, after, then, next, now, at first, suddenly, earlier, while, during,* and *yesterday.* These words do not give exact times, but they help you understand the time order.

Read a summary of "Dvora's Journey" on the next page.

In 1904, Dvora's family escaped from Russia into Poland. From Poland, they expected to go to the United States.

First, they traveled across Russia in a horse-drawn cart. Then they came to the river that separated Russia and Poland. They waited inside a hut for five days until the guide led them across the river.

Finally, the time came for them to cross. They could hardly wait until it was dark.

That night they waded across the icy river into Poland. The first part of the trip to the United States was over. The next part would begin soon. A year later they would be in America.

Notice how this summary uses one date and many time words to help you follow the time order.

Knowing the time order of certain events can help you discover other information that is not directly given. Use the date and time-order clues to answer this question: By what year did Dvora's family plan to be in America? How do you know this?

Textbook Application:
Time Order in Social Studies

Read the article on the next page that tells how a young American Indian woman helped a group of explorers. As you read, notice the dates and time words that help you follow the order of events. The sidenotes are a guide.

She was only 16 years old at the time of her greatest adventure. She was a **Shoshone** (shuh·SHOH·nee) Indian. At her death in 1812 only a few people knew her name. Today we know **Sacajawea** (sa·kuh·juh·WEE·uh) as an American hero who helped our country grow from coast to coast.

This date gives you a general idea of the historical time period in which Sacajawea lived.

Why was Sacajawea important? Let's go back hundreds of years before she was born. People from Europe were exploring America then. They could travel only as far as the Rocky Mountains. The ragged mountains were a huge wall blocking the way. It would take many years before the region could be settled.

This is a clue that you are about to be given some background information.

The Spanish came first. Spanish settlers pushed north from Mexico in the 1700's. Next came French fur traders from Canada. They found many Indian tribes living here. Yet Americans in the East knew very little about the Rocky Mountains in the early 1800's. Was it possible to take a wagon through the mountains? Could a person go by river from the Atlantic to the Pacific? No one could say for sure.

Notice how the dates and time words in this paragraph tell you the order of events.

Lewis and Clark

President Thomas Jefferson sent two men to find out. Their names were **Meriwether Lewis** and **William Clark.** Lewis and Clark with a small group of men left St. Louis, Missouri, in May 1804. They spent the summer and fall going up the Missouri River. In November of that year, they stopped at an Indian village to spend the winter. The village lay at the edge of the Rocky Mountains. The hardest part of their journey was just ahead.

Sacajawea now enters our story. She was the wife of a trapper who was staying at the village. Lewis and Clark hired the trapper to help them find a way through the mountains. Sacajawea joined them because she could speak to the Indians.

Across the Rockies

In the spring the party started up the Missouri again. One day one of their boats tipped over. All their goods fell into the icy water. Sacajawea did not waste a moment. She jumped in and saved almost everything.

This paragraph contains additional dates and time clues. What are they?

This time clue tells you when Lewis and Clark's group started up the Missouri River. Use clues from earlier paragraphs to figure out what year it was.

Now the party was in the mountains near Shoshone country. Lewis and Clark set up a meeting with the Shoshones to buy horses from the Indians. The Shoshones did not want to sell their horses. Sacajawea stepped forward. The Shoshone chief gasped in surprise. Sacajawea was his sister! He had not seen her in five years.

Sacajawea persuaded her brother to sell the horses. The Shoshones also helped guide the group through the mountains.

Lewis and Clark reached the Pacific after much suffering. Then they turned around and made the same trip back. They traveled 8,000 miles (about 12,900 km). <u>The trip took them nearly three years!</u> They had gone from the Mississippi River to the Pacific Ocean, opening up the land to Americans. Sacajawea had helped them do it.

—*States and Regions,*
Harcourt Brace Jovanovich

You read earlier that the starting date of the trip was in May 1804. Use the time clue in this paragraph to determine about what year it was when the group finished their trip.

Reading about a series of events can sometimes be confusing, especially when the events are not described in order. As you read, remember to use time clues to help you place events in their proper order.

Young Reader's Choice
Award Author

A boy's voyage home takes a detour when he is shipwrecked. Read to find out how he and a wild horse stay alive—and learn to trust each other—on a deserted island.

The Black Stallion

by Walter Farley

Alec was returning to America on a ship from Bombay, India, when a storm struck. The ship was split in two! Alec stood in line for the lifeboat until he remembered that the black stallion was tied up in a stall. The horse would surely die if Alec didn't turn him loose.

The horse was a wild stallion. He had never carried a rider, and he hated being tied up. Most of the ship's crew thought the Black was a mean horse. Alec knew better.

Alec freed the Black in time. Together they jumped into the ocean just as the ship was sinking. After a very long swim, the Black pulled Alec ashore on a small island. There Alec made a rough shelter for himself out of wood he gathered on the shore. He found fresh spring water and food— some berries and fish. Alec also began to make friends with the wild black stallion.

Days passed, and gradually the friendship between the boy and the Black grew. The stallion now came at his call and let Alec pat him while he ate. One night Alec sat within the warm glow of the fire and watched the stallion eating moss beside the spring.

The flame's shadows reached out and cast ghostlike patterns on the Black's body. Alec's face became grim as thoughts rushed through his brain. Should he try it tomorrow? Did he dare try to ride the Black? Should he wait a few more days? Go ahead—tomorrow. *Don't do it!* Go ahead—.

The fire burned lower and lower. Yet Alec sat beside the fire, his eyes fixed on the black stallion.

The next morning Alec woke from a fitful sleep to find the sun high above. He looked for the Black, but the horse was not in sight. Alec whistled, but no answer came. He walked toward the hill. The sun blazed down and the sweat ran from his body. If it would only rain!

When Alec reached the top of the hill, he saw the Black at one end of the beach. Again he whistled. This time there was an answering whistle as the stallion turned his head. Alec walked up the beach toward him.

The Black stood still as he approached. Alec went cautiously up to him and placed a hand on his neck. "Steady," he whispered, as the warm skin quivered slightly beneath his hand. The stallion showed neither fear nor hate of him. His large eyes were still turned toward the sea.

For a moment Alec stood with his hand on the Black's neck. Then he walked toward a sand dune a short distance away. The stallion followed. Alec stepped up the side of the dune, his left hand in the horse's thick mane. The Black's ears went forward. His eyes followed the boy nervously—some of the wildness returned to them. His muscles twitched. For a moment Alec could not decide what to do. Then his hands gripped the mane tighter and he threw himself on the Black's back. For a second the stallion stood still. Then he snorted and plunged. Alec felt the mighty muscles heave. Then he was flung through the air, landing heavily on his back. Everything went dark.

Slowly Alec opened his eyes. The stallion was pushing him with his head. Alec tried moving his arms and legs, and found them bruised but not broken. Wearily he got to his feet. The wildness had once more disappeared in the Black. He looked as though nothing had happened.

Alec waited for a few minutes. Then once again he led the stallion to the sand dune. His hand gripped the horse's mane. This time he laid only the upper part of his body on the stallion's back, while he talked soothingly into his ear. The Black's ears moved back and forth as he glanced backward with his dark eyes.

"See, I'm not going to hurt you," Alec whispered. After a few minutes, Alec carefully slid onto the horse's back. Once again, the stallion snorted and sent the boy flying through the air.

Alec picked himself up from the ground—slower this time. When he had rested, he whistled for the Black again. The stallion moved toward him. Alec stepped on the sand dune and once again let the Black feel his weight. Gently he spoke into a large ear, "It's me. I'm not much to carry." He slid onto the stallion's back. One arm slipped around the Black's neck as he half-reared. Then, like a shot from a gun, the Black broke down the beach. His action shifted, and his huge strides seemed to make him fly through the air.

Alec gripped the stallion's mane. The wind screamed by and he couldn't see! Then down through a long ravine he rushed. Alec's blurred vision made out a black object in front of them, and as a flash he remembered the deep gully that was there. He felt the stallion gather himself. Instinctively he leaned forward and held the Black firm and steady with his hands and knees. Then they were in the air, sailing over the black hole. Alec almost lost his balance when they landed but recovered himself in time to keep from falling off!

The jump had helped greatly in clearing Alec's mind. He leaned closer to the stallion's ear and kept repeating, "Easy, Black. Easy." Alec kept talking to him.

Slower and slower ran the Black. Gradually he came to a stop. The boy let go of the stallion's mane, and his arms circled the Black's neck. Wearily he slipped to the ground. Never had he dreamed a horse could run so fast! The stallion looked at him, his head held high, his large body only partly covered with sweat.

That night Alec lay wide awake, his body aching with pain, but his heart pounding with excitement. He had ridden the Black! He had conquered this wild, unbroken stallion with kindness. He felt sure that from that day on the Black was his—his alone! But for what—would they ever be found? Would he ever see his home again? Alec shook his head. He had promised himself he wouldn't think of that anymore.

The next day he mounted the Black again. The horse half-reared but didn't fight him. Alec spoke softly in his ear, and the Black stood still. Then Alec touched him lightly on the side, and he walked—a long, loping stride. Far up the beach they went.

Then Alec tried to turn him by shifting his weight and gently pushing the stallion's head. Gradually the horse turned. Alec took a firmer grip on his long mane. He pressed his knees tighter against the large body. The stallion broke out of his walk into a gallop. The wind blew his mane back into the boy's face. The stallion's stride was effortless, and Alec found it easy to ride. Halfway down the beach, he was able to bring the stallion back again to a walk, then to a complete stop. Slowly Alec turned him to the right, then to the left, and then around in a circle.

Long but exciting hours passed as Alec tried to make the Black understand what he wanted him to do. The sun was going down quickly when he walked the stallion to the end of the beach. The Black turned and stood still. A mile of smooth, white sand stretched before them.

Suddenly the stallion bolted, almost throwing Alec to the ground. He picked up speed with amazing swiftness. Alec hung low over his neck, his breath coming in gasps. Tears from the wind rolled down Alec's cheeks.

Quickly the stallion neared the end of the beach. Alec thought that his breathtaking ride of yesterday was to be repeated. He pulled back on the mane. Suddenly the Black's pace slowed. Alec flung one arm around the stallion's neck. The Black shifted into his fast trot, which gradually became slower and slower, until Alec had him under control. Overjoyed, Alec turned the stallion and rode him over the hill to the spring. Together they drank the cool, refreshing water.

With the days that followed, Alec's mastery over the Black grew greater and greater. Alec could do almost anything with him. The wildness of the stallion disappeared when he saw the boy. Alec rode him around the island and raced him down the beach. Without realizing it, Alec was improving his horsemanship. He had reached the point where he was almost a part of the Black as they raced along.

One night Alec sat beside his campfire and stared into the flames that reached high into the air. He was deep in thought. The ship had left Bombay on a Saturday, the fifteenth of August. The shipwreck had happened a little over two weeks later, perhaps on the second of September. He had been on the island exactly — nineteen days. That would make it about the twenty-first of September. By now his family must think he is dead! He had to find a way out. A ship just had to pass the island sometime.

For the first time, Alec thought of the coming cold weather. The heat had been so strong upon the island since his arrival that it had never entered his mind that it would soon get cold. Would his shelter give him enough protection?

He rose to his feet and walked toward the hill. The Black, standing beside the spring, raised his head and whistled when he saw him. He followed Alec as he climbed to the top. The boy's eyes swept the dark, rolling sea. The stallion, too, seemed to be watching — his eyes staring into the night, his ears pointing forward. An hour passed. Then they turned and made their way back to camp.

A wind started blowing from out of the west. Alec built up the fire for the night, then crawled wearily into his shelter. He stretched out and was soon asleep.

He didn't know how long he had been sleeping, but suddenly the Black's shrill scream woke him up. Sleepily, he opened his eyes. The air had grown hot. Then he heard a crackling noise above. His head jerked upward. The top of the shelter was on fire! Flames were creeping down the sides. Alec leaped to his feet and rushed outside.

A strong wind was sweeping the island. Right away he knew what had happened. Sparks from his campfire had been blown upon the top of the shelter and had easily set fire to the dry wood. He grabbed a large shell and ran to the spring. Filling it, he ran back and threw the water on the flames.

The Black walked nervously beside the spring, his nostrils quivering. Alec rushed back and forth with his shell full of water, trying to keep the fire from spreading. But it had a good start and soon the whole shelter was on fire. Smoke filled the air. The boy and the horse were forced to move farther and farther back.

Alec knew that the fire could not spread much farther. The island was too barren of any real fuel. But right now the flames were burning everything in sight. They roared and reached high into the air. There was nothing that Alec could do. The one thing he really needed — his shelter — was gone. And there was no more wood.

The fire burned a long time before it started to die down. Then the wind, too, began to slow. Alec sat beside the spring, watching the flames, until the first streaks of dawn

appeared in the sky. He blinked his smoke-filled eyes and gritted his teeth. He wasn't licked yet! He'd find some way to make a shelter. If that didn't work, then he'd sleep outside like the Black.

His mind made up, he set out for the beach. Perhaps some wood had been swept onto shore during the night. The Black trotted ahead of him. Then Alec saw him snort and rear as he reached the top of the hill, and plunge back down again. Alec hurried forward. From the top of the hill, he looked down. Below him was a ship anchored four hundred yards off the island!

He heard voices. He saw a rowboat being drawn up on the beach by five men. Alec didn't believe what he saw. Unable to shout, he rushed down the hill.

"You were right, Pat, there *is* someone on this island!" he heard one of the men shout to the other.

The other replied, "Sure, and I knew I saw a fire reaching into the sky!"

Alec's eyes blurred; he couldn't see. He stumbled and fell and then jumped to his feet. Again he rushed forward. Then they had their arms around him.

Words jumbled together and stuck in Alec's throat as he looked into the five pairs of eyes staring at him. Then he found his voice. "We're saved!" he yelled. "We're saved, Black, we're saved!"

Discuss the Selection

1. How did the horse and Alec help each other to get to the island?

2. What did Alec do to stay alive on the island?

3. What part of the story did you think was the scariest?

4. What was the first clue the author gave you that the Black was beginning to trust Alec?

5. Why did the ship come to the island?

6. How was Alec's kindness toward the stallion unexpectedly rewarded?

Think and Write

Prewrite

Pretend you are shipwrecked like Alec. If you had a choice, what animal would you like to have with you? Why? What would the island be like? What would you do for food and shelter? Would your animal be a pet or a helper? Make a list of things you would do on your island.

Draft

Pretend you are a reporter and are assigned to write a short news story about someone who has recently been rescued from a deserted island. Tell how he or she lived on the island. How did he or she eat? Sleep? Dress? Now imagine that the same person was shipwrecked but had an animal as company. How did the animal help the person? Include these details in your news story. Remember, a good news story answers the questions *who, what, when, where,* and *why.*

Revise

Read your news story. Does it have an opening, or a beginning sentence, that makes readers want to continue reading? Does your story answer all of the questions? Is it interesting to the reader? Make any necessary changes to your story so that it answers the questions and is interesting to your reader.

John Newbery Medal Author

Roads

by Rachel Field

A road might lead to anywhere—
    To harbour towns and quays,
Or to a witch's pointed house
    Hidden by bristly trees.
It might lead past the tailor's door,
    Where he sews with needle and thread,
Or by Miss Pim the milliner's,
    With hats for every head.
It might be a road to a great, dark cave
    With treasure and gold piled high,
Or a road with a mountain tied to its end,
    Blue-humped against the sky.
Oh, a road might lead you anywhere—
    To Mexico or Maine.
But then, it might just fool you, and—
    Lead you back home again!

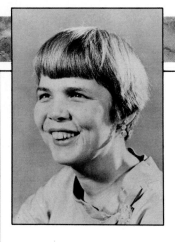

Jean Little

When Jean Little was young, she had a turtle that she named after the British poet Robert Browning. The name she gave her pet was an early sign of Jean's interest in literature. She may not have known then that she wanted to write books. However, she did know that she loved reading them.

Jean Little was born in Taiwan in 1932. Her mother and father were American doctors who had gone to Taiwan to live. Jean was blind when she was born, but she did gain some sight as she grew older. Jean was lucky because her mother, father, two brothers, and sister often read books to her. She listened to many stories. At an early age, Jean was able to read on her own.

When Jean was seven, the Little family left Taiwan and moved to Canada. There, Jean had some problems. The children at school made fun of her because of her poor eyesight. She just did not seem to fit in. Jean began spending more and more time in the library. She liked being around books better than she liked being with people her own age.

Jean's feelings about life changed the more she read. With each new book, she dreamed and thought about a career as a writer. Jean's love for literature grew.

Growing up with poor eyesight was not easy. Still, Jean has achieved a lot in life. She has chosen to make the most of the *ability* part of her sight dis*ability*.

Jean studied English language and literature at the University of Toronto. Then she began a career teaching children with handicaps. Working with these children led her to believe that she should be writing books in which disabled boys and girls could see themselves. Jean Little's first books, then, were for the children in her own classes.

Parts of Jean Little and her life are in her later books as well. She writes about children who have cerebral palsy. She tells about blind and mentally retarded children. The children in Jean Little's books are different. However, this does not mean that they are weak. They are true-to-life characters who learn to live with themselves as they are.

Jean Little's books have been translated into many languages. As a result, she is a pen pal to children across the world. Some of her books have won important prizes.

Jean Little has been brave as she faced life. She has not let her poor sight keep her from doing things. You will be reading a selection from Jean Little's book *From Anna*. As you read, think about how Anna, too, had to be brave to face her problems.

Canadian Children's
Book Award Author

Read to discover how a girl gets a fresh start in a new country.

Anna's New Beginning

by Jean Little

Germany in 1934 had a new leader: Adolf Hitler. His hatred of the Jewish people was just beginning to change the country. The Solden family was not Jewish but sensed that soon all Germans might be in danger. Anna, the youngest of the Solden children, also faced personal challenges, both at school and at home.

At school, Anna was failing. When she tried to read, the letters jiggled on the page. At home, Anna's father and mother argued. Papa had once promised his "darling Anna" that she would grow up where thoughts are free. To keep his promise, he feared they might soon have to leave Germany. Mama did not think that they should leave.

Also, Papa had announced that everyone in the family must learn to speak English. Only Anna and her mother were slow to learn the new language.

It was a good winter, a lovely spring. Anna took for granted that the storm had blown over, that eventually Papa would even forget about the English lessons.

Then one morning early in June, 1934, a letter came from Canada. It was not from Anna's uncle in Canada, Uncle Karl; it was from his lawyer. And overnight, Anna's sometimes happy, often unhappy, but always familiar world turned upside down.

"Anna! You are going to be late for school," Mama called. "And there is a letter here for you from Canada, Ernst, which looks important."

They went to the table. The letter lay at Papa's place. He opened it and read it. Then his hands clenched, half crumpling the page.

"What is it?" Mama cried, hurrying to him.

Papa had to wait a moment. Anna saw him swallow.

"My brother Karl is dead," he said then. "He had a heart attack. He has left me everything he owned."

There was a babble of voices.

"Oh, Papa, how awful!" said Gretchen, who remembered Uncle Karl from when she was a small girl and he had visited Germany and stayed with them.

"Papa, are we going to be rich, then?" That was Rudi.

"Rich," Fritz echoed longingly, but he stopped there. Something in Papa's face silenced him.

"Poor Papa," Frieda chimed in, kicking Fritz.

It was then that Papa said the unbelievable thing. He did not ask anyone. He just made a statement, a flat, hard statement of fact.

"No, Rudi, we will not be rich. Karl was only a grocer with a small store, and Germany is not the only country that has been suffering from a depression. This is our chance. We will go to Canada."

"Canada!"

In every voice there was the same feeling that Anna had heard months before in Mama's. Canada was not a place to go to; Canada was a geography lesson.

"Mr. Menzies suggests we come in September." Papa went on as though he heard no outcry.

"Who is Mr. Menzies? What does he know about what we do?" Mama's words cut through the air as shrilly as a whistle.

"He is Karl's lawyer. I had written to Karl before, asking what our chances would be in Canada. He offered to take us in, but I wanted my own business. He said there was no place for a German English teacher. Now I shall be a grocer. I did not want Karl's

charity, but it seems he has given it to me after all."

Papa got up, letter in hand, and strode out of the room. There were tears on his cheeks. Anna saw the tears and could not move. She could not think. Mama, though, started after him, but at the last minute she saw the clock, gasped, and stopped to hustle the children off to school, refusing to answer any questions.

"Go! Go!" she almost screamed at them. "As though things aren't bad enough with this in your father's head!"

She whirled away then and left them without her "Good-bye." As Anna went out, closing the door behind herself, she could hear Mama right through the walls.

"Ernst, Ernst, I will not go. I tell you *I will not go!*"

Then, pausing, she heard Papa, not so loudly, but in a voice like iron. "We are all going, Klara. Whether you understand or not, whether you come willingly or not, we are going. You must start to get ready."

Papa bought their tickets. They were going by steamship. It should have been exciting. To Fritz and Frieda it was. They began to brag.

However, Papa even put a stop to that, the moment he found out about it. "I don't want you talking about the fact that we are going," he told the whole family.

"If you'd only explain, Papa," Rudi answered, "then we'd know what to say. People ask us questions, you know."

"You may tell people your uncle has died and we have been left a business in Canada. Say that I have to go and look after it. Say we have all decided to go. You don't need to say more than that. I do not want you to talk about it any more than you have to. It is not safe to say too much."

Papa sounded so serious. The children knew there was much he was not telling them. Mama thought he was wrong, but even Rudi believed Papa. He was too unhappy himself to be doing it for some foolish reason.

That was when Anna knew he did not want to go either, that he was going because of his promise to her that she should grow up where thoughts are free and because of his love for all of them — Rudi, Gretchen, the twins, even Mama, who was still fighting against him. Poor Papa!

Finally it was time. They were going tomorrow, away from their home, to a land where people spoke English.

Everything was packed. They sat on boxes to eat their last meal at home.

"It feels lonely here," Frieda whispered.

Papa laughed all at once. It was as though he had been afraid but his fear was suddenly vanishing. He could see where he was taking them, and it was a fine, safe place.

"Let's not be lonely," he rallied them. "Why, we all have each other. We can make a fresh start together, we Soldens. We just need some courage. What's the bravest song you know?"

It was Gretchen who said it, not Anna.

" 'Thoughts Are Free,' Papa," she cried.

Anna felt much braver as their voices chased back the shadows and filled the emptiness with joyous sound.

Suddenly, Anna's voice faltered and broke off. Nobody else had seen, but Mama was crying again. Her cheeks were wet with tears. As the others swept on into the wonderful second verse and the triumphant finish, Anna once more felt alone and afraid. Then she saw her father smile at her mother, and she looked at Mama again.

The tears were still there, but Mama was singing as bravely as anyone.

The family stood in a huddle near the barriers in the waiting room at Toronto Union Station, in Canada. After leaving the ship in Halifax, they had come the rest of the way by train. There had not been money enough for berths. Anna had sat up for thirty-six hours, leaning against Papa whenever she dozed, and now she swayed on her feet. If only she could lie down somewhere!

"Mr. Menzies will be here any minute," Papa spoke again, anxiously scanning the faces of people near them.

Anna had let her eyelids close for just one second. Now she opened them wide in astonishment. Papa, who insisted that they all speak English, had spoken in German! He must really be worried.

Finally a man approached and spoke to Papa.

"Ernst Solden?"

"Yes, yes. You must be Mr. Menzies."

The men shook hands. Mr. Menzies was tall and his hair was gray.

"My wife, Klara," Papa began introducing them. "My oldest boy, Rudolf . . . Gretchen . . . Fritz and Elfrieda, our twins . . . and this is Anna."

126

Anna blinked at hearing Rudi and Frieda called by their real names. Mr. Menzies smiled politely.

"You two certainly look like your father," he told the older ones. "And the twins are very like you, Mrs. Solden."

Anna was startled again. She had never heard her mother called "Mrs." before. It made Mama seem a stranger.

Moving automatically, she followed the others out of the station, across the street, and into a restaurant. There she munched on a sandwich—something she had never eaten before—and sipped from a tall glass of milk.

"Franz Schumacher said he'd meet us here," Mr. Menzies was explaining to her parents. "He's a doctor and was a great friend of Karl's. We'll need two cars to get you and your bags to the house," Mr. Menzies said. "Dr. Schumacher is late. A last-minute patient, I suppose."

The words blurred in Anna's head. She dropped her sandwich half-eaten. By the time Dr. Schumacher came hurrying in, she was sound asleep in her chair. This time, she missed the introductions. She did not rouse until a deep voice, close beside her, said, "I'll carry the little one."

Mama objected. "She is much too heavy to carry. Wake her up. Anna . . . Anna!"

I can't, Anna thought groggily, keeping her eyes shut.

Strong arms gathered her up.

"She's not heavy at all," Dr. Schumacher grunted, shifting her to get a better grip. Anna flicked open her eyes for one split second, just long enough to see the big, friendly face. What had he said? Could she really have heard?

If the doctor knew she was awake, he made no sign. "Light as a feather—really!" he said to Mama.

Anna lay perfectly still in his arms. She kept her eyes tightly closed and she did not smile.

Yet she loved Franz Schumacher from that moment.

"When you get settled and a bit rested," the doctor said, "bring the children around to my office to have their medical examinations for school."

"School!" Fritz echoed, horrified.

The doctor looked back at the boy and laughed.

"Yes, school," he said. "It starts a week from Tuesday."

Dr. Schumacher's waiting room was shabby and crowded. When the Soldens arrived, the two boys had to stand up against one wall with their father because there were not enough chairs.

When he had finished examining Rudi, Gretchen, and the twins, Dr. Schumacher stretched out a broad hand to Anna. She slid off her father's knee at once and put her hand in the doctor's. Papa smiled. So someone else had discovered a way to reach his Anna!

"Let me hear you read the letters on this card," Dr. Schumacher said to Anna.

Anna froze. Reading! She couldn't . . .

She looked where he was pointing. Why, there was only one letter there. That was easy! She did know the names of the letters now.

"E," she told him.

"And the next line down?" Dr. Schumacher asked.

Anna wrinkled up her forehead. Yes, there *were* other letters. She could see them now, when she squinted. They looked like little gray bugs, wiggling.

"They're too small to read," she said.

Ten minutes later, when Dr. Schumacher was very sure about Anna's eyesight, he came out to the waiting room with Anna.

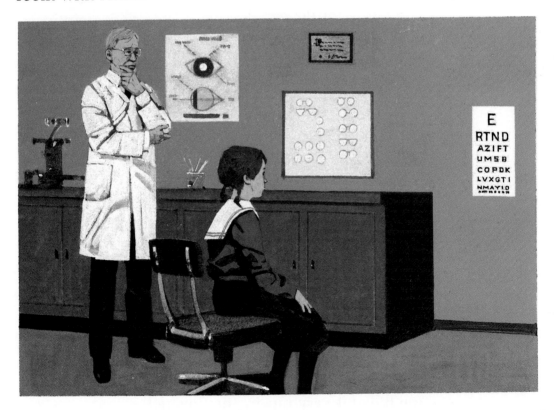

"She sees very poorly, very poorly indeed," he said. "She should be wearing glasses. She probably should have had them two or three years ago. Before we go any further, I want to have her examined by an eye doctor."

It was all like a nightmare to Anna. Once more, she had to read letters off a faraway card. Once again, she could only see the big E. The new doctor peered into her eyes with a small bright light. He made her look through a collection of lenses. All at once, other letters appeared.

"F . . . P," Anna read in a low voice. "T . . . O, I think . . . Z."

"Now read these," the eye doctor said, pointing to the next row of letters. These letters were too small for Anna to read.

Dr. Schumacher then took her to yet another room where she sat on a chair and was fitted for frames. When they were back in Dr. Schumacher's office, the grown-ups took the chairs.

"Even with the glasses, she will not have normal vision," Franz Schumacher explained. "She'll have to go to a special class, a Sight Saving Class," he went on. "Lessons are made easier there for children with poor eyesight."

"Not go to school with the others!" Mama wailed, hoping she was not understanding.

Dr. Schumacher switched back to German. He spoke gently, soothingly.

"It is a nice place. She'll like it there. You will, Anna. You'll like it very much," he finished.

Anna did not look up or answer. Dr. Schumacher had become part of the bad dream in which she was caught. She hardly heard what he said. What she did hear, she did not believe. How could she like school?

Then, three days before school was to begin, Anna's new glasses arrived. Perched on her nub of a nose, they looked like two round moons. She longed to snatch them off and hurl them into a far corner. Instead, she peered through them suspiciously.

For one startled moment, an utterly new expression came over her small, plain face, a look of intense surprise and wonder. She was seeing a world she had never guessed existed.

"Oh, Anna, you look just like an owl," Frieda laughed, not meaning any harm.

The wonder left Anna's face instantly. She turned away from her family and stumped off up the stairs to her alcove where none of them could follow without permission. Papa, though, came up alone a minute or two later.

"Do you like them, Anna?" he asked quietly.

She almost told him then. She nearly said, "I never knew you had wrinkles around your eyes, Papa. I knew your eyes were blue, but I didn't know they were so bright."

But Anna remembered Frieda's laughing words. How she hated being laughed at!

"Do I *have* to keep wearing them, Papa?" she blurted. Papa looked sorry for her, but he nodded.

"You must wear them all the time and no nonsense," he said firmly.

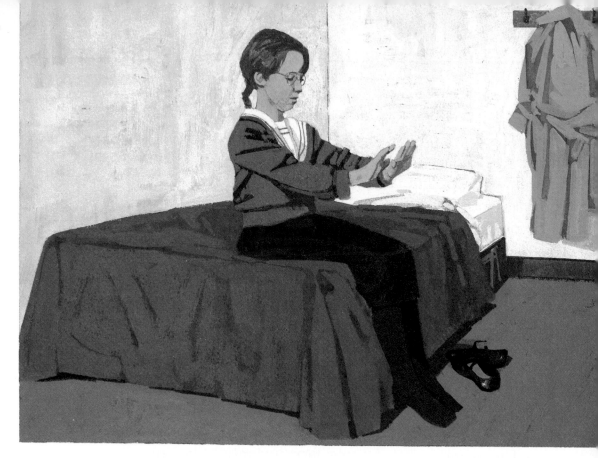

Anna reddened slightly. It was not right, fooling Papa like this. She was not ready to share what had happened to her. Even her father might not understand. She could hardly take it in herself.

"All right, Papa," she said, letting the words drag.

When he had gone, she lifted her right hand and held it up in front of her. She moved her fingers and counted them. Even though the light was poor, she could see all five. She examined her fingernails. They shone faintly and they had little half-moons at the bottom. Then she leaned forward and stared at her red wool blanket. It was all hairy. She could see the hairs, hundreds of them.

Everything, everywhere she turned, looked new, looked different, looked miraculous.

When Dr. Schumacher arrived to take Mama and her to the new school, Anna was ready with a bright bow on each of her thin braids.

"It is so kind of you to take Anna to this school," Mama fussed, getting herself and Anna into their coats.

"Nonsense," Dr. Schumacher said, "I know Miss Williams. I can help with the English, too. It won't take long."

The three of them found nothing to say to each other as they rode along. When they got out in front of the school, Anna marched along between her mother and the doctor. She tried to look as though this were something she did every day, as though her heart were not thudding so hard against her ribs it almost hurt. Franz Schumacher reached down his big warm hand and gathered up her cold little paw. His hand felt just like Papa's. She left her hand where it was and felt braver.

Miss Williams was the first surprise in what was to be a day of surprises.

"It's lovely to have you with us, Anna," she said when Dr. Schumacher drew Anna forward and introduced her and Mama.

The teacher had a low, husky voice, and her smile was so honest that even Anna could not doubt she meant it. She looked at Anna almost the way Papa did.

She doesn't know me yet, Anna reminded herself, not smiling in return. She hasn't heard me read.

"I've brought you a real challenge this time, Eileen," Dr. Schumacher said in an undertone.

Challenge.

Anna did not know that word. Did it mean "stupid one"? But no, it couldn't. Franz Schumacher still had her hand in his, and the kindness of his grasp had not changed as he said it. Anna kept the new word in her mind. When she got home, she would ask Papa.

Fifteen minutes later she sat in her new desk and watched her mother and Dr. Schumacher leave the classroom.

"Don't leave me!" Anna almost cried out after them, her courage deserting her. She must not cry. She must *not*!

"You can sit next to Benjamin," Miss Williams said. "Ben's been needing someone to keep him on his toes, haven't you, Ben?"

Quickly, she told Anna the names of all the other children in the class. The names flew around Anna's ears like birds, each escaping just as she thought she had it safely captured.

"You won't remember most of them now," the teacher said, seeing panic in the child's eyes. "You'll have to get to know us bit by bit. I think you and Ben will probably be working together," Miss Williams went on.

"Now you know us well enough to begin with," the teacher said. "It's time we got some work done in this room."

Anna, who had been relaxed while studying Ben, froze. What now? Would she have to read? She sat as still as a trapped animal while Miss Williams went to a corner cupboard. In a moment, she was back.

"Here are some crayons, Anna," she said. "I'd like you to draw a picture. Anything you like. I'll get the others started and then I'll be free to find out where you are in your schoolwork."

Anna did not take the crayons. She did not know anything she could draw. She was nowhere in her schoolwork. She wanted Papa desperately.

And what did "challenge" mean?

"Draw your family, Anna," Miss Williams said. "Draw your father and your mother, your brothers and your sisters—and yourself, too, Anna. I want to see all of you."

The feel of the box, solid and real, brought back Anna's courage. The crayons were big and bright. They looked inviting. The teacher put paper on the desk— rough, cream-colored paper. Lovely paper for drawing. Six pieces, at least!

"Take your time," Miss Williams said, moving away. "Use as much paper as you need."

Anna took a deep breath. Then she slowly picked out a crayon. She knew how to start, anyway.

She would begin with Papa.

A while later, Miss Williams came and bent above her.

"Who are they, Anna?" she asked.

Slowly Anna began to explain in German.

Miss Williams did not stop her and tell her to talk

English instead, but when Anna pointed and said *"Mein Papa,"* the teacher answered "Your father. My, he is tall, isn't he?"

"Yes," Anna replied in English, only half aware she was switching. She was intent on making sure Miss Williams understood her drawing.

"They are gone on . . . to the sea," she fumbled, looking in vain for an English word for "holiday."

"I thought they had," Miss Williams said.

It was not such a terrible day. Not once did the teacher ask Anna to read from a book. She printed the story of Anna's picture on another piece of paper. The letters were large and black. Anna read each line as it appeared. She did not panic. She did not think of this as reading.

"You like drawing, don't you, Anna," Miss Williams said, picking up the picture and looking at it again, smiling at the bright colors, the liveliness of the twins.

Anna did not answer. She was too startled, even if she had known what to say. She had always hated drawing in school.

"You like reading, too. I can see that. And your English! I can hardly believe you've been in Canada such a short time. You are amazing, Anna."

Miss Williams was not nearly as amazed as Anna Elisabeth Solden. She, Anna, like reading!

She wanted to laugh, but she did not. She still did not even smile openly.

All the same, Anna felt something happening deep inside herself, something warm and alive. She was happy.

When school was over, she walked past her own house and went on to the store where Papa was hard at work. She waited off to one side. When the customers were gone, she stepped up and leaned on the counter.

"Papa, what is a challenge?" She had said the word over and over to herself all day long so she would be able to ask.

Papa scratched his head.

"A challenge," he repeated. "Well, it is . . . something to be won, maybe. Something special that makes you try hard to win it."

Anna thought that over.

"Thank you, Papa," she said, turning away.

"But school," her father cried after her. "Tell me about it."

"It was fine," Anna said over her shoulder. Then she twirled around unexpectedly and gave him one of her rare half-smiles.

"It was a challenge," she said.

"Something special," she repeated, as she started for home. "Dr. Schumacher thinks I am something special, like Papa said. But why something to be won?"

She gave a little hop all at once. She would not mind going back tomorrow.

"It is a challenge," she said over again, aloud, in English, to the empty street.

She liked that word.

1. What gave Anna a "fresh start" in Canada?

2. How did the character Anna change during the story?

3. Why do you think Mrs. Solden was so upset about having to leave Germany to go to Canada?

4. What was the first clue the author gave that helped you know that Anna might need glasses?

5. How did you feel when you realized that Anna could finally see?

6. How did Anna's glasses change her feeling about school?

7. How did the move to Canada turn out to be "a blessing in disguise" for Anna?

Thinking About "Detours"

The characters you have traveled with in this unit have taken you to many different places. You have been with Alec on a deserted island, and you have waded through a river with Dvora. You have watched as Juan and Anna began new lives in countries strange to them, and you have been trapped in a library with Mary Rose and Jo-Beth. All of these characters made detours that led them in new directions.

Some of the characters had no control over the detours their lives took. All they could do was make the best of their situations, just as Alec did. Other characters had a choice as Tom had a choice. Each of these characters chose his or her detour because it seemed like the best thing for him or her to do. You, too, may experience detours in which you have no control and detours in which you find new choices.

As you read other selections, think about the qualities the characters have to help them to accomplish the things they do. Think about the feelings that they experience during their adventures. How do they remind you of people you know? How are they different?

1. Think about Juan in "How Juan Got Home" and Uncle Joe in "Making Room for Uncle Joe." Both had to get used to living in a new place. How were their problems alike? How were their problems different?

2. Mary Rose and Jo-Beth were "prisoners" in a library. Alec was a "prisoner" on a deserted island. How were these two "prisons" alike? How were they different?

3. In which stories did the characters take an *unwanted* detour to escape from danger?

4. Whose detour became a new way of life? Explain.

5. The detours you have read about have been mostly about someone being trapped somewhere unexpectedly or having to leave suddenly to go somewhere else. However, sometimes your mind takes detours when you start daydreaming. Can you think of some pleasant detours you have taken when your attention wandered? Explain.

6. How are the writings of Betsy Byars and Jean Little alike? How are they different?

7. Which selection in this unit did you like the best? Why?

Unit 2

Skylights

What idea comes to your mind when you think of a *skylight*? You might think of a skylight as a window in a roof, facing the sky, that lets in light. You might think of one of the many lights that shine far off in space, such as the moon and the stars. You might even think of other lights in the sky, such as fireworks.

A different kind of skylight could be any kind of window that lets you look into the future.

In "Skylights," you will read about the sun and stars. You will read about other objects in space. You will also find information that gives you a peek into the future: a "window" that lets you look beyond the present time.

As you read the selections, think about how many different kinds of skylights there can be!

Read on Your Own

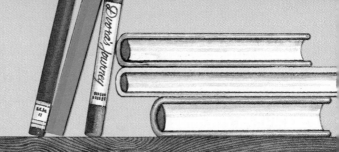

Sun and Light *by Neil Ardley. Watts.* The experiments in this book will help you understand the energy of the sun.

A Book of Flying Saucers for You *by Franklyn M. Branley. Crowell.* For many centuries, in many different places, people have reported seeing unidentified flying objects (UFOs). This book gives one explanation.

Stowaway to the Mushroom Planet *by Eleanor Cameron. Little.* Davie and Chuck return to the Mushroom Planet to find Mr. Bass and to bring Mr. Theo home to Basidium. A stowaway hides on board and makes a lot of trouble for the space travelers.

Mishmash and the Robot *by Molly Cone. Houghton.* Even though Mishmash now lives with someone else, he is still Pete's best dog. When he becomes friends with a robot and mysterious things happen, Pete must save his old dog.

Miss Pickerell Tackles the Energy Crisis *by Ellen MacGregor and Dora Pantell. McGraw.* This is the story of what happens when Miss Pickerell, her cow, and the mayor travel to England.

Black Suits from Outer Space *by Gene DeWeese. Putnam.*
Calvin discovers that a stray cat is an alien from outer
space. A ring he finds leads him to other aliens
disguised as men in black suits. A spaceship is lost,
and Calvin and his friend Kathy must find it.

The Donkey Planet *by Scott Corbett. Dutton.* Two
scientists are tricked by an evil scientist into
traveling to another planet, where they are changed
into a donkey and a twelve-year-old boy. They must
escape from this planet.

Nelson Malone Meets the Man from Mush-Nut *by
Louise Hawes. Dutton.* Many strange things happen to
Nelson, but the strangest is a summer camp run by
outerspace men who take the campers to their planet
and then return them to Earth.

Star Ka'at *by Andre Norton and Dorothy Madlee. Archway.*
A spaceship of cats comes to Earth to rescue their
kinsmen left behind ages ago. They make contact
with a young boy, recently orphaned, and a girl
living with her grandmother. The cats are in hopes
that they can save Earth from a disaster.

In this selection, you will read about one very special "skylight" and how we are learning to use its energy.

Putting the Sun to Work

by Jeanne Bendick

It's a hot summer day. You, your family, and some friends decide to drive to a park near the beach for a cookout.

When you walk over to the beach, the sand and the rocks are so hot that they hurt your bare feet. You put on sneakers in a hurry. The water is so

bright, shining in the sun that you can hardly look at it.

While the charcoal fire is starting to burn in the cookout stove, you go for a swim. The water feels good. It is warm at the top, but cooler down around your toes. After you swim, you dry yourself with a towel.

For lunch there are hot dogs, corn, salad, rolls, and fruit. By the time the corn and hot dogs are cooked, all the towels are dry. You had spread them out on the rocks, in the sun.

While you were having fun at the beach, work was being done. Energy from the sun was doing the work.

Heat energy from the sun dried the towels. It heated the sand, the rocks, the water, and the air.

Light energy from the sun was working on the beach, too. It supplied the daylight. It made the sand bright and the water sparkling.

The sun also supplied the energy that grew the food you ate.

Solar Energy

As long as the sun shines, the earth will not run out of energy. The sun pours more energy onto earth than we can ever use. Most of that energy comes to us as heat and light.

Energy from the sun is called solar energy. Anything to do with sun is called "solar." The word began with the Roman word for the sun, which is *sol*.[1]

---

[1] sol [säl]

Solar energy is a safe kind of energy. It doesn't cause pollution or have dangerous leftovers. That is why scientists and inventors are trying different ways to capture and use the sun's energy. They hope to find a way for the sun to do some of the jobs other types of fuels have been doing for a long time.

To make the sun do work like that, scientists have to solve some problems. They have to collect the sun's energy. Collecting sunshine isn't easy, and sunshine isn't easy to store, either.

Still, people have been using solar energy to help do their work for a long time. There are old ways and new ways of catching sunshine and putting it to work.

Catching Sunshine

If you were building a house in a place that had cold winters, would you build the house with the windows toward the sun or away from it?

You would probably build the house with the windows toward the sun. That way, sunlight could pour in to warm the house. People have been building houses that way for a long time.

Is it possible to catch even more of the sun's heat in a house? Yes, it is. Some houses also collect the sun's heat on the roof, move the heat indoors, and store some of it to use later. A house like that is called a solar house.

People who build solar houses have learned how to do those things by noticing how the earth itself uses solar energy.

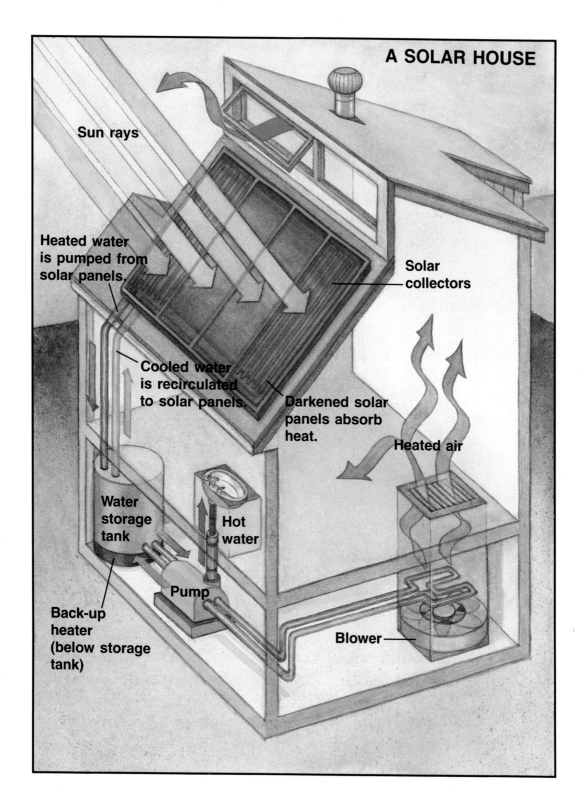

A SOLAR HOUSE

Sun rays

Heated water is pumped from solar panels.

Solar collectors

Cooled water is recirculated to solar panels.

Darkened solar panels absorb heat.

Heated air

Water storage tank

Hot water

Back-up heater (below storage tank)

Pump

Blower

151

Remember the beach we talked about earlier? Remember the hot sand and the hot rocks? Some materials take in heat energy from the sun and hold it. These materials absorb the heat. Sand and rocks do this. So do some other solid materials, such as metals. Water absorbs the sun's heat, too.

Color can also be important. Dark, dull colors absorb heat. Light-colored, shiny surfaces reflect heat. They bounce it back. That's why people wear dark clothes to stay warm in the winter and light-colored clothes to stay cool in the summer.

Storing Heat

The longer it takes something to heat up, the longer that thing holds the heat. Materials that heat up fast also cool off fast.

If you were to go back to the beach in the evening after sunset, the sand and the rocks, which heated up fast, would be cool. The water, which heated up slowly, would still be warm.

It takes a long time for the sun to heat the water in a big lake or the ocean. By the end of summer, however, a large body of water will have caught and stored enough heat from the sun to last for a long time.

Water stores heat very well. That's why land near a large body of water stays warmer in the winter than land far away from the water. The stored heat in the water helps warm the land around it.

Slowly, all winter long, heat from the water moves out into the cold air. Heat always moves that way—

from a warmer place or thing to a cooler one. Once you know which way heat moves, you can understand how things get hot and how they lose heat.

Remember when the hot sand on the beach burned your feet? Heat from the sand was moving into your cooler feet! Once you understand how heat moves into things, through things, and out of things, it is easy to see how a solar house works.

In many warm places around the world, there is a lot of sunshine all year long. In those places, a solar house can supply all the heat and hot water most families need. A solar house in a cold climate often needs some kind of backup heater. The heater is used when the weather is very cold, or if the sun does not shine for some days.

Keeping Heat in One Place

Once the house is warm, what keeps the heat from moving out of the warm house into the cool outside air?

Remember the sneakers you put on when the hot sand was burning your feet? They kept the heat from moving from the sand into your feet. The sneakers were insulation. *Insulation* is any material that keeps heat (or other kinds of energy) from moving from place to place.

Insulation in a house keeps heat from moving out of the house in the winter. It also keeps heat from moving into the house in the summer.

It does not take a lot of heat to make a house comfortable. Solar energy can do that job in many areas of the world.

What about work that takes more heat, such as cooking dinner? Or still more heat, such as melting steel? Can the sun do work like that?

satellite

space telescope

calculator

solar furnace

1. What special "skylight" did you just read about? Why is it so special?

2. How can we put the sun to work?

3. Do you think we are using the sun's energy enough now, or should we be using it more? Explain your answer.

4. How did reading about a cookout at the beach prepare you to understand how solar heating works?

5. Why should we begin to use the sun for energy rather than using energy made from fuel?

6. What kinds of work that affects your life does the sun do? Explain your answer.

Prewrite

Discuss what you learned about solar energy in this selection. Where does it come from? How do we collect it? How do we use it? Copy and complete the chart on the next page by listing the main features of solar energy in the column labeled *Main Features*. If what you have listed is an

156

advantage of solar energy, put a check mark in the column labeled *Advantage.* If what you have written is a disadvantage, put a check mark in the column labeled *Disadvantage.*

SOLAR ENERGY		
Main Features	**Advantage**	**Disadvantage**
▬▬▬	▬▬▬	▬▬▬
▬▬▬	▬▬▬	▬▬▬
▬▬▬	▬▬▬	▬▬▬

Draft

Write a summary of what you have learned about solar energy. Remember that a summary is short. It gives only the main points. It combines ideas and leaves out details. Use the ideas from your chart to help you write the summary.

Revise

Read your summary. Is it too long? How is it organized? Does it include the main features of solar energy? Have you put in anything that is not necessary? Make whatever changes or cuts are needed to improve your summary.

Kim is both proud and embarrassed about her family's energy-saving home. Read to find out how her family proves that "different" can be better.

Those Weird Wagners

by Bonnie Bisbee

Tom Barton leaned forward and tapped me on the shoulder. (Just my luck: He sits right behind me in class!) "What was that crazy thing I saw in your garage the other day, Kim?" he asked me in a loud voice. I didn't answer him or turn around.

"It looks like a big laser-gun for blasting something out of the sky. Ha-ha-ha-hee-haw!" Tom's laugh reminded me of a donkey's bray. A few kids sitting nearby snickered as Tom hopped up onto his chair.

"Are the weird Wagners going to fend off invaders from space? Zap, zap, zap!" he said, pretending to be shooting a gun into the air.

"That's not a laser!" I said hotly. "It's a solar mirror, if you want to know. It gathers the sun's energy and focuses it in one place for cooking. Next summer we'll be able to have a cookout without using any fuel at all!"

Tom sneered and shook his head as he climbed back into his seat. "You Wagners are hopeless energy nuts," he said. "First you put that crazy-looking wind thing in your backyard to make electricity. Then you put up those weird glass-covered boxes—what do you call them, 'solar water heaters' or some dumb thing. Now there's this hamburger and hot dog laser. What are you going to do next, get some hungry sheep to 'mow' your lawn so you won't have to use any gasoline? Ha-ha-ha-hee-haw!"

I blushed, because that's exactly what we'd do if we had more space. Then we'd be able to make nice warm, energy-saving sweaters from their wool.

Tom started to say something else, but our teacher, Mr. Huffler, came back into the room just then. He looked serious. The room stopped buzzing as everyone shut up.

"I have an announcement to make," Mr. Huffler said. "A bad snowstorm is coming, so the bus drivers want to get you home early."

I looked outside, and sure enough, the sky was heavy with dark gray clouds, and a few flakes were already falling.

"Now don't push and shove," Mr. Huffler said as we grabbed our books and coats. "You'll all be safely home before the storm hits. You can go now."

As we crowded out the door, Tom yelled above the noise, "Hey, Kim, I hope you don't want to take a shower when you get home. Those wonderful solar water heaters aren't going to do you much good during this storm. Ha-ha-ha-hee-haw!"

This time I think I did a pretty good job of ignoring Tom. But how I hated that stupid laugh!

As soon as I got home, I turned on the news. "The radio says this storm could reach 'blizzard proportions'!" I announced. "I hope that Mom gets home from work okay."

Just then the front door flew open. A snow-covered Mom came in, along with a blast of cold air. I ran to greet her.

"That storm is fierce!" Mom said, closing the door with effort. "I'm glad to be home."

Mom hung up her coat and walked over to our wood stove to warm up. I followed her.

"Tom Barton calls us the 'Weird Wagners'!" I blurted out. "He says lots of other people call us that, too."

My sister, Leslie, backed me up. "People think we're nuts," she said. "The other day Mr. Jacusi across the street asked me about our windmill. He called it another of our 'dopey gadgets.' "

Mom raised her eyebrows. "Lots of people are making their own energy these days. We're not the only ones."

"We're the only ones in our neighborhood who do!" I said. "And Tom's told the kids at school about some of our disasters—like the time we tried to make fuel from sugarbeets. He blabbed about how we goofed and how the mess could be smelled clear down the block."

Just then Dad walked in from the kitchen. "We've had our ups and downs, all right, and it cost us a bit to get started," he said with a smile. "But we've got some pretty good stuff working for us now."

"That's right," agreed Mom. "Now we don't have to depend on anyone for energy—not the electric company, not the oil company, nobody. So let 'em laugh."

Leslie joined in. "Who cares if people make fun, Kim? Our place is really neat!"

"I know, but sometimes I wish our house were a bit more . . . well, normal!"

"Don't pay attention to Tom and he'll give up his teasing," advised Dad.

"But I have to listen to that stupid laugh!" I said with a look of disgust.

Mom spoke up suddenly. "You know, all this talk makes me think of something. It was getting dark on my way home. But I didn't see any street lights or even house lights burning on our block—except here!"

Just then the doorbell rang. The wind sprang inside as I opened the door. I was surprised to see who was there.

"Tom Barton! Mr. and Mrs. Barton and little Ann! Come in!"

Tom wouldn't look at me as I led the bundled-up family into the living room. For once he wasn't laughing.

Mrs. Barton looked around curiously at the cozy, well-lit room. "The wind and snow have knocked some power lines down," she explained. "No one in the neighborhood has electricity — except for you folks."

"At home we can't cook dinner, have hot baths, or watch TV," Mr. Barton said. "But the real problem is that we can't heat Ann's bottle, and she's getting hungry."

"We can easily heat her bottle on the woodburning cook stove in the kitchen," Dad said.

"Why don't you folks stay for supper?" Mom invited. "We'll make a big pot of soup. Our solar-heated greenhouse supplies us with lots of fresh vegetables. We won't have to worry about getting to the supermarket for more food."

"We'd love to stay. Thanks!" said Mr. and Mrs. Barton together.

"Anyone who wants to can have a shower," Leslie said. "Our solar water heater won't do much for us tonight. But our garbage will!"

The Bartons looked at each other kind of funny until Leslie started to explain. "We dump our garbage and other wastes into a big tank in the basement. The wastes digest, or break down, and we collect the gas that forms. And now we can use it to fire up our regular water heater."

I remembered what Tom had said earlier in the day—about our being out of luck when the sun wasn't shining. I looked over at him, but he was just looking at the floor.

"I wonder what the news is on this storm?" Mr. Barton said. Leslie ran to turn on the radio.

"Our wind machine and our sun-powered 'photo-cells' give us enough electricity for just about everything," Dad said.

"The power is stored in batteries in the basement, to use as we need," Mom added.

". . . *worst storm to hit Riverdale in years,*" the radio said. "*Half of the town is now without electricity.*"

Mrs. Barton suddenly said, "We always thought you were . . . well, different. But now I think I'd like to put some of your ideas to work at *our* house."

I glanced at Tom. He looked down at the floor some more. His face was turning a funny shade of red.

"Making power from wind, wood, wastes, and the sun can work for almost everyone," I said. "And it's pretty easy on the environment." (Our wood stoves were making too much smoke, but we were working on that.) "Besides," I continued, "with home-made energy you can smile when the power lines blow down!"

"We haven't smiled at our electricity bills lately," Mr. Barton said. "And they're going to go even higher. Your way of doing things makes pretty good sense, I guess."

Mom and Leslie went to warm the baby's bottle and to make hot cider for everyone else. Dad started the soup. I set the table while listening to the wind blow and our guests chatting by the stove. The snow piled up outside, but we were warm and happy.

"Can I help you?" a familiar voice offered. I whirled around. For the first time all evening, Tom's brown eyes looked straight at me.

"I'm sorry I teased you, Kim," he said with a sheepish smile. "I'm going to tell everyone at school how the Not-So-Weird Wagners saved my family from freezing in the dark! . . . Hey, do I smell gingerbread baking?" He sniffed like a hungry hound.

I smiled sweetly. "Yes, Tom," I said. "But why do you think you'll be getting some?" And then I added quickly, "Just kidding—ha-ha-ha-hee-haw!"

1. How did Kim's family prove that being "different" can sometimes be better?

2. Name three of the energy-producing gadgets the Wagners had in their home.

3. Which of the Wagners' gadgets do you think was the most interesting? Why?

4. When did you first begin to think that the Wagners were the only family to have electricity during the storm?

5. Why did the Wagners want to make their own energy?

Prewrite

Not too long ago, the Wagners' "weird" ways of producing energy might have seemed like something from science fiction. Now, we know that energy can be produced in these ways. Other ideas that seem weird, or strange, today could be real tomorrow. Let your imagination go, and discuss what life in the future might be like.

Make drawings or diagrams, or cut pictures from magazines, to show a new way of doing something. You might want to show a new kind of transportation, shelter, heat, food, clothing, education, or communication.

Draft

Choose one of the new ways of doing things that you have explored, and write a short description of it. For example, you might have designed a new kind of car or house, a new way of shopping, or a new way of feeding people. Tell all about your new idea—describe it carefully.

Revise

Read your description. Could someone else get a clear picture of your new invention and how it works? Have you explained how your invention would be of help to people? Add or change whatever you can to make your description clearer.

Narration

Narration is one of the four major forms or categories of writing. It is the kind of writing in which the author's main intent is to tell a story, or narrative.

The word *narrative* means story. A narrative may be real, or it may be fiction. A narrative may take the form of a poem or a story. It may be as short as a paragraph or as long as a book, but it always tells a story.

Narrative writing can inform the reader and give information about a topic. However, in a narrative the author is telling a story while giving that information.

Read the following paragraphs. Decide which is an example of a narrative.

A. Energy from the sun is called solar energy. Anything to do with the sun is called "solar." The word began with the Roman word for the sun, which is *sol*.

B. "Why don't you folks stay for supper?" Mom invited. "We'll make a big pot of soup. Our solar-heated greenhouse supplies us with lots of fresh vegetables. We won't have to worry about getting to the supermarket for more food."

Which of the paragraphs is an example of a narrative? How do you know? Passage B is an example of a narrative because the paragraph tells part of a story. The paragraph is from the story "Those Weird Wagners." Paragraph A is from the article "Putting the Sun to Work." This paragraph mainly presents information; it does not tell a story.

A narrative needs a narrator, someone to tell the story. The person telling the story might be an unseen storyteller or narrator, or it might be a character in the story. If the author uses an unseen narrator who is watching and reporting the action, we say the story is told from the *third-person point of view*. If the author uses a character in the story as the narrator, we say the story is told from the *first-person point of view*. In a first-person narrative, the reader finds out what the narrator-character says, does, thinks, feels, and observes because the character tells us. It is almost as if the narrator-character is speaking to the reader. Words that indicate first-person point of view are *I, me, my, mine, us,* and *our*.

Read the following paragraph. It is the first paragraph from the story "Those Weird Wagners."

C. Tom Barton leaned forward and tapped me on the shoulder. (Just my luck: He sits right behind me in class!) "What was that crazy thing I saw in your garage the other day, Kim?" he asked me in a loud voice. I didn't answer him or turn around.

from *Those Weird Wagners*
by Bonnie Bisbee

The author is using Kim Wagner to tell the story. The pronouns *I, me,* and *my* and the phrases *tapped me, asked me,* and *I didn't answer* help you know that Kim is the narrator-character. "Those Weird Wagners" is an example of a first-person narrative.

Suppose the author had chosen to write the story from the third-person point of view. Read the paragraph below to see how the story might have begun.

D. Tom Barton leaned forward and tapped the girl in front of him on the shoulder. "What was that crazy thing I saw in your driveway the other day, Kim?" he asked her in a loud voice. She didn't answer him or turn around.

Both paragraphs are clearly the beginning of a narrative. However, there is a difference. Read paragraph **C** again. Notice that when Kim is the narrator-character, you find out what happens, but you also learn through her words what she is thinking and how she feels about what is happening.

Read paragraph **D** again. You know what is happening, but you don't know about Kim's thoughts or feelings. You will only know these if the unseen narrator tells you.

Once an author decides to write a narrative, then he or she must decide who is going to tell the story. If the author wants the storyteller to be able to describe all the characters and actions in the story and comment on what they think and feel, the author will write a third-person narrative. The storyteller, the unseen narrator, supplies all the information that the reader needs.

If the author decides that a character in the story

will tell his or her own story, then the author will write a first-person narrative. The narrator-character must provide all the necessary information not only about himself or herself, but also about the other characters, as well as the setting and events in that story. The reader will know what is happening only through the narrator-character's eyes and will be told what is happening through what the narrator-character says or what is said to him or her.

Read the next two sets of narrative paragraphs. Think about what you are learning about the characters, the setting, and the events in each and how you are learning it. The sidenotes will help you.

A. When satellite control called me, I was writing up the day's progress report in the Observation Bubble—the glass-domed office that juts out from the axis of the Space Station like the hubcap of a wheel. It was not really a good place to work, for the view was too overwhelming. Only a few yards away I could see the construction teams performing their slow-motion ballet as they put the station together like a giant jigsaw puzzle. And beyond them, twenty thousand miles below, was the blue-green glory of the full Earth, floating against the raveled star clouds of the Milky Way.

"Station Supervisor here," I answered. "What's the trouble?"

from *Who's There*
by Arthur C. Clarke

The personal pronouns *me* and *I* should help you know who is telling the story.

Phrases such as *I could see* and *I answered* are additional clues.

How are you learning what Sarah is doing and thinking?

The narrator is giving background information about Ponder's Mill and Sarah to establish the setting and major character of the story.

B. After her talk with Poppa, Sarah listened even harder whenever she heard Halley's Comet mentioned. Everybody in Ponder's Mill had been talking about it.

Ponder's Mill was the only place Sarah Lewis had ever lived. She'd been born there in 1900.

Sarah was able to find Ponder's Mill on only one map, because the town was so small. That was in the Goode's School Atlas. There was a big double page that showed the north central United States. Ponder's Mill was near the top edge of Nebraska. The day she found the map, Sarah moved the page closer and closer to her face. At first the heavy black lines around the different states became blurred. Next the red lines that were the railroads and the blue lines that were the rivers disappeared. Finally her nose was almost against the paper. All she could see was the small dark circle that stood for Ponder's Mill.

Then Sarah pretended she was going inside the circle. She pretended she stepped through the circle and was suddenly on the courthouse lawn at the bottom of Main Street. She pictured herself walking west between the elm trees.

from *The Year of the Comet*
by Roberta Wiegand

How do you learn about Sarah in "The Year of the Comet"? Who is telling the story in "Who's There"? Which of the two sets of paragraphs is a personal narrative? Remember that a narrative is a story and that a narrative may be real or it may be fiction. A narrative may be as short as a paragraph or as long as a book, but it must tell a story.

The person telling the story, or the narrator, may be an unseen narrator who is watching and reporting the action, or it may be a story character who is telling his or her own story.

Noting whether a selection is an informational article or a narrative will help you set your purpose for reading. If the selection is an informational article, you should look not only for the information, but also for the way the author is presenting that information. If the selection is a narrative, you know that someone will be telling a story.

Before you begin to read a selection, set your purpose for reading. As you set your purpose, try to figure out if the author's intent was to present information or tell a story. Remember that

- a narrative is a story;
- a narrative has a storyteller or narrator;
- the narrator may be the author or a character in the story.

The next time you write, try writing a narrative. Write one in which a character is the storyteller and uses the words *I, me, my, mine.* Then try writing a story by having a third-person or unseen narrator tell the story. Remember that your narrative may be real or fiction, but it must tell a story.

Children's Choices Author

In this selection, two brothers look at the night sky together and solve a puzzling question.

Einstein Anderson and the Night Sky

by Seymour Simon

Einstein Anderson was an average-size twelve-year-old boy in the sixth grade. Sometimes his light-brown eyes had a faraway look when he was thinking about some important problem in science. But Einstein was not always serious. He loved jokes of all kinds and liked to make puns, the worse the better.

Adam was Einstein's real name. But almost everyone called him Einstein, after the most famous scientist of the twentieth century. Adam had been interested in science for as long as he could remember. He talked about science, read about science, experimented in science, and even solved puzzles by using science. For years, even his teachers had called him by the nickname Einstein.

"Tonight is the big event," said Einstein. "I've finished my telescope's tripod, and we can go out in the backyard and do some stargazing."

"It's about time," said Dennis, his younger brother. "You've been working on that thing for months now. And you said the telescope was ready to use weeks ago. Why couldn't we look at the stars just by holding the telescope in our hands?"

"It wouldn't work," Einstein explained. "An astronomical telescope is too powerful to be hand-held. You'd never be able to keep it steady enough to observe anything."

"Then how come sailors are always looking through telescopes that they hold?" Dennis asked.

"That's not the same thing," said Einstein. "A ship's telescope may have a magnification of ten or fifteen. But even a small astronomy scope will magnify forty or fifty times. And the higher the magnification, the steadier the mounting you need. Wait till it gets dark—you'll see why the tripod is so important."

That night the boys ate dinner quickly and did the dishes in record time. However, it was dark by the time they carried the telescope and its mounting out to the backyard.

"That doesn't look much like a telescope to me," Dennis said after Einstein had set up everything. "Where's the glass lens at the front?"

"This is a reflecting telescope, not a refractor," Einstein said. "Refractors gather light by means of a glass lens at the front end of a tube. That's the kind of scope that most people recognize. But a reflector gathers light by means of a curved mirror at the bottom of a tube. A reflector is easier to build and much less expensive for the same size."

"Whatever you say, Einstein," said Dennis. "Let's look at some stars."

"Before we look," said Einstein, "let's wait a few minutes for our eyes to become dark-adjusted. Close your eyes for a little while. After your eyes adjust to the dark, don't look directly at my flashlight. If you look at a bright light, you'll lose your dark-adaptation quickly."

"Okay," said Dennis. He closed his eyes. "Are you thinking of becoming an astronomer?" he asked.

"I might," Einstein said. "Of course you know that an astronomer is a night watchman with a college education," he continued.

"Ha, ha," said Dennis, opening his eyes. "Could we look at some stars now?"

"Sure," said Einstein. He set up the telescope on the heavy tripod and pointed it at a spot in the Milky Way. Then he motioned Dennis to look through the eyepiece.

"Wow!" Dennis exclaimed, "I see so many stars I can't even count them. What am I looking at?"

"That's a small section of the Milky Way," said Einstein. "It's a huge mass of millions and millions of stars. They're so far away that without a telescope they just look like a band of hazy light. The Milky Way is a group of stars called a galaxy. Our sun is part of the Milky Way, out toward one edge. You're looking toward the center of the galaxy."

"Let's look at that bright star next," Dennis said, pointing.

"That's not a star. It's a planet," said Einstein.

"How can you tell without even looking through a telescope?" asked Dennis. "I thought planets move around in the sky so that they're in different spots all the time."

"That's true," Einstein admitted. "I'm not sure which planet it is, but I do know it's a planet."

Can you solve the puzzle: How can Einstein tell a planet from a star without using a telescope?

"It looks like a star to me," said Dennis.

"There's a difference," Einstein explained. "Except when they are high overhead, stars twinkle when you stare at them. Planets usually shine with a steady light."

"Why is that?" asked Dennis.

"Stars are so far away from us that they look like points of light even through the biggest telescopes. Planets are much closer than stars. A bright planet will look like a disk even through my little telescope. We get many light rays from a planet but only one ray from a star. The earth's atmosphere can interfere with a star's light much more easily than with a planet's light. When it does, the stars appear to be twinkling."

Einstein looked through his telescope at the planet. "I think the planet is Jupiter," he said. "The four faint points of light you can see nearby are Jupiter's moons. Just think. Jupiter's moons were first seen by the great scientist Galileo with a small telescope more than three hundred years ago."

Einstein paused and smiled. "You know that some people say Galileo would have been a great movie fan because he liked to watch the stars so much."

"Ugh!" said Dennis. "I think you should stick to being a night watchman."

1. How did Einstein tell the difference between a planet and a star without using a telescope?

2. What is the difference between a reflecting telescope and a refractor?

3. Why do you think that Adam didn't mind his nickname?

4. What did the boys do before they looked at the stars? What tells you they did this?

5. Why did the boys wait for the tripod to be finished before they used the telescope?

6. How can the saying "Things are not always what they seem" apply to this selection?

Think and Write

Prewrite

Einstein Anderson built his own telescope. In the story, he tells how it is made. Think of something you know how to make. It could be a model rocket, a folded-paper design, a milkshake, or a puppet. Think of the materials you need and the steps you take to make it. If possible, make it and notice exactly what you do.

Draft

Write a set of directions for making whatever you have chosen. List the materials first. Then list the steps necessary to make it. Follow this model:

HOW TO MAKE A ▬▬▬▬
Materials:
1. ▬▬▬▬▬▬▬▬▬▬▬▬▬▬
2. ▬▬▬▬▬▬▬▬▬▬▬▬▬▬
3. ▬▬▬▬▬▬▬▬▬▬▬▬▬▬
4. ▬▬▬▬▬▬▬▬▬▬▬▬▬▬
5. ▬▬▬▬▬▬▬▬▬▬▬▬▬▬
Steps to Take:
1. ▬▬▬▬▬▬▬▬▬▬▬▬▬▬
2. ▬▬▬▬▬▬▬▬▬▬▬▬▬▬
3. ▬▬▬▬▬▬▬▬▬▬▬▬▬▬
4. ▬▬▬▬▬▬▬▬▬▬▬▬▬▬
5. ▬▬▬▬▬▬▬▬▬▬▬▬▬▬

Revise

Read your directions. Have you included everything you need? Are the steps in the right order? Could someone else make the same thing by following what you have written? Make any necessary changes, so that someone can follow your directions.

Until We Built a Cabin

by Aileen Fisher

When we lived in a city
(three flights up and down)
I never dreamed how many stars
could show above a town.

> When we moved to a village
> where lighted streets were few,
> I thought I could see ALL the stars,
> but, oh, I never knew—

>> Until we built a cabin
>> where hills are high and far,
>> I never knew how many
>>   many
>>   stars there really are!

*Join Kate and Vinny to find out why
their class visited a planetarium.*

Indoor Stars

by Linda Beech

"Will the stars twinkle the way they do in the
sky?" Kate wondered. "What will the planets look
like?"

Kate and her partner, Vinny, hurried to catch up
to the rest of their class. They were in New York
City visiting the Hayden Planetarium, which is part
of the American Museum of Natural History.

Kate knew that a planetarium is a place in which projectors and other machines show the Sun, Moon, planets, and millions of stars just as they look in the sky. Still, Kate was curious. What would these indoor stars be like?

At the planetarium Kate and Vinny found seats in the Sky Theater. The theater was round, and the seats were arranged in rows of circles facing the center. A large projector stood on a platform in the middle of the room. Blue and red lights surrounded it.

"That projector looks like a huge bug!" Kate whispered to Vinny. "I wonder how it works."

Just then the lights dimmed, and the show began. Kate and Vinny looked up in amazement. The ceiling of the theater was really a huge screen shaped like a dome. During the show the ceiling became the night sky. It was on this dome that the projector shone images of the stars and planets.

The program had several parts to it. The first part was about Halley's Comet. This comet was first seen sometime before the year 240 B.C. Like all comets, Halley's Comet travels along a certain path through the solar system. This path circles the Sun. Halley's Comet is well-known because it circles the Sun quite often—once about every seventy-six years. Also, as it moves closer to the Sun, the comet can be seen from Earth.

The program that Kate and Vinny watched showed that people had seen Halley's Comet many times in the past. A famous Italian artist, Giotto di Bondone, even showed the comet in one of his paintings in 1301. Kate and Vinny also learned that Halley's Comet last appeared in 1986.

As Vinny watched the show, he thought, "How do they make the comet move?"

Kate was thinking about something else. "I wonder if the stars look the same now as when Halley's Comet was first spotted," she said to herself.

The next part of the program honored the fiftieth birthday of the planetarium. Many people, events,

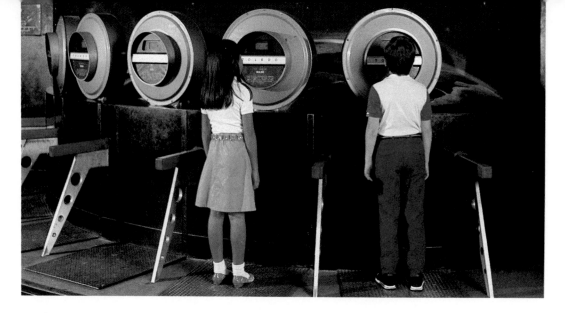

and inventions from the last fifty years were shown through pictures. The program also showed how people's ideas and knowledge about our world and space have changed.

Kate and Vinny's teacher talked to the class when the program was finished. "This planetarium is part of the American Museum of Natural History," she said. "The stars, too, are very much a part of natural history. Today, we know so much more about natural history because of what has happened in the last fifty years. Computers, rockets, and space flights have helped us learn a lot."

Then the class was allowed to look at the science exhibits in the planetarium. One of the favorites was called "Your Weight on Other Worlds." Vinny discovered that he would weigh 91 kilograms on the planet Jupiter and 980 kilograms on the Sun.

"How much do you weigh on Earth?" asked Kate.

"I won't tell you," said Vinny, "but I'll give you this hint. My weight on the Sun is 28 times what it is on Earth."

Kate laughed. "I'll figure it out and tell you how much you weigh later," she said. "In the meantime, here is a problem for you. I weigh 36 kilograms on Earth. How much do I weigh on Mars if my weight there is one-third of my weight on Earth?"

Vinny said he would think about it. Then they walked over to another exhibit. This one showed how old they would be on other planets. "Oh, look!" cried Kate. "If I lived on Mars, I would only be five years and five months old."

Vinny said, "You could move to Mercury. On that planet you'd be over forty-five years old!"

The exhibit explained that each planet rotates, or turns, at a different speed. This means that days are not the same length on every planet. Some days are longer and some are shorter than on Earth. Just as the days are not the same length on every planet, neither are the years.

It was now almost one o'clock. Kate and Vinny didn't want to be late. They had been chosen from their class to interview the head of the planetarium, Dr. William Gutsch. They were going to ask him questions about the planetarium and then share the information with the class. They rushed to his office.

Kate and Vinny found Dr. Gutsch easy to talk to as he explained his answers to their questions.

Vinny: How does the big projector work?
Dr. Gutsch: Inside each of the large balls is a light bulb, or lamp. Around these lights are lenses. Behind each lens is a glass plate. Part of the sky is on each glass plate. The light from the

lamps shines through the lenses, which then project that part of the sky onto the screen.

Vinny: You mean that all of the stars are really inside the projector?

Dr. Gutsch: Yes, Vinny. The images for the stars, Sun, planets, and Moon are all in there. We don't have to change what is in this projector because the sky, or what we can see of it, has changed very little in ten thousand years.

Kate: Why does the projector move?

Dr. Gutsch: When the projector moves, the stars or planets on the screen move. In this way, it is possible to show how the sky looks at different times of the year.

Kate: I see lots of things around the sides of the dome. Are they projectors, too?

Dr. Gutsch: Yes. There are about a hundred small projectors that we use for different effects. Each has a special purpose. For instance, one projector shows how Halley's Comet moves along its path.

Vinny: Our teacher wanted us to ask about a laser light. Do you have one?

Dr. Gutsch: Yes, we do. It is a powerful thin beam of light that we use to write or draw things on the screen.

Kate: The show we saw about Halley's Comet was so interesting! Did you do it all by yourself?

Dr. Gutsch: No, not really. Putting together a planetarium show is something like making a movie. I write the scripts, hire people to read them, and work with artists, composers, sound engineers, and many others.

Kate: And you have real stars as the stars of your show!

Dr. Gutsch: I guess you're right, Kate.

Vinny: How do you get all the parts of a program to work together?

Dr. Gutsch: Much of this is done by computer. The computer tells each projector when to flash something on the screen and how long to keep it there. It also coordinates the sound track, the laser light, and the other parts of the show.

Kate: There were a lot of people here today. Is the planetarium always this busy?

Dr. Gutsch: The American Museum–Hayden Planetarium is one of the world's largest and busiest planetariums. More than one hundred and fifty thousand students come to see its shows each year. Thousands of other people, both New Yorkers and visitors, also come.

Kate: I'm glad we were some of your visitors.

Vinny: I am, too.

Kate and Vinny thanked Dr. Gutsch for his help and promised to return to see other shows.

"By the way, Vinny," said Kate as they got on the bus, "the answer to your problem is 35. You weigh 35 kilograms."

Vinny laughed. "That's right. And you would weigh 12 kilograms on Mars. But really, Kate, I hope you don't go there. There's so much we can still learn on Earth."

Kate agreed. "We sure learned a lot today."

1. Why did Kate and Vinny's class visit the planetarium?

2. How was a computer used in the show at the planetarium?

3. What did you learn about planetariums that you did not know before you read this selection? Tell where you found the information.

4. What other questions would you have asked if you had been interviewing Dr. Gutsch?

5. Do you think Kate and Vinny learned all that they wanted to about the planetarium? Explain your answer.

6. How can a planetarium help people learn more about space than they can learn just by studying the sky with a telescope?

Think and Write

Prewrite

In the story, Vinny and Kate interviewed Dr. Gutsch. They asked about the planetarium and how the projectors worked. They also could have asked him questions such as those on the next page.

- How did you become interested in astronomy?
- What do you like best about your job?
- Have you ever discovered a new comet or star?

If you had a chance to interview someone, what kinds of questions would you ask? Discuss this with classmates and make a list.

Draft

Pretend you are going to interview someone, maybe a movie star, a politician, a wildlife expert, or a musician. Choose one of these or someone else who interests you. Then write five questions to ask the person. Discuss the list you made with your classmates to hear their ideas. Think of questions that will tell you something interesting about the person.

Revise

Read your questions. Are they questions you would want answered? What kinds of answers do you think you would get? Would the answers interest others who may hear the interview? Do you want to change any of the questions? Make the necessary changes to improve your questions.

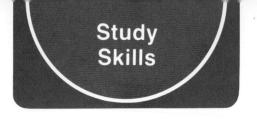
SQ3R

Would you be surprised to learn that there is a study plan that works well and doesn't take a long time? You might even be surprised to learn that it works well for many students in all of their subjects. This plan will help you to obtain good results and to use your study time in the best way. The plan is called SQ3R.

What is SQ3R? **SQ3R** is a five-step plan that will help you to organize your study time and to remember more of what you study. The *S* and *Q* stand for *survey* and *question*. The three *R*'s stand for *read*, *recite*, and *review*.

What can SQ3R do for you? This plan will help you to set a purpose for reading *before* you begin to study. Setting a purpose will make it easier for you to understand and remember the material *after* you have read it.

Here are the five steps of the SQ3R plan. Read each step carefully.

1. Survey

Survey means "to look over." When you begin to study, take a few minutes to get an idea of how the material is put together. Look at each page that you will be reading. Look for headings that divide the material into sections. If there are pictures, look at them and read the captions that go with them. While you are looking over the material, try to predict what it will be about. Think about what you already know about the subject.

2. Question

Question yourself about the kind of information you want to get from the study material. The best way to do this is to read the title and any headings and try to turn these into questions. Ask yourself, "Who? What? Where? When? Why?" and "How?" For example, if you were surveying a science text and you saw the heading *Indoor Stars,* you might ask yourself these questions: "What are indoor stars?" or "Where can indoor stars be found?" or "Why is a star indoors?" By asking yourself questions such as these, you are establishing a purpose for reading the material. Trying to answer the questions as you read will help you to understand and remember more of the selection.

3. Read

You have already surveyed the material and have an idea what it will be about. You have also prepared some questions to be answered. Now you need to do a careful reading. As you **read,** try to understand all the important points the author is making. You may want to reread some sections to be certain you understand them fully. You may also want to take notes on any important information.

You should plan to use the longest part of your study time for this step.

4. Recite

Recite, in SQ3R, means "to put the facts and the ideas you read into your own words and say these words out loud to yourself." Putting the facts and the ideas into your own words will help you to remember them.

When you get to this step, you should be able to answer the questions you asked yourself in step 2. If other questions are asked at the end of the section or chapter, try to answer them also. If you have trouble answering any questions, go back and read the material again.

5. Review

Review the material by looking back over it. Reviewing the material will help to remind you of what you have studied. Look back at the headings and answer again the questions you asked yourself in step 2. Look back at any boldface words in the material or any notes that you may have taken.

You will find this step more helpful if you allow some time to pass between step 4 and your review. If you have done steps 1 through 4 well, you should be able to do a quick review after an hour, a day, or even if several days have passed since you studied.

When you use SQ3R, first *survey* the material. Then ask yourself *questions*. Next, *read* carefully to find the answers. Then put the important facts and ideas from the material into your own words, and *recite* these words to yourself. At a later time, *review* the material. Remember, you should give steps 2, 3, and 4 the most time as you study.

Textbook Application:
Using SQ3R in Science

Read the following selection, using the SQ3R plan. Remember, first survey the selection. Predict what you will find in it, and think about what you already know about the subject. Then ask yourself some questions based on the headings you see. Use the sidenotes to help you practice your new study plan.

The Planets

Without a telescope, planets and stars look alike. Ancient astronomers learned to tell them apart. They observed that some space objects kept the same positions in the sky night after night. Other objects slowly changed their positions. These objects were the planets traveling around the sun. A **planet** is a large space object that moves around the sun. The ancient people called these moving objects "planets." The word "planet" meant "wanderer." Today we still call these objects planets.

Planets travel around the sun in paths called orbits. An **orbit** is the path an object follows when it revolves around something else. Planets close to the sun revolve around the sun in a short time. Their orbits are small when compared to those of more distant planets.

Noticing the title is part of the *survey* step. In the *question* step, you would change this heading into a question, such as "What are planets?"

Pay attention to boldface words. Why do you think these words appear this way?

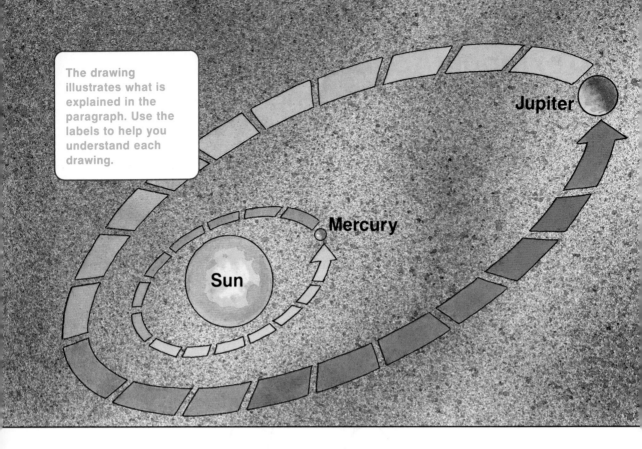

The drawing illustrates what is explained in the paragraph. Use the labels to help you understand each drawing.

Jupiter

Mercury

Sun

The time it takes a planet to make one complete orbit around the sun is called a year. How does the length of a year on Jupiter compare to a year on Mercury?

A planet is kept in its orbit by a force called gravity. If there were no gravity, a planet would move in a straight line in space. The sun's gravity changes the direction of the motion of a planet. Because of the sun's pulling force, a planet orbits the sun in an oval shaped pathway or **ellipse** (ih·LIHPS).

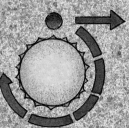 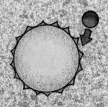 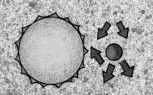

**Planet moving
in straight line**

**Gravity pulls planet
toward sun**

**Planet remains in
orbit around sun**

> After you study each picture, *recite* the main ideas of what you have read so far.

The size and shape of each planet's ellipse is different. The size and shape of the ellipse depends upon the planet's distance from the sun. The speed of a planet may also change as it goes around the sun. If the ellipse is more oval, the speed changes greatly. A planet with a more rounded ellipse travels at almost the same speed throughout its orbit.

Suppose your class could blast-off right now and take a tour of the solar system. What planets would you want to visit? What would you like to learn about each of the planets you visit?

—*Accent on Science,* Charles E. Merrill

> Try to answer these questions. How did you decide?

The SQ3R study plan can help you get the most out of what you read. As you study, remember to

- *survey* the material;
- ask yourself *questions*;
- *read* carefully to find answers to your questions;
- *recite* the facts and ideas in your own words;
- *review* the material at a later time.

John Newbery Honor
Award Author

In this selection, you will learn about a space station soon to be built. Read to find out why a space station is needed.

A Giant Step into Space

by William Steele

When pioneers moved west across North America, they began by building small outposts. From the outposts, they went out to explore new lands. We are about to build an outpost in space: a space station.

The National Aeronautics and Space Administration (NASA) plans to build the space station early in the 1990's. It will be in orbit about four hundred kilometers above Earth.

It will not be the first space station, but it will be the first permanent one. An American space station called *Skylab* was launched in 1973. It stayed in or-bit for six years. The Soviet Union put a space station called *Salyut 6* in orbit in 1977. It stayed there for almost five years. Another Russian space station, *Salyut 7*, was launched in 1982. The new space station will be larger and better equipped than any of these.

A Funny Shape

The station will probably look like a bunch of huge metal cans hanging on a long stick. The "cans" will be about fourteen me-ters long and five meters across. They will be that size and shape so they can fit in the space shuttle.

200

The crew of the station will live in one area of the station. They will work in other areas. The station will look as if it has wings. The "wings" will be panels that make electricity from sunlight. The "stick" will be a huge beam that holds it all together.

The station will be one hundred and twenty-two meters long and will weigh over two hundred thousand kilograms. Space shuttles will carrry it into orbit. It will take six shuttle flights or more to carry all the pieces up. More pieces may be added later.

Six or eight people will live in the station at first. Each person will have a "bedroom" about the size of a closet. A crew will stay on the station for about three months. Then another crew will take their place. Space shuttles will be visiting the station all the time, bringing food and other supplies.

The United States will build most of the station. Other countries will also work on it. In 1985, Canada, Japan, and the European Space Agency decided to help. (The European Space Agency is run by a group of countries.)

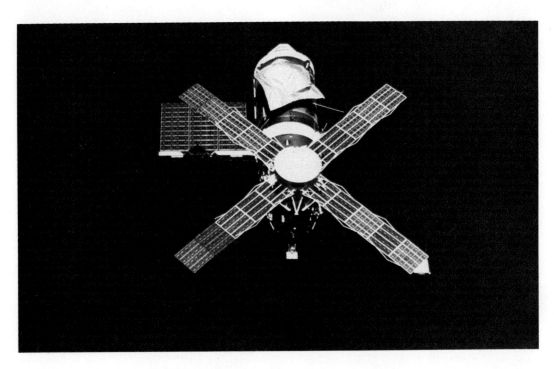

The station will be used as a factory and as a laboratory. It will also be used as a base from which to repair satellites. In time, it may be a starting place for trips to the moon and to other planets as well.

Factories in Space

Some products can be made better in space than on Earth be-cause the space station will not feel the pull of Earth's gravity. Medicines, metal alloys, and elec-tronic computer chips may all be made in space someday.

When medicines are made, the end product is sometimes a mixture. This mixture includes the needed medicine as well as substances that are not wanted. One way to make medicines pure is

with an electric current, which pulls the mixture apart. On Earth, the pull of gravity weakens the electric current. In space, this system works much better. It makes medicines that are much purer than any made on Earth.

Alloys are made when different metals are melted and then mixed together. The alloys are often stronger or better in some way than the metals from which they were made. The more smoothly an alloy is mixed, the better it will be. On Earth the heavy metals sink to the bottom and the light ones come to the top. In space they will mix together smoothly.

Electronic computer chips must be made out of material that is both very pure and very smoothly mixed. Space is the perfect place

to make them. Chips made in space may be better than any that have ever been made on Earth. These chips could make much faster computers.

It is important that these products can be made better in space. It is also important that they can be made for less money in space. Companies will have to pay NASA for letting them use the space station. Therefore, they will want to be sure that their products can be made cheaply. NASA needs to find companies that want to make their products in space. The money they give NASA will help NASA to pay for the space station.

High-Altitude Science

Some scientists want to study how plants grow and animals act without gravity. Some want to see how low gravity affects people. Other researchers in space want to find cures for some diseases.

Astronomers do not need to get away from Earth's gravity. They would like to get outside of Earth's layers of air. The atmosphere blocks light from stars far away. It also makes the view through a telescope fuzzy. Telescopes for studying the stars and planets will float near the space station. They will not be attached to it. This is so they won't shake every time someone on the station moves around.

An Orbiting Repair Shop

There are hundreds of small satellites in orbit around Earth. Sometimes they need repairs. Astronauts now use the space shuttle to fly up to a satellite to repair it. The people on the space station will be able to get to the satellites much more easily.

The space station may also be used as a base for workers. These workers will build huge satellites. The satellites will gather the sun's heat, turn it into electricity, and send the electricity back to Earth.

New Worlds to Explore

Once the station is built, it can be used as a base to send explorers out to other parts of space.

The spaceships we have sent away from Earth so far have been very small. They are small because the whole ship has to be

blasted free from Earth's gravity by one rocket. Out in space, we can build much larger ships. Also, less rocket fuel will be needed to launch a ship to another planet when the ship is already in orbit.

After the pioneers built their outposts in the Old West, more people came. The outposts grew into cities. Then people went out from those cities and built new outposts.

Someday, NASA's small space station may grow into a city in space. There may be more space stations in other orbits. The next project may be to build a base on the moon, or send a ship to explore Mars. The space station is just the first step!

1. Why is a new space station needed?

2. Name three ways in which the new space station will be used.

3. What would you like most about living and working on a space station? Why? What would you like least? Why?

4. Find the sentence that tells how the crew will get food and supplies during their three-month stay aboard the space station.

5. How is a space station like an outpost in the Old West?

6. How would the saying "Necessity is the mother of invention" apply to people living in the first space station?

Prewrite

Think about what it would be like to be a space pioneer. Does it seem exciting to you? What would be the best thing about living or working on a space station? Copy the chart on the next page and add to it. In each column, write words that you think would make someone want to live or work in space.

ADVANTAGES OF LIVING AND WORKING IN SPACE	
Living	**Working**
adventure	research
exploration	satellites

Draft

Write an advertisement for life on a space station. Use the words on your chart to give your readers a sense of excitement about this wonderful and exciting opportunity. Convince them that being a space pioneer is like being a pioneer in the Old West.

Revise

Read your advertisement. How does it make you feel? What words did you use to convince your readers? Does it need to be made stronger? Make any changes necessary to improve your advertisement.

Tyro is faced with a life-threatening situation and must make a difficult decision. Read to find out what happens to Tyro.

Australian Children's Book
of the Year Award Author

The Fallen Spaceman

by Lee Harding

The alien starship circled Earth many times before the spaceman fell.

The people inside the starship looked a little like us, but they were different in many ways. They came from another world in a distant part of the galaxy.

They were small, like children, with tiny arms and legs. They had large eyes and pale faces and no body hair at all, not even eyelashes. The tops of their heads were as smooth and as shiny as apples.

Their voices were strange. To our ears, their speech would sound more like music.

They moved around carefully. They were not very strong, and their soft bones could be easily broken. They had made many clever machines to do most of their work. This gave them time to think and to play and to enjoy themselves. In this way they were most like us.

As they passed Earth on their way to another star, they were curious and decided to study our world for a while. They swung their great starship into orbit and watched us through powerful telescopes.

They could not be seen from Earth, because they had a way of making their starship invisible. That way, they could carry out their work undisturbed.

They drew maps of our world, and their powerful cameras made an important record of our way of life. After several long days, they finished their study and began their journey once more.

They set their course for a star far away. The whole ship began to shake as the mighty engines roared and pushed away from Earth at a tremendous speed. In a matter of hours, they would be clear of the solar system and heading toward another star.

Except that they had made a terrible mistake. They forgot that one crew member, Tyro, was outside, working on the hull.

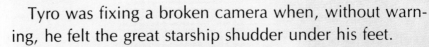

Tyro was fixing a broken camera when, without warning, he felt the great starship shudder under his feet.

He recognized at once the deep vibration of the atomic engines starting up. Puzzled, he wondered what the engineers were doing. He didn't understand why he hadn't been called inside. It was not safe to be working on the hull when the engines were being tested.

Tyro looked quickly toward the enormous tail of the starship, where the great engines pointed at the stars. At that moment the hull shook below him and the rockets fired.

The stars blurred and spun about him. The shock of the starship taking off sent him spinning away into space. He tumbled over and over like a wheel through the deep darkness of space. He was knocked unconscious.

In a matter of seconds, the starship was many miles away. Soon they would discover that one of their crew was missing. By that time, they would be in another part of the galaxy.

In the meantime, Tyro kept falling. Spinning and falling in all directions, while the big blue Earth swam below him.

It was some time before Tyro regained consciousness. When he did, he saw the stars spinning around outside his faceplate. He knew that something terrible had happened.

He leaned forward in his safety harness and moved one of the control levers. Small rockets fixed to the outside of his spacesuit fired for a few seconds and were able to stop his wild tumbling. Once the stars finished their mad dance, there was nothing else for him to see.

Where was the starship? Why hadn't they come back for him?

Tyro shivered. Never before had he felt so alone and afraid.

His spacesuit was huge. It was as tall as a five-story building. He sat safely inside it, in the center, protected by his netting, like a spider in his web.

He was small and weak, but his spacesuit had great power. It was built like a small starship. In front of him was a control panel with many instruments. Behind it was a small computer that helped him to control its movements.

He moved another lever . . . then another. The spacesuit began to turn around. The stars moved to one side. The great blue globe of Earth came into sight as he watched through his faceplate.

A great sadness came over him when he realized he was lost. What would he do if the starship did not return? He could not stay up here forever! His air would run out in a few more hours.

Better to take his chances on the strange world below! If he could reach it in safety, he would be able to stay alive until the starship returned . . . if it ever returned.

His head was clear now. He studied the control panel carefully. He had made up his mind to go down and take his chances. There was no time to lose. Every minute that ticked away used up a little more of his precious air supply.

It was a long way down to Earth. The trip would take several hours, and there was much that worried Tyro about the journey.

He would fall at a great speed. He would fall so fast that his spacesuit would be burned up like a meteorite if he didn't use his rockets carefully. With luck he would make a safe landing with fuel left over.

The computer plotted a safe downward course. Tyro sat back and waited while it took over the controls and got the strange journey under way.

He felt his shoulder rockets fire, gently pushing him down. He began to fall feet first and very fast.

Tyro was frightened for the first few minutes. After a while, though, he got used to the strange feeling and sat back in his safety harness.

He thought about the unknown world below. He didn't know much about Earth. He was a cameraman, not a scientist. All he knew about Earth was the talk he had heard around the ship. He had heard that the people of Earth were large and warlike, with loud voices.

He would have to find somewhere to hide from the people of Earth while he waited for the starship. That might not be so easy. For the moment all he thought about was a safe landing.

Faster and faster fell the spaceman. Soon the Earth had pushed everything else aside and filled his view. He could see land, green and brown, through the gaps in the fleecy clouds. The great oceans threw back bright sunlight and hurt his weak eyes.

The oceans worried him. He didn't want to come down there! What he needed was a deep forest, far away from any cities. There he hoped he would be safe.

He entered Earth's atmosphere at a terrific rate. Clouds rushed past his faceplate and it grew suddenly hot inside the spacesuit. He raced across oceans and mountains, forests and jungles, deserts and rain forests. Cities flashed by below the huge feet of his spacesuit. He saw all the Earth, but too fast for his tired eyes to follow.

The computer saw and recorded everything. It sorted through this information, looking for a safe place to land. Tyro could never have made such a swift descent without its help.

Faster and faster he fell. It was so hot inside the spacesuit that he could hardly breathe. He looked away from the controls and out through the faceplate. He was over land again, falling toward a wooded mountain range.

He wondered if he would make it alive. The heat was burning him up. His eyes stung and his skin had begun to dry up. Two miles up and falling! The wind batted at his spacesuit like an angry fist.

The forest, rich and green, raced up from below. The computer was leading him toward a small clearing in the trees. Tyro felt a warm feeling of relief. He closed his eyes and waited.

He was only a few hundred feet above the forest when the computer fired the braking rockets to slow his fall. It should have worked, but something inside the computer slipped. It corrected too much. The spacesuit came to a sudden stop in midair. It bobbed around as though a giant, invisible hand were shaking it.

Tyro was thrown forward. Only his safety harness saved him from dashing his head against the control panel. He looked about, wild-eyed with surprise. Whatever was happening?

The spacesuit danced across the sky like something gone mad, rockets blazing. The fall had been checked, but the powerful push of energy had thrown the spacesuit wildly off course.

Tyro saw what was happening. He reached forward to take the hand controls, but nothing happened. The levers were useless in his tiny hands!

Slowly the spacesuit came about as the dazed computer sensed what had happened. By then, though, it was too late to avoid disaster.

Tyro almost made it. The top branches of the trees were even with his faceplate when the rockets coughed and died. The last drop of rocket fuel had been used up trying to bring the spacesuit under control.

The spaceman fell.

The air screamed past his faceplate. He closed his eyes and waited. The ground rushed up to meet him. The tearing, crashing noise outside grew even louder.

The spacesuit slammed into the ground. The shock shook every bone in Tyro's body. The spacesuit toppled over and buried its great helmeted head in the ground. Tyro passed out. His last conscious thought was that he was down at last and alive.

For a long time after he regained consciousness, Tyro was too sore to move. His chest was badly bruised where his safety harness had held him down—but it had saved his life.

He wondered how much time had passed since the crash and how much air he had left. He sat up and rubbed his aching arms and legs. From the angle of the spacesuit, he realized it had fallen on one side.

He couldn't see a thing through the faceplate. The helmet had dug deeply into the ground, making it impossible to see anything outside. Inside the spacesuit it was dark.

He moved a switch. He felt better when a weak light flooded the inside of the spacesuit. It seemed that not everything had been damaged by the fall.

After some time, he noticed an unusual quiet inside the spacesuit. There was not even the soft purr of the control computer to break the silence.

The computer . . . now he remembered.

The computer had made a mistake. That mistake had almost cost him his life. If the spacesuit was damaged beyond repair, it could still cost him.

Tyro tried the controls. Nothing happened. He tapped out a message directed to the computer. Again, there was no answer. He might well be alive, but his spacesuit seemed quite dead.

Just when he was about to give up, there was a soft hum from the control panel. A few weak lights lit up. One of them showed "Computer Ready."

Tyro took a deep breath and leaned back in his seat.

"All right," he said in his strange musical speech, "how bad is it? Let me have a full report."

It took a few seconds before the computer replied in a mechanical copy of Tyro's voice.

There has been some damage, it croaked. Tyro could tell that the voice coil had been badly damaged by the fall. *It will take some time to find out how badly.*

"Be as fast as you can," he ordered. "I want to know how much damage has been done."

The computer hummed quietly to itself as it went about this important business.

Tyro sat back, weak and sore. His senses reached out and made contact with the outside world.

The forest felt warm and kind. Nothing to fear out there.

Yet, there was something else. Something that moved. He could feel it. It was coming closer.

A shadow fell across his faceplate. It shut out what little light found its way in through the dust and dirt that covered the glass.

He heard scraping sounds. Something was scratching away at the dirt covering his faceplate.

Tyro tensed and sat forward. There was nothing he could do! There might be some dangerous animal outside, trying to get in. Given time, his spacesuit would repair itself. Then he would be more than a match for any life form on this planet but not now. Not when he was still helpless!

The scraping continued. A few inches of sunlight crept into the spacesuit. Tyro saw large white fingers nervously scraping the dirt away.

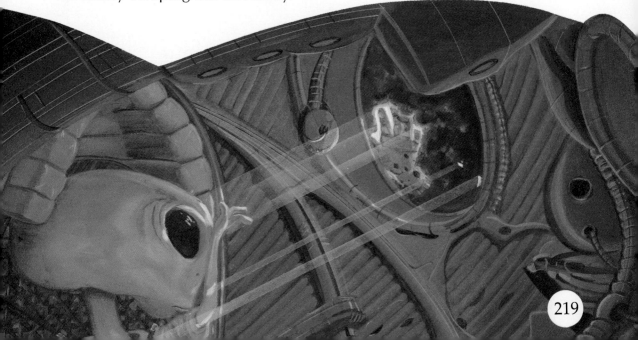

Tyro was surprised. The fingers were so like his own, only much longer. A wave of relief washed over him. No animal then, but a creature like himself.

He held his breath and waited while the busy fingers completed their work. The scraping stopped. There was a long pause and then the shadow moved again, blocking out the sun.

A strange face was staring in through the faceplate at him.

Tyro crouched low in his seat. The stranger's face was bigger and longer than his own. A great thatch of hair sprouted from the head. The eyes were wide and startled. Tyro could feel great waves of uneasiness reaching into his mind.

For a moment he managed a weak smile. It seemed that the alien outside was as worried as he was!

They stared at each other through the faceplate. A strange silence drew them together. When another few moments had passed, the stranger's face pulled back slowly from the darkened glass. It disappeared to one side, allowing the sunlight to come streaming in.

Tyro sat quite still for some time. He waited for his wildly beating heart to quiet down, and for the computer to deliver its final report.

Still, he could not erase from his mind the image of that strange and disturbing alien face.

Discuss the Selection

1. What accidentally happened to Tyro?

2. What happened after Tyro reached Earth?

3. In which situation did you think Tyro was in the most danger?

4. How does the author let you know that something is going to happen to Tyro?

5. What do you think will happen to Tyro next?

6. How does this selection show that new experiences can be frightening?

Think and Write

Prewrite

Imagine what it would feel like to find yourself alone in another world. Would you be frightened? Would you be curious about this new place? Would you be lonely? If you were in Tyro's place, what would you do first after landing on Earth? Discuss your ideas with a classmate.

Draft

Continue to write the story of Tyro, the fallen spaceman. What do you think would happen next? Write your ideas in the order that you think they would happen. Here are some questions you might use:

- What would Tyro find when he left his spacesuit?
- Would people be friendly to him?
- Would he run into danger?
- What would he think of Earth and the people living on Earth?

Revise

Read your story. Have you told at least two things that happened to Tyro? Would what you have written make someone want to go on reading? Add or change whatever you can to make your story interesting.

Fantasy and Science Fiction

There are many kinds of fiction. You have learned that in realistic fiction, the characters and the setting are believable even though the story is not true. The characters and the events could actually exist.

You have also learned that fantasy is one type of fiction and that in fantasy, things happen that could not happen in real life. Sometimes, the characters seem real but the world in which they live is magical. Fantasies can take you to the bottom of the sea or to an unknown world. Fairy tales, folktales, myths, legends, and all science fiction are fantasies.

Science fiction mixes the real with the fantastic. It allows characters to do many of the imaginative things that are characteristic of fantasy. However, most science fiction deals with scientific possibilities and the changes these advancements may bring. Unlike fantasy, science fiction suggests possibilities about life in the future. A science fiction writer includes descriptions based on scientific facts in a make-believe world, and tries to make them believable.

Read the following paragraphs. Think about the realistic details in the story and also think about what makes this story science fiction.

The alien starship circled Earth many times before the spaceman fell.

The people inside the starship looked a little like us, but they were different in many ways. They came from another world in a distant part of the galaxy.

As they passed Earth on their way to another star, they were curious and decided to study our world for a while. They swung their great starship into orbit and watched us through powerful telescopes.

They could not be seen from Earth, because they had a way of making their starship invisible. That way, they could carry out their work undisturbed.

They drew maps of our world, and their powerful cameras made an important record of our way of life. After several long days, they finished their study and began their journey once more. They set their course for a star far away.

from *The Fallen Spaceman*
by Lee Harding

The realistic details are the telescopes, Earth, the stars, the starship, and space travel. You know that this story is science fiction because the creatures in the starship could make their ship invisible, and they set their course for a star far away.

Remember that in science fiction, the characters, the setting, and the plot may or may not be believable and that the author is using some current or projected scientific fact as a basis for the story.

This selection, presented in play form, gives information about the parts of a computer. Why do you think the parts of a computer are amazing?

The Talking Computer

by Murray Suid

CHARACTERS:

Person	Mouse	Screen
CPU	Microphone	Speaker
Disk Drive	Light Pen	Printer
Program	Byte	Modem
Keyboard	Main Memory	

The scene is a science museum. A sign reading "Welcome to the Talking Computer Exhibit" hangs center stage. Note: **All Parts** *means that all characters except* **Person** *and* **CPU** *speak the given lines together.*

Person: This is the science museum's new talking computer. Since hearing is believing, I'll just turn it on.

All Parts: Hello. We are the parts of a computer. We're here to tell you what we do and how we work.

Person: That's great.

All Parts: (*All parts shout out.*) I'll go first because I'm the most important. You are not! I am! No, I am!

CPU: (*blows a whistle and everyone quiets down*) That's better.

Person: Who are you?

227

CPU: I'm the Central Processing Unit, or CPU for short. You might call me the computer's brain. I do the math and thinking work. I also tell the others what to do.

Person: I guess *you* are the most important part.

CPU: Not really. We're all important. Would your brain be much use without your heart, your skin, your . . .

Person: I see what you mean.

CPU: To know how a computer works, you have to learn about *all* of us. Isn't that right, everybody?

All Parts: Sure! We're all important!

Person: So, who goes first?

All Parts: Me! Me! Let me! Let me!

CPU: (*blows whistle again and waits for quiet*) You can see why a CPU is needed. Let's begin with you, Disk Drive. After turning the computer on, people often use you or your cousin Tape Drive.

Disk Drive: I knew I was the most important part.

All Parts: Boo! Hiss! That's not so! Boo!

CPU: (*blows whistle*) Cut that out. Our guest doesn't want to hear bragging and arguing. Now, Disk Drive, just tell what you do in plain English. Okay?

Disk Drive: Okay. I'm something like a record player, only I play magnetic disks. (*holds up a disk*) Disks or tapes store words, numbers, pictures, and programs. A program is . . .

Program: (*interrupting*) Stop! Don't tell what I do. I'll talk for myself.

Disk Drive: Excuse me, Program.

Program: You're excused. Now, a program is a list of instructions a computer follows in doing a job. It's like the script for a play. But in this case the actors are the computer's parts. For example, a checkers program tells the screen how to make a checkerboard pattern. It also tells the CPU how to make moves.

Person: Can that program play chess, too?

Program: Nope. Every time you ask the computer to do a different job, you need another program. There are thousands of ready-to-use programs for everything from doing mathematics to drawing pictures. Plus, you can always write your own programs.

Person: I see why computers are so popular! With different programs, one machine can be used in lots of ways. But how does it work?

Program: Put the disk or the tape into the drive. Then use the keyboard . . .

Keyboard: Did I hear someone say *Keyboard*? That's me. My keys can send signals directly to the CPU. After you put a disk into the disk drive, you type the name of the program.

Person: You mean like "Checkers"?

Keyboard: Yes. Then you push my *return* or *enter* key. That tells CPU what you want. Without me, nothing would happen.

Mouse: What about me, Keyboard?

Person: Who are you?

Mouse: I'm Mouse. I can do a lot of Keyboard's work, only faster. Plus, I can draw pictures. Some people think that I look like a mouse crawling around when I am doing my job.

Microphone: And what about me? Some computers let people use a microphone to tell CPU the job they want done. In the future I may be the main way people talk to computers.

Keyboard: We'll see.

Light Pen: Speaking about seeing, don't overlook me, Light Pen. (*holds up package with bar code*) I can read the bar codes used in stores and libraries. Keyboard, Mouse, and Microphone can't do that! So there.

CPU: No bragging! What matters is that each of you can let the user talk to me in electrical code. In most computers, the code is made up of messages called *bytes*. Each byte stands for a letter, a number, or a symbol.

Byte: I work the way a finger code works. Suppose you want to send a message to someone across the room. First you both agree that one finger up is C, two fingers up is A, and three fingers up is T. Then you could send the word *cat* in this way. (*Byte holds up one finger, then lowers the hand, then raises the hand and holds up two fingers, then lowers the hand, then raises the hand and holds up three fingers.*)

Person: But there are no fingers inside the computer.

Byte: That's true. Instead, I'm made up of eight electrical signals. By using different ones, I can send 256 different messages. (*Byte moves fingers up and down to make different patterns.*)

Person: I could never make sense of all these bytes.

CPU: I'm made so I can figure out this kind of message quicker than you can blink your eye. When a user asks for a program stored on a disk, I instantly send a signal—using the same electrical code—telling Disk Drive to send the program to Main Memory.

Main Memory: That's me. I'm the place where programs stay while being used. I also hold some of the data—words and numbers—that the computer is working with.

CPU: After Disk Drive has done its job, I send another signal, using different bytes, to Main Memory. I ask it for the program's first instructions.

Byte: (*running to Main Memory*) May I have the first instruction, please?

Main Memory: I send the first instruction, also in code, back to the CPU.

Byte: (*running to the CPU*) Tell the screen to print a message saying that the program is ready.

Screen: I'm something like a TV screen. Without me, the computer couldn't tell the user anything.

Speaker: Really? In some computers, a speaker like me can talk to the user in a voice that sounds almost human. Why, in a few years electronic speakers may replace screens completely.

Screen: I doubt it. Can you *show* pictures and colors the way I can?

Speaker: No, but can you play music the way I can?

CPU: (*blows whistle*) Cut it out! The point is that my job is to take the program's instructions from Main Memory one at a time. I then make sure they're carried out.

Person: Do you always have the other parts do the work?

CPU: No. Sometimes I do it. Part of me does the math and thinking work. In a way, I send messages to myself.

Person: What happens next?

CPU: After I deal with the first job, I ask Main Memory for the next thing to do. In some programs, thousands of little jobs have to be done before the big job is done. When the big job is finished, the result may be flashed on the screen or sent to the printer.

Printer: Like a typewriter, I put words and numbers on paper. I can even print pictures.

CPU: Sometimes, the information is sent to the modem.

Modem: My job is to change the code inside the computer into a different code that can be sent over phone lines to other computers.

CPU: But often the information will be stored for later use. In most computers, information can't be kept in Main Memory. When the computer is shut off, that erases everything. For safekeeping,

information must be sent to the disk drive where it is put on a disk.

Person: Whew. You're really kept busy sending and receiving signals.

CPU: That's true. Most modern computers can move around a million or more messages each second.

Person: How do you do it so fast?

CPU: My main moving parts are electrical signals. Electricity travels at the speed of light. That's the fastest thing in the universe. Also, while I'm big in this play, I'm small in real life. I fit onto a tiny chip of silicon that's smaller than your fingernail. Many of the signals I send and receive travel less than a quarter of an inch. Since the trips are short, they don't take a long time.

Person: Well, all of you parts are amazing!

All Parts: Thanks. We like you, too.

Person: Shall I turn you off now?

All Parts: Yes, but before you do, we have one last message.

Person: What is it?

(*All Parts say nothing, but for three seconds they signal by rapidly moving their fingers up and down.*)

Person: Could you say it in English?

All Parts: Sure. This is *the end*.

1. Which parts of the computer do you think are amazing? Why?

2. How are the keyboard, the microphone, the mouse, and the light pen similar?

3. Which part of the computer in the play did you think acted like a teacher or a coach? Explain your answer.

4. When did you realize that the author had given each part of the computer human characteristics? Why do you think the author did this?

5. What did you learn must happen for a computer to work best?

6. Many things are done better by a team than by one person. How does this idea apply to the selection?

Think and Write

Prewrite

The parts of a computer cannot do much by themselves. Together, though, they are very powerful. Think of some ways that people work together to do things they cannot do alone.

Here are some examples:
- a baseball team
- an orchestra
- a big-city newspaper

What does each person do in each of these? What would happen if one part of the group or team were missing? Discuss this with some classmates.

Draft

Choose one example of people working together to make or do something. Write a short play in which each person explains what he or she does. Use "The Talking Computer" as a model for writing your play.

Revise

Read your play. Would it be fun or interesting to listen to or watch? Is it clear what each person does? Is it also clear how they work together? Make whatever additions and changes are needed to improve the play.

Bar and Circle Graphs

You know that you can learn many things by reading words and sentences. Did you also know that you can learn many things by studying pictures and drawings? A **graph** is a special kind of drawing that shows how two or more things are related. A graph can sometimes show information more clearly than words.

There are different kinds of graphs. Two of these are bar graphs and circle graphs.

Bar Graphs

You know that a bar graph compares one thing with another. In order to get information from bar graphs, you must learn to "read" the bars. Look at the bar graph below.

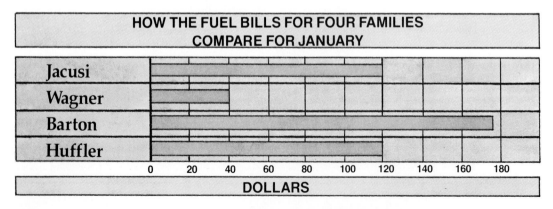

HOW THE FUEL BILLS FOR FOUR FAMILIES COMPARE FOR JANUARY

Jacusi
Wagner
Barton
Huffler

0 20 40 60 80 100 120 140 160 180

DOLLARS

The words above the graph are the title. The title tells what the graph is comparing—the fuel bills for four families during the month of January. The words at the left side of the graph tell the different subtopics being compared—four families. The numerals at the bottom of the graph give amounts. The label below the numerals tells that the numerals stand for dollars.

From this graph you can tell how much each of the four families spent for fuel during January. Look at the subtopic *Wagner*. Notice that the bar next to the name *Wagner* ends at the numeral 40. You can tell this by looking at the bottom of the graph. How much did the Wagners spend for fuel during January? You know from this bar graph that the Wagner family spent forty dollars for fuel during January.

The graph below tells the same information, but the information is arranged differently. The first graph you studied is a horizontal bar graph; this graph is a vertical bar graph.

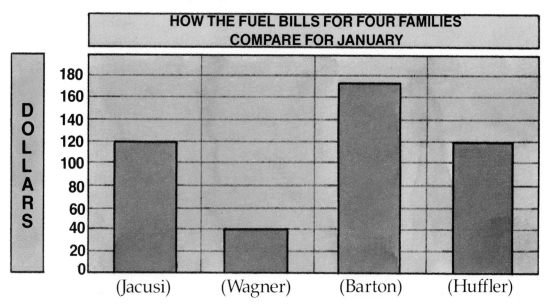

Circle Graphs

Another kind of graph is a circle or pie graph. A circle graph compares information by showing how a whole can be divided into parts. The following circle graph is another way of looking at how four families spent money on fuel during January. Read the graph and answer the questions.

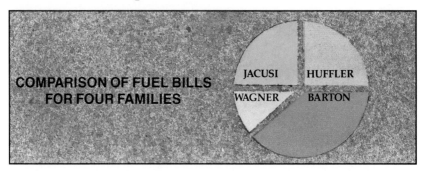

COMPARISON OF FUEL BILLS
FOR FOUR FAMILIES

JACUSI   HUFFLER

WAGNER   BARTON

What does the circle graph tell? The title of the circle graph tells what is being compared. The graph compares the fuel bills for four families. Which family spends the largest amount on fuel? The Bartons have the biggest part of the circle, so they spend the largest amount on fuel. Which family spends the smallest amount on fuel? The Wagners spend the smallest amount on fuel. They have the smallest space on the circle graph. Which families spend the same amounts on fuel bills? The Jacusis and Hufflers spend the same amounts on fuel, so their spaces are the same size on the circle graph.

Notice that the bar graph shows how much money each family spent and gives exact figures. The circle graph, however, shows the relationships of the amounts of money that each family spent on fuel, but it does not tell the exact dollar amount. No dollar figures are given.

Here is another example of how a circle graph and a bar graph can provide different information about the same topic. As part of a math project, Kim surveyed the students in her school to find out who had computers and what additional items had been bought for use with these computers. She made a circle graph and a bar graph to show the results. Look at the two graphs that Kim made and then answer the questions in the paragraph below.

ITEMS BOUGHT
BY
FAMILIES WITH COMPUTERS

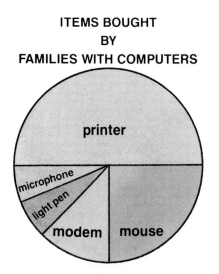

ITEMS BOUGHT
BY
FAMILIES WITH COMPUTERS

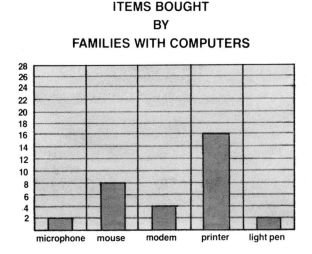

According to the circle graph, which item was the one most often bought by families with computers? By looking at the circle graph, you can tell that the printer was the item most often bought. Exactly how many printers were bought? You cannot find out by looking at the circle graph. You can find out, however, by looking at the bar graph. How many were bought? The answer is "16 printers." As you can see, each of the two graphs provides different information about the same item. The circle graph shows that printers were bought most often. The bar graph tells exactly how many printers were bought.

Robots can be used in many different ways. As you read, think about how a robot could be most useful to you.

Ready, Set, Robots

by Lisa Yount

The new workers are skilled, and they do many jobs. Some help put cars together. Others move packages in a warehouse. A team of them runs a supermarket in Japan. A few are learning to cut the wool from sheep in Australia. Some walk on the ocean floor. One has stood on the red sands of the planet Mars, where no human being has ever gone.

The new workers are robots. Over twenty thousand are on the job worldwide—and that number is growing all the time. Robots can work all day and all night.

This robot is putting a car together. It works at a factory in Turin, Italy.

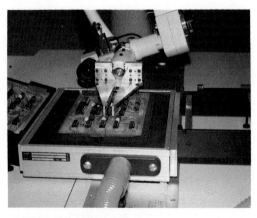

A robot's computer "brain" tells it what to do. This robot is making a part that may go in another computer.

Robots never become sick or tired. They do jobs that are too boring, dangerous, or difficult for people to do.

Of course, these machines cannot really think as people do. A robot's "brain" is a computer. People must plan every step of an action they want a robot to do. Then they write a set of instructions, called a program, for the robot's computer. The computer follows these instructions and makes the robot's body move. Television cameras act as "eyes" and send pictures to the robot's computer brain.

Where Robots Work

Most robots today work in factories. Many car factories in Japan, the United States, and other countries use robots. Almost all the workers in one Japanese factory are robots. One set of robots can paint a car after other robots have assembled the car. Another kind of robot can sort machine parts more quickly than people can. It pulls out any parts that are not made right.

You may soon see robots in stores, too. They already do most of the work in the big Seiyu market in Yokohama, Japan. A robot cart rolls along the market's aisles. Signs on it show what foods are on sale that day. A "butcher" robot slices meat, following orders that buyers give by pressing buttons. The robot then weighs the meat, wraps it, and shoots it out a slot. Other robots work at night, when the store is closed. They bring carts of food out of a warehouse behind the store. People put the food on the market's shelves.

Robots can go where people cannot. One kind of robot works on the bottom of the sea. It is guided by a person on a nearby ship. A television screen aboard the

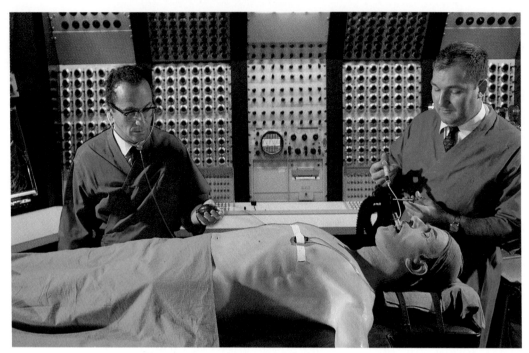

The "patient" on this operating table is really a robot. It is helping these people learn how to be good doctors.

ship shows the person what the robot "sees" below. To make the robot move, the person moves a robot arm on the ship. This sends a message to the robot on the ocean floor. That robot moves its arm in the same way that the arm on the ship was moved.

The two *Viking* landers that visited Mars in 1976 were also a kind of robot. Signals from Earth controlled them. The robots took pictures of the planet and tested its soil.

Other Ways Robots Help

Robots can help people become better doctors and nurses. Some robots are programmed to act as a real person would when given certain medicines. Other robots will "bruise" or "bleed." By practicing with the robots, people learn how to help the injured and sick.

Robots can work for disabled people, too. People who cannot move their arms and legs may be able to move their heads to guide a robot that can feed or dress them. Some people may need to wear a robot arm and hand, which can pick up an egg without breaking it. A scientist in Japan is working on a robot "guide dog" for blind people. A talking robot that can read books to blind people is already in use.

Police and fire fighters use robots, too. Police departments use robots to take bombs apart. Robots can also act as guards. There are robots that visit classrooms to tell children about safety. Robots that can walk up walls may soon help fire fighters save people in burning buildings.

A robot "nurse" gives this disabled man a drink.

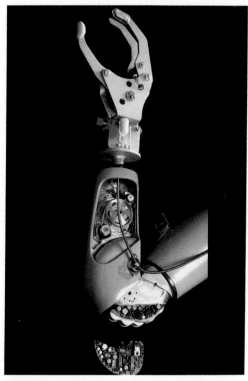

If someone loses an arm in an accident, a robot arm can take its place. This arm was made at the University of Utah.

Would you like this robot to visit your classroom or stay in your home?

OPD2 belongs to the police department in Orlando, Florida. OPD2 is telling these children about safety.

Robots can help children learn. A talking robot helped fourth-grade children in New York for several years. When a student gave the right answer to a question, the robot would tell a joke or a riddle. Children in a New Mexico classroom learned about computers by writing programs that told a robot how to do different jobs. Robots have been used to teach languages to children, as well.

People also use robots just for fun. Some amusement parks and restaurants have robots that sing, dance, play the piano, or tell jokes. A few even have robots that bring the food you order.

Robots in the Future

People even have robots in their homes. Today, though, most of these robots are just costly toys. Some can speak a few sentences. Some can roll across the room to greet a guest—if their owners tell them where to go. One day, perhaps, home robots may answer the door, cook the food, or walk the dog.

No one knows how robots will change our lives. Some people think that robots will take jobs away from those who need them. Others think robots will let people do more exciting jobs or have more free time. Whatever happens, you are likely to see more and more robots as you grow up. Maybe someday you will even have a robot of your own!

WABOT-2 *is a Japanese robot. It can read music and play the piano.*

When this robot is finished, "he" may speak or sing. Robots like this can be found in some restaurants and amusement parks.

This robot was made by a Swiss clockmaker and his son in 1774. It writes messages.

1. If you could design a robot to work for *you,* what kinds of jobs would it be able to do?

2. Name four ways in which robots are being used to help people.

3. Do you think a robot would make a good friend? Explain your answer.

4. How do you know *who* is responsible for making the robot a successful machine?

5. Why are more and more robots being used every day?

6. How does the saying "There are two sides to every story" apply to this selection?

**Think
and
Write**

Prewrite

Imagine you have a robot of your very own. Copy and complete the chart on the next page. List five things you would like your robot to be able to do. Think of things that would help you the most.

My robot would . . .
1. clean my room
2.
3.
4.
5.

Draft

Write a speech to give to your parents. Tell them why you should have a robot of your own. Here are some points to think about:

- How the robot would make life easier for you
- How the robot would make life easier for your parents
- How the robot would make your life more fun

Revise

Read your speech. Is it convincing? Have you given examples to support your reasons for wanting a robot? Will your parents agree with your reasoning? Add or change whatever you can to make your speech more convincing.

Alfred Slote

Alfred Slote, a well-known author, was first encouraged by his oldest son and a librarian to write children's books. Both his sports fiction and his science fiction are about young people, what happens to them, and how they handle it.

Alfred Slote's career has taken many interesting turns. After attending the University of Michigan, he served in the Navy during World War II. After the war he returned to the university to finish his studies. Later he went back to school, this time in France. There he wrote his first book. When he returned to the United States, he became an English teacher at a Massachusetts college.

Alfred Slote has strong feelings about reading. He believes that reading is the most important thing a child can do. "You only know what your eyes can see and your ears can hear," he says. "This firsthand knowledge is good, but it is not enough to cope with the world we live in." He believes that books go beyond firsthand knowledge to help us see life from other points of view. "If you read," he says, "you have a better chance to understand human relationships."

Alfred Slote likes to visit schools to talk with students who read his books. He says, "Children really keep you on your toes. They make you think."

One day he was with a group of fourth-grade students. One boy asked him, "Why did you write *My Robot Buddy*?"

Very slowly Mr. Slote began to answer. He said, "I think I wrote it . . ." Then he paused to think about why. While Mr. Slote was pausing, the boy tried to help him. He said, "Oh, you wrote it all right. Your name is on the cover."

If he had been given enough time, Alfred Slote could have answered that question. *My Robot Buddy* was different from the sports fiction he had written. It was a type of science fiction that allowed him to use more of his imagination. He says, "The *Robot Buddy* books are mysteries set in the future. They are not pure science fiction. I use the future because nobody knows exactly what it's going to be like, and my guess is as good as any. It gives me a lot of freedom as a writer."

When children ask him how to become a writer, he tells them to read. "Not every reader becomes a writer," he says. "But no one ever became a writer who wasn't a reader."

Alfred Slote has written many children's books. Two of his sports books are *Jake* and *Hang Tough, Paul Mather*. Other titles in the *Robot Buddy* series are *C.O.L.A.R.*, *Omega Station*, and *The Trouble on Janus*.

As you read "My Robot Buddy," think about what Alfred Slote's picture of the future is.

Children's Choices Author

In this science fiction story, read to find out how a ten-year-old boy gains a new friend on his birthday.

My Robot Buddy

by Alfred Slote

I had no business wanting a robot for my birthday. My folks weren't well off. My father needed the mobile telephone for his solar car. He needed the mobile telephone for business. I needed a robot for pleasure.

My folks and I live out in the country, and after school there was no one my age around. On the Read/Screen I had seen pictures of kids who had robots that acted like brothers and sisters to them. They could talk with them, play ball with them. I wanted someone like that, someone I could talk with, throw a ball with, go fishing with, climb trees with.

So I bugged my parents about a robot for a long time. If they talked about the latest line of solar cars, I talked about the latest line of robots. "You know," I'd say, "I saw on the Read/Screen that the newest robots look more like people than people do."

"Is that so, Jack?" Mom would say, and change the subject.

When that didn't work, I'd march around the room pretending I was a robot. Robots have that stiff-in-the-knees walk, and I got so I could robot-walk perfectly.

"Hey, look at me," I'd shout, and march around until Dad would ask me to remember that I wasn't a robot, and couldn't become one no matter how hard I tried, and to please stop shaking the house. When I wouldn't stop, he would say I looked sleepy.

That was a cue for bed.

About a week before my tenth birthday, I put on a big "look-at-me-pretend-I'm-a-robot" show, and I got sent up to bed early again. I lay in bed and knew I was being a pest, but I also knew I had to have someone to play with after school, or I'd go nuts.

I guess Mom thought the same thing. I heard her saying downstairs, "Frank, I think we're going to have to get him his robot."

"We can't afford it, Helen," Dad replied. "Nor does he really need one. If *you* wanted a robot to help us with the housework, I could understand that, but just because Jack is bored . . ."

"Couldn't we get one robot that would do both?" Mom was thinking that she could kill two birds with one stone.

"I don't think so," Dad said. "My guess is that it's fairly simple to program a robot to do jobs, whether they're housework, gardening, or factory work. But to show emotions, hold a conversation, think, be a companion—those are complicated responses, and programming a robot to do things like that must be expensive. I don't think we can afford that kind of robot, Helen."

"All right, Frank, then I think we ought to move back to the city where Jack can have other children to play with."

Now Mom was hitting Dad where it hurt. He hated cities. He hated the feeling of people crowding him. He hated driving in traffic. Dad had grown up in Metropolis III in the northeast, and after college he had worked as an engineer on a space shuttle. When he'd made enough money, he had bought our house in the country, away from modern life and other people. He said people who lived in cities were growing soft. He wanted me to chop wood and dig gardens and climb trees. I didn't mind country life, except that I was lonely. I didn't want a robot to do my chores for me. I just wanted someone to play with.

"Helen," Dad said, and I could tell from the way he said Mom's name that he was weakening, "buying an expensive robot means no mobile telephone for my car. It means my business won't get bigger. That means constant trips to the home office to report in orders, which means less time that I can spend at home."

"Frank," Mom said, "measure your business against your son's happiness."

Dad was silent for a moment. "You're right," he said at last. "We'll buy him his robot."

I clapped my hands and started to shout with happiness, but I had the sense to shut up.

"What was that?" Mom asked.

"Probably a branch falling on the roof," Dad said.

The next day Dad asked me if I wanted to take a tour of a robot factory on Saturday. Saturday was my birthday.

"A tour?" I asked innocently. "What for?"

"Well," Dad said casually, "you're always talking about robots. Perhaps it'll cure you to go through a place that makes them."

"Suppose it doesn't cure me."

"I'll take that chance," Dad said.

On Saturday, Mom, Dad, and I drove in Dad's solar car to Metropolis VII. Metropolis VII is a small satellite city that had been moved down from the northeast after a pollution crisis and rebuilt by the river. Mom liked it. She liked the shops and the parks and the theaters and the art we saw along its moving sidewalks. Even the industrial section was pleasant to drive through. Trees had been planted everywhere.

Dad drove up one ramp and then another, and in a few moments we saw a big sign that said: *Atkins Robots, Inc., The Very Best in Robots.*

Behind the sign was a circular white building.

"Here we are," said Dad.

It didn't look the way I thought it would. I had expected something much larger and straighter, like the factories where solar cars and spaceships are made.

We drove up the ramp right into the building and came to a sign that blinked:

Stop.

Dad stopped the car.

The sign then blinked:

Leave your motor on.

Blink:

Now leave the car.

"Why, they're treating us as though *we* were the robots," Mom said with a nervous laugh.

"It looks pretty efficient," Dad said.

As we got out of the car, a door to the building opened and a man in a chauffeur's uniform came toward us. He had that stiff-in-the-knees walk. He was a robot.

"You may go inside, if you please," said the robot-chauffeur. "I will park your car."

We watched the robot-chauffeur get in our car and drive it away smoothly.

"I would never have known except for how he walked," Mom said. "Now what do we do?"

"We go inside, just as he told us," Dad said. He looked at me. "Excited, Jack?"

"Yes, aren't you?"

Dad nodded. "I'm curious, I'll confess."

We went through the door the chauffeur had come out from, and we found ourselves inside a green room. There was a desk in the middle of it, and behind the desk was a blond lady in a white uniform. On her uniform was a small label that said: *Atkins Robots, Inc.*

She smiled brightly at us. "May I help you?"

"We're the Jameson family," Dad said. "I made an appointment for a tour."

"Of course. Won't you be seated? Dr. Atkins himself will give you the tour."

She checked our name on a list, took a piece of paper out of a drawer, and then left the room, walking stiff in the knees. "Hey," I whispered. . . .

"We know," Mom said.

"There probably isn't a human being in the place," Dad said.

"I wonder if Dr. Atkins will turn out to be a robot," I said.

"It's scary," Mom said.

"I like it," I said.

Dad smiled. "Well, it's a form of living advertising."

"If you can call it living," Mom said.

"I can, and I do," said a voice behind us. We all turned. Standing there was a tall, thin man wearing a green smock and carrying a clipboard with papers on it.

"When robots are well-built and well-programmed, they have lives of their own," the man said. "And who is to say really whether a human being in his human-ness is any more alive than a well-programmed Atkins robot in his robotness?"

He looked right at me as he asked that, but I wasn't going to answer him. For one thing, I didn't know if he was a robot or a human.

"A human," he answered my unspoken thought, and that gave me goose pimples. "I am Dr. Atkins. And you, I take it, are the Jameson family. If you will please follow me, we will begin our tour of the factory."

We followed Dr. Atkins into a small room in which were three chairs facing a blank white wall.

"Please sit down."

Dr. Atkins stood next to a side wall that had a panel of buttons on it.

The lights in the room grew dim.

"Our factory is made up of five *P* departments: Production, Programming, Physiognomy—"

"What's that mean?" I whispered to Mom.

"*Physiognomy* means 'face,' " Dr. Atkins said. He had good ears all right. "The fourth *P* is Personality, and finally there is the Power department. We will now begin the tour."

He pushed a button. It was completely dark in the room now. Suddenly the wall in front of us began to move. What kind of tour was this? I had thought we would go through the factory. But here the factory appeared to be moving while we were sitting still. The wall now seemed to be melting in front of our eyes. We were looking right through it into a long room. In the middle of the room was a conveyor belt with robots lying down on it. Standing above them, working on them, wiring them, soldering connections, attaching terminals, were other robots. Robots were manufacturing robots!

"In Production," Dr. Atkins's voice rang out, "we construct the outer shells and the inner hardware. Atkins Robots, Inc., produces fifteen robots per day. Not many compared with the output of large factories, but we take pride in the quality of our custom-made, long-lasting, lifelike robots."

Suddenly Production disappeared. The wall was dim again, and the factory once more appeared to move behind the screen.

"We are now coming to our second *P* department—Programming."

A scene lighted up in front of us. Seated at a row of machines with keyboards were a dozen older people punching out computer data cards.

"These people are your computer experts, I take it," Mom said.

"You are half-right, Madam," Dr. Atkins said. "They are computer experts, but they are not people. They are robots. Our most expensive robots. We have programmed them to program other robots. These Programming robots are never allowed to leave the factory. We keep them under lock and key at all times. The ransom we would have to pay a robotnapper to get a Programming robot back would be exorbitant."

Dr. Atkins paused. "That means 'very expensive,' young man."

"Thanks," I said.

Programming disappeared. The factory appeared to glide along behind the wall again.

"Now we are coming to Physiognomy—which means, young man?"

"Faces," I said.

"Very good. Suppose you wanted a robot as a companion. What kind of face would you like your robot to have?"

I knew what was going on. I was going to pick out a face for my birthday present.

"Can I see some?" I asked.

I saw more than some. So many faces flashed on the screen, I couldn't keep up with them. There were boy faces and girl faces, funny-looking faces and good-looking faces. There were faces with pug noses, long noses, big ears, little ears, buckteeth, little teeth, no teeth; redheads, blondes, dark-haired kids. Freckles, pimples . . . it was as if every face you ever saw in your life was passing in front of your eyes, and never the same face twice.

"Do you see any face you like, Jack?" Mom asked.

"Lots," I said. "Hey, there's a swell face."

The face that I liked held still on the screen. It was a boy who looked about my age. He had red hair and freckles. He was grinning. It was a friendly face.

A light flashed on the screen and then a voice said, "Physiognomy pattern A-1-Y17."

"Is that his name?" I asked. The screen went black.

"That is his facial pattern," Dr. Atkins said. "The person who buys him names him."

The factory views began moving across the screen again.

"What kind of name would you give to that face, Jack?" Mom asked.

"I don't know. 'Bob' . . . no, he doesn't look like a Bob. Red-haired, freckles, grinning . . . I've got it— 'Danny'! That's a good name for a redhead with freckles. Danny!"

"Danny One," said Dr. Atkins.

"One?"

"In case he gets rebuilt. The owner may want a similar model.

"We are now arriving at our Personality department." We were looking into another room. This one had a gigantic computer in it.

"Young man, if you were to have a robot for a friend, what kind of personality would you like him to have?"

"Like mine," I said.

"That is not very helpful," Dr. Atkins said. "How would you describe your personality?"

I glanced at my folks, but they didn't say anything. My dad's eyes were twinkling.

"Nice. . . . I think."

"And what exactly does 'nice' mean?"

"Well," I said, looking at the computer where a single light was going on and off, "I'm happy . . ." Suddenly a whole battery of lights went on and cards started going through the machine. "I like outdoor things. I like baseball and football and I like to fish. I'm a good tree climber and a pretty fast runner. Gee, I guess I like most everything."

I thought the computer would go wild. Green lights, yellow lights, red lights, cards going in and out, and bells sounding.

"Hmmmm," said Dr. Atkins, "you are a happy, all-around boy. Happiness is very difficult to program, and a robot who liked to do all those things would be as close to a real ten-year-old boy as possible. That would make Danny One a very expensive robot."

The screen went dim. The factory started moving again.

Dad cleared his throat. "I . . . uh . . . don't suppose there's any inexpensive way you could program for happiness."

"No, Mr. Jameson," Dr. Atkins said. "I'm afraid you have to be born a human being to be able to feel happiness for free: a nice day, a pretty sunset, a birdcall . . . enjoyment like this, people get just by being alive. But a robot must be programmed to enjoy things like that, and I'm sorry to say, that is very costly. Ah, now we are arriving at our final P department: Power."

We were looking into a dark room that had a solid screen at the end of it. In the screen were hundreds of small holes with light bulbs above and below them. Looking up at the screen were stiff, shadowy figures. They were holding wires in their hands.

"The bulbs you see on the screen stand for voice calls from Atkins robots in the field. The hum you hear in the background comes from nuclear generators stored below this level. In this room we can monitor the energy cells of every Atkins robot no matter where on

earth it is. If an Atkins robot needs an emergency charge, it can radio in to our Power department and receive one. Of course, you can recharge an Atkins robot by merely plugging it into your home nuclear power core. But should your robot run out of energy on the road or should your home nuclear core be damaged, the robot itself can call in and request a charge."

A bulb began flashing. Instantly, the low-pitched hum grew louder. A robot figure moved quickly.

"There are earphones below your chairs," Dr. Atkins said. "You can hear a robot calling in for an emergency charge if you put them on."

We did, and this is what we heard:

"Vic II. Vic II. Code 89C1, located in Agricultural Region 14. I have been working all night in the fields and need an emergency charge."

"All right, Vic II," said a Power department robot. "You'll be plugged in immediately."

A Power department robot climbed a little ladder and plugged a wire into the hole below the flashing light.

"When this happens," Dr. Atkins explained, "a bill is sent to the owner. Naturally, emergency charges are not included in the original price of our robots."

"Naturally," Dad said with a sigh.

"However, if you look after your robot, this should not happen."

"You are receiving now, Vic II," said the Power department robot in our earphones.

"I am receiving now. Thank you, Power department," said Vic II.

"Every Atkins robot has a built-in two-way radio so it can communicate with Power in emergencies. The radio is a simple affair with an on-off button located on the robot's belly."

"A belly button!" I exclaimed.

"Precisely," Dr. Atkins said. "In robots, it is a communication source. Our tour is now over."

The images behind the walls stopped. The lights went on. The room was the same as when we had started—which was no surprise, since we had never left it.

"Are there any questions about Atkins robots?" Dr. Atkins asked us.

I had a question all right, but it wasn't for Dr. Atkins. It was for Mom and Dad. It was: When do I get my robot? But I was afraid to ask. These were really expensive robots. Now I understood why. And Dad really needed a mobile telephone for his solar car.

Suddenly there was a knock on the door.

"Come in," Dr. Atkins said.

The door opened. A red-headed kid with freckles was standing there. He had a paper in his hand.

"Happy birthday, Jack," Mom said.

"Happy birthday, Jack," Dad said.

They were both smiling at me. I stared at the red-headed kid.

"Happy birthday, Jack," the kid said, grinning. "I'm Danny One. Here's my printout, Dr. Atkins. I hope he likes me."

"I'm certain he will, Danny One," Dr. Atkins said. "After all, it isn't given to every ten-year-old boy to create a friend. Now, let's check this over . . ." Dr. Atkins examined the paper Danny had given him. "According to the printout Danny One is programmed to play baseball. He bats right and throws left. In football, he can punt, kick, and throw a pass. He knows how to tackle and block. He is not a fast runner."

"I'm a little stiff in the knees, Jack," Danny said apologetically.

I laughed. "Hey, he's for real."

"He is a real robot," Dr. Atkins corrected me. "Programmed also to play basketball, climb trees, fish, and carry on general conversations. He has been programmed for a fourth-grade education in geography, arithmetic, history, and spelling. He can also do light chores around the house"—Dr. Atkins looked at me severely—"like any well-mannered ten-year-old boy. Ahem.

"Happy birthday, young man. May you enjoy your robot friend Danny One. Take good care of him."

Danny One and I stood there grinning at each other. This was both our birthdays.

1. How did Jack get his new friend?

2. Why was Danny One such an expensive robot?

3. Name the five *P* departments of Atkins Robots, Inc.

4. Do you think that Jack might want to rebuild Danny One in the future? Explain your answer.

5. What sentence on page 265 tells you that the homes in this story used nuclear energy?

6. Why did Jack's parents decide to get Danny for him?

Thinking About "Skylights"

"Skylights" began with an article about the most important light in the sky for us. You read about how we have begun to use the sun's power. You also read about ways to use other energy sources around us.

People have always been fascinated by objects in the sky. We even recreate images of the night sky in planetariums. Einstein Anderson and his brother Dennis studied the night sky with the same kind of instrument that Galileo used long ago.

You read about how we plan to reach out toward the stars by building a space station. You saw, too, how our imagination leaps ahead of known scientific facts and creates science fiction stories about beings from outer space. Maybe someday we will learn whether or not there really is life like Tyro on other planets.

Space travel is just one of the possibilities of the present and of the future. You also read about parts in computers that millions of people now use; you read about the kinds of robots we already have; and you read Alfred Slote's story about robots in the future.

Watch for other views of the sky in selections you read. Look, too, for the imaginative skylights that let you look to the future.

1. In "Those Weird Wagners" you read about how Tom Barton made fun of the Wagner family partly because they used solar energy. Do you think Tom Barton would have acted differently if he had read "Putting the Sun to Work"? Why or why not?

2. If Einstein Anderson went to the Hayden Planetarium, what do you think he would find most interesting? Why?

3. Suppose that Tyro had a chance to meet Einstein Anderson. If there were a way for them to understand one another, what do you think they would enjoy talking about together?

4. The author of "My Robot Buddy," Alfred Slote, writes stories that take place in the future. Imagine that he wrote a story that takes place on the space station you read about in "A Giant Step into Space." What do you think his story would be about?

5. How did reading "The Talking Computer" help you to better understand how robots work in "Ready, Set, Robots"?

6. Which "Skylight" selection did you enjoy reading about the most? Why?

Unit 3

Symphonies

A symphony is a piece of music written to be played by an orchestra. To play a symphony well, the musicians in the orchestra need to work as a team. The many different sounds of the instruments must *blend* together to make one complete and beautiful sound. Such blending can be found in other forms of expression, too. For example, some paintings have been called "symphonies of color."

In "Symphonies," you will read about people who have found their own special forms of expression. Some of these people perform music; others dance, write, or paint. Through practice and with great determination, all have learned to do something that is important to them.

As you read the selections, think about how all these forms of expression are alike and different, yet special.

Read on Your Own

The Glorious Fourth at Prairietown *by Joan Anderson. Morrow.* The Carpenter family travels from Pennsylvania to Indiana in 1836 and celebrates the Fourth of July.

Music Lessons for Alex *by Caroline Arnold. Clarion.* After attending her first concert, Alex asks for music lessons. We follow Alex as she begins her lessons and works with other students. We then attend Alex's concert.

The Photo Dictionary of the Orchestra *by Melvin Berger. Methuen.* The best way to appreciate an orchestra is by listening, but reading about the musicians and their instruments is also fun.

Ballet Company *by Kate Castle. Franklin.* You will see everything that goes into putting on a ballet at the Royal Ballet in London. There is a lot more than dancing!

The Skates of Uncle Richard *by Carol Fenner. Random.* Nine-year-old Marsha dreams of becoming a figure skater but has difficulty with her uncle's old skates. With his help and encouragement, she learns how to use the skates and is on her way.

Two Piano Tuners *by M.B. Goffstein. Farrar.* Debbie lives with her grandfather, Reuben Weinstock, the greatest piano tuner in the world. She wants to be just like him, even though he would rather she become a concert pianist.

The Muffin Fiend *by Daniel Pinkwater. Lothrop.* A fiend from outer space has stolen all the muffins in Vienna, and Inspector LeChat enlists the help of Mozart, the famous composer and muffin lover. The silly mistake that trips up the culprit is as funny as this book.

The Purim Goat *by Yuri Suhl. Four Winds.* A poor Jewish boy in Poland cannot bear to have his goat slaughtered, so he teaches her to dance.

Frederick *by Leo Lionni. Pantheon.* All the mice are getting ready for winter, but it appears that Frederick is not doing any of the work. When the food they have worked to store begins to run out, the other mice are delighted that Frederick is a poet who was storing up beautiful words to share!

Randolph Caldecott
Medal Illustrator

As you read this autobiography, notice how some of the artist's early life is reflected in her artwork.

Self-Portrait: Trina Schart Hyman

by Trina Schart Hyman

The author, Trina Schart Hyman, is a well-known artist. She has won awards and honors for her illustration of children's books. She drew the pictures in this selection.

Trina Schart Hyman usually expresses herself through her colorful drawings. In this selection she also paints pictures with words. As you read, you will see that the author's language and her art are both colorful.

The Farm

I was born forty-two years ago in Philadelphia, Pennsylvania. We lived out in the country about twenty miles north of the city. Our house was in one of the very first housing "developments" built during the Second World War. It was a little square brick house on a

276

corner of new green grass. My father planted a tiny willow tree and a golden ash in the front lawn. My mother made a big garden in the backyard.

Those six blocks of new houses seemed out of place. The rest of the landscape was open, grassy fields, some thick patches of woods, hidden rocky streams, and just a few old houses. The old houses had lawns so richly green and soft, and trees so big and gnarled and ancient, that I knew that they all belonged rightfully in their places.

The farm was the oldest of the old places. It was set back from the road. You could see it from the corner of our yard. Even so, you had to walk the length of two fields and then down a long avenue of trees before you could get to the house.

A WALK TO THE FARM TO BUY EGGS, IN 1942

It was a long, low, stone farmhouse with at least forty rooms, three chimneys, and a slate roof. It had an enormous stone barn, a mossy spring house, and a hidden rock garden. It also had several flower gardens, a large vegetable garden, and a lovely pond fed by ancient springs. It had horses, cows, chickens, geese, sheep, goats, and lots of dogs and cats.

The barn was always filled with hay. It was a dark, sweet, dusty landscape that reached four stories high. The deep, rich smell of animals and drying clover was so thick it seemed touchable, like velvet. The people who owned the farm were the King and Queen to me.

The Queen wore farmers' overalls, heavy boots, faded shirts, an old sailor's hat, and beautiful old rings on her long fingers. She was always darkly tanned. She had a bony face and a smile with long white teeth. She was an artist. She painted pictures of people who were as mysterious as she.

I can remember one of the first drawings I worked on. It was of the Queen with a big basket of eggs on her arm. I didn't think her overalls were pretty. So I drew her in a beautiful long dress with lots of little egg-shaped polka dots.

I never saw the King. I learned later that he was a farmer and an archaeologist. He spent most of his time in faraway countries.

One spring, years later, when I was in art school, the farm was sold. Men and machines came and tore it down. They ripped up the grand old trees and burned them in a big fire. They smashed the old stone walls. They beat on the solid old barn, with its families of rats and birds, until it finally collapsed and died. Then they plowed it under with their bulldozers.

I SHOW THE QUEEN MY DRAWING.

I learned something that day. I learned that everything changes, and nothing is safe. I still have dreams about the farm. It was my first kingdom and, in a way, my first real home.

Little Red Riding Hood

I was a really strange little kid. I was born scared of anything and everything that moved or spoke. I was afraid of people, especially. I was afraid of all people— kids my own age, all grownups, even my own family. I was afraid of dogs (until my parents bought me a puppy of my own), horses, trees, grass, cars, and streets. I was afraid of the stars and the wind. Who knows why?

My mother is a beautiful woman with red hair and the piercing blue gaze of a hawk. She never seemed afraid of anyone or anything. It was she who gave me the courage to draw and a love of books. She read to me from the time I was a baby. Once, when I was three or four, she was reading my favorite story. Suddenly the words on the page, her spoken words, and the pictures in my head fell together in a blinding flash. I could read!

The story was *Little Red Riding Hood.* It was so much a part of me that I really became Little Red Riding Hood. My mother sewed me a red cape with a hood that I put on almost every day. On those days, she would make me a "basket of goodies" to take to my grandmother's house. (My only grandmother lived in Rhode Island, three hundred miles away. That didn't matter, though.) I'd take the basket and carefully walk through the backyard, "going to Grandmother's house." My dog, Tippy, was the wolf.

My Father and the Museum

My father worked as a plumbing and heating supplies salesman. He loved music and singing, walking quietly in the woods, and fly-fishing. He could play almost any musical instrument. The one he played most often was a concertina. A concertina is like an accordion. It was beautiful, with inlaid pearl and wood designs on it. He played the harmonica, too. Sometimes he played both at once, holding the harmonica on a brace around his neck.

He also told the best stories. When I was a tiny little girl and still afraid of the stars, he sometimes took me for walks at night. He told me magical stories about the stars and of the many gods who created the universe.

I had to have braces on my teeth for nine years. So my father drove me into the city to the dentist every Saturday morning. I'm sure he would much rather have spent the time fishing the quiet backwaters that he loved. But for me, those city trips were journeys into a magical kingdom.

Some Saturdays, after the dentist, I got to go to the Philadelphia Art Museum. I should have been afraid of that grand building, but I wasn't. I loved it. I loved the halls full of paintings. I loved the tapestries and glass and wood. I even loved the furniture that the artists who had done the paintings must have used!

There's a painting by Brueghel[1] in a hallway. It shows a fat man with red stockings, running, running. His hands are clutching at his hat and his satchel. He is running away from a hillside full of sheep! Why?

---

[1] Brueghel [broo′gəl]

There is a dark tree to the far right of the painting. A bird is perched on the only branch in a yellow sky. I could feel his fear. Why is the man so afraid? If you look closely, there is a wolf in with the sheep, sneaking closer and closer. Oh no! He's really Little Red Riding Hood! Oh, Brueghel, I love you.

School

In school, I couldn't ever concentrate on what I was supposed to be learning. All I wanted to do was to be left alone. I wanted to read books or listen to music, or to draw pictures of witches and princesses. I should have been learning fractions.

After I finished high school, I went to art school in Philadelphia. Then everything changed. Suddenly, I was not only *allowed* to draw all day long, I was *expected* to! I was surrounded by other artists all day. We talked, ate, lived, and dreamed about art. It was as though I had been living, all my life, in a strange country. There I could never quite fit in — and now I had come home.

THE PIGEON LADIES: 1958

After the first year of basic drawing, painting, print-making, and design classes, I majored in illustration. My best friend, Barbara, was an illustration major, too. Barbara and I went everywhere together. We'd walk all over the city. We'd draw everything we would see: people, streets, doorways, subways, trees, piles of trash. If we discovered a "new" street, we were as excited as if we'd found a new world.

Whenever we had any free time, we'd walk to the art museum. We'd wander through its miles of beautiful rooms and quiet halls, looking at paintings and drawing from them. And every day for lunch, rain or shine, we went to Rittenhouse Square. We took our sketch books, hamburgers, and a big box of saltines for the pigeons. We were comrades. We were *artists*. Everything was exciting and beautiful. We loved it all.

1. What important people in Trina's early life are reflected in her drawings?

2. What would Trina rather have been doing in school instead of learning fractions?

3. Why do you think Trina liked the painting by Brueghel so much?

4. What did Trina learn the day the farmhouse was torn down? Find the sentence that helps you learn that.

5. Trina Schart Hyman began drawing at an early age. How does she use this talent today?

6. Many things must be combined to create an interesting picture. What must Trina blend to create her pictures?

Prewrite

In the selection, Trina Schart Hyman describes a painting by the artist Brueghel. Use her words to help you imagine what the painting looks like. If you need to, reread that part of the story that tells about Brueghel. Then select one of Trina Hyman's illustrations that you might like to describe. Copy and complete the chart below by listing descriptive phrases that apply to the illustration you selected.

Description of a Trina Schart Hyman Illustration	
Characters	
Location	
What is happening	

Draft

Now write a paragraph using some of the phrases you used to describe the Trina Schart Hyman illustration you selected. Tell what is in the picture, where things are placed, and what is happening. Say something about the colors, shapes, shadows, and light you see. Finally, tell what the feeling, or mood, of the picture is.

Revise

Read your description. How closely does it match the picture? Could someone else figure out which picture you have described? Add or change whatever you can so your reader could identify the picture you described.

Wind Circles

by Aileen Fisher

Without a pen,
without a hand,
without a pair of glasses,

The broken stalks
so bent and tanned
among the scattered grasses

Draw curves and circles
in the sand
with every wind that passes.

And *I*
can't draw them half as grand
in school, in drawing classes.

National Council of Teachers
of English Award for
Excellence in Poetry Poet

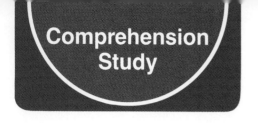

Fact and Opinion

Some sentences state facts. Other sentences give opinions. Read the following sentence.

Trina Schart Hyman illustrates children's books.

The sentence states a fact. The statement can be proved. There are sources of information that you could check to find whether Ms. Hyman illustrates books and what books she has illustrated. A **fact,** therefore, is something that can be proved.

Another kind of statement gives an opinion. An **opinion** tells what a speaker or writer feels, thinks, or believes. An opinion may be based upon facts, but it is a judgment. An opinion cannot be proved.

Sometimes writers signal opinions by using signal words such as *I think, in my opinion,* or *it seems to me.*

Read the following sentence.

I think that Trina Schart Hyman is the best artist in the world.

There is no way to prove that Trina Schart Hyman is the best artist in the world. That's the writer's opinion. Others might agree with the opinion, but it is still an opinion. The words *I think* signal that an opinion follows. However, sometimes opinions are given without signal words.

Writers often present both facts and opinions in the same article, and sometimes the opinions are given without the use of signal words. You may agree that all the facts are true. However, you may not agree with the opinions. Before you can judge the opinions, you must be able to separate them from the facts.

Now read the following paragraph. In it the writer gives both facts and opinions. Which are the facts? Which are the opinions? How do you know?

Many Americans carry around America's most beautiful memorial—the Lincoln penny. In 1909, the United States created the Lincoln cent. It was first made on the date that would have been President Lincoln's one-hundredth birthday. It took the place of the Indian head coin. There could not have been a better way of honoring Abraham Lincoln. Not only is it America's most beautiful memorial, but it is our most useful one.

The first sentence gives an opinion that would be impossible to prove: The Lincoln penny is "America's most beautiful memorial."

The next three statements are facts. You could prove each of these by reading history books, encyclopedias, or other records to see when the first Lincoln pennies were made. By checking to see when Abraham Lincoln was born, and adding one hundred years, you could prove when that coin was made.

The statement that says that "there could not have been a better way of honoring Abraham Lincoln" is an opinion. There is no way of proving it.

The last statement repeats the first opinion and also states another opinion about the penny being our most useful memorial. In both the first and last sentences, the word *most* is a clue word that the writer is giving an opinion. Other words such as *best* and *worst* can also be used as clues to an opinion.

In the paragraph about the Lincoln penny, the writer gave opinions and used facts to back up those opinions.

As you read, look carefully for facts and opinions. Remember, facts can be proved. Opinions tell how someone feels or what someone thinks.

Read the following paragraphs. As you read, think about which statements are facts, which are opinions, and which opinions are supported by facts. Look also for clue words that signal an opinion.

Drawing involves making a design of some kind on any useable surface. Some artists draw with chalk or charcoal, while others use crayons, pencils, or ink. The most interesting pictures are made when artists scratch their drawings into surfaces.

While ancient peoples used clay and stone as drawing surfaces, later civilizations used parchment. Paper is the best drawing material because it is inexpensive and easy to carry.

Textbook Application:
Fact and Opinion in Health

In textbooks, authors usually state facts. However, authors may sometimes state their opinions. Most support their opinions with facts. Supporting opinions with facts leads to sound conclusions. Read the following articles, looking for facts and for opinions based on facts. The sidenotes will help you.

How Can You Meet Your Needs?

What can you do if your needs are not being met? Sometimes you can change the way you look, think, or feel. Sometimes you can meet your needs by changing your actions. You can do something that makes you feel good about yourself. Then you can meet the need to be proud of yourself. You can be more friendly. That can bring you closer to others and satisfy another need.

This sentence is one of several opinions in the paragraph. Can you find one more opinion?

Thinking About Yourself

Amy liked to watch television. But that kept her from doing her homework. Sometimes her work was messy or late. Then she could not feel proud of herself. She felt angry with herself all the time.

Amy decided to do something to change the way she felt. She thought about herself for a while. Then she made

This is a fact that could be proved by talking with Amy. The remaining sentences in the paragraph and in the following paragraphs support that fact.

two lists. One list showed things about herself that she liked and did not want to change. The other list showed things about herself that she wanted to change.

Amy started watching less television. That gave her more time for homework, so her work was always neat and on time. She also had more time to practice the piano. She spent more time in her garden. And she made some new friends.

Amy has changed her way of acting. Her new actions have changed her way of feeling. Now she is not angry with herself all the time. By changing some of her actions, Amy helped satisfy her need to feel proud of herself.

—*HBJ Science,* Harcourt Brace Jovanovich

There are no sidenotes for the next article. As you read, look for opinions and for supporting facts.

PHYSICAL ACTIVITY
Daily Activities

Think about all the things you do each day. The days of most people your age are filled with activities. "Activities" are things to do.

To do some activities, you need to move your body very little. Drawing is such an activity. But to do other activities, you must move your body a lot. Skating is such an activity. These kinds of activities are called *physical* [FIHZ·ih·kuhl] *activities.*

Kinds of Physical Activities

There are many kinds of physical activities. Some kinds of physical activities can be done indoors. Other kinds of physical activities must be done outdoors. What are some physical activities that you have done indoors? Which have you done outdoors?

Some kinds of physical activities must be done alone. Other kinds of physical activities can be done with other people. Some people choose to compete, or try hard to win, in physical activities. People compete in some physical activities alone. In other physical activities, people compete as a team. But not everyone likes to compete in physical activities. Some people like to do physical activities just for fun.

—*Good Health for You*, Laidlaw Brothers

The authors have an opinion about why people participate in physical activities. What is their opinion? Is it supported by facts? What facts are given?

Remember, facts can be proved or supported. Opinions are judgments and cannot be supported.

Read to find out how one man made his dream of dancing come true not only for himself but also for others.

Ballet Is for Everyone

by Susanne Banta Harper

Arthur was tired. But he was happy and excited, too. He could hardly wait to tell his family and friends the good news.

"I did it," he told his best friend. "I passed the audition." Arthur Mitchell had been accepted to study dance at the New York City School of Performing Arts.

"Congratulations," his friend said, and he made a prediction. "You're going to be one of the best dancers at the school. I know it."

When classes began, it was clear that Arthur Mitchell did have exceptional talent. He was especially good at jazz dancing. He could move sleekly like a cat or rapidly like a fly. He could make angry, sharp movements or jaunty,

bouncy ones. When Arthur danced in the jazz style, he was part of the music.

But Arthur studied more than just jazz dancing. He also studied ballet. He worked to train his legs to turn outward as classical ballet required. He practiced the exercises at the *barre* with special care so that he would develop the control of his body needed to perform the difficult steps perfectly. He loved the jumps and turns. When he leaped into the air, he seemed to fly. When he turned on one foot, he seemed to spin like a top. The harder Arthur worked at ballet, the more he came to love it.

Arthur kept in touch with his old friends as he studied. He told them that ballet was very hard work. "But," he said, "I think I would like to make it my career."

Some of his friends tried to discourage him. "Stick with jazz, Arthur," they said. "Ballet is for white people."

Arthur considered that advice. In the early 1950's there were no black dancers in any major ballet company. But Arthur Mitchell loved ballet.

I know it won't be easy, he thought. But I have worked hard and plan to work even harder. I know I can do it.

His mind made up, Arthur Mitchell entered the School of American Ballet. My friends are wrong, he thought. Ballet is for everyone.

Some of the students and some of the parents did not like having Arthur at the school. One father complained, "I do not want my daughter to dance with that black boy. He should not be here." Some other parents agreed.

The teachers at the school did not agree. They could see how talented Arthur Mitchell was. They encouraged him to continue. While Arthur was at the School of American Ballet, his abilities were noticed by the directors of the New York City Ballet. They invited him to join their company. Arthur was thrilled.

In 1955 Arthur Mitchell became the first black dancer to perform with a major ballet company. Audiences quickly came to love him and his wonderful dancing.

Arthur had succeeded in doing what he set out to do. He received praise from dance critics and warm applause from audiences, who loved him. He became a leading dancer. Yet at times he was troubled. He thought of the children in Harlem, where he had grown up. Those children had never seen ballet and did not have the opportunity to study it.

Ballet is for everyone—I am an example of that, he thought. But maybe that is not enough.

Finally, Arthur Mitchell decided to leave the New York City Ballet, and he announced what he was going to do. "I must try to bring ballet to other black people. I am going to start a new ballet company, a black ballet company."

Again some of his friends warned him. "Don't do it, Arthur," they said. "It's impossible. Where would you get the dancers?"

"I will recruit and train young people from Harlem. I will teach them to be first-rate dancers," Arthur replied.

The task before Mitchell was enormous. Also, the money to carry out his dream was scarce. At first all he could afford for his new dance school was a rented garage. Later the school moved to a church basement. The school attracted many students. Arthur made them work hard to master the classical technique. "I can do it, and you can, too," he told the students when they became discouraged.

After much hard work and training, Arthur Mitchell decided that he had a group good enough to perform for the public. The Dance Theater of Harlem was born. They performed many classical ballets. When they danced *Swan Lake,* the audiences saw swans gliding gracefully through the sad story. When they danced *Firebird,* audiences responded excitedly to the rapid leaps and turns of the magic bird. When they performed *Dougla,* which the Dance Theater of Harlem made famous, audiences responded to the jazz rhythms with enthusiasm. The Dance Theater of Harlem was a success wherever it went.

Eventually, the reputation of the company became so great that many dancers were eager to join it. One day when Arthur Mitchell was holding auditions, some of the dancers who competed were not black. He decided to hire some of them.

Later he was criticized by some people for hiring white dancers for the Dance Theater of Harlem. They said that they thought his company was for black dancers. Why hire white dancers?

"That's easy to explain" was Arthur Mitchell's answer. "The Dance Theater of Harlem needs dancers. And, as we have proved, ballet isn't just for white people or just for black people. Ballet is for everyone."

1. How did Arthur Mitchell help others make their dreams of dancing come true?

2. How did Arthur's opinions differ from those of his friends over the years?

3. Do you think it was difficult for Arthur to switch from jazz dancing to ballet? Explain your answer.

4. What words did the author use to help you picture the ballets *Swan Lake* and *Firebird*?

5. How did Arthur answer people who criticized him for hiring white dancers?

6. Musicians in an orchestra must work together to create harmonious music. Why is it important for dancers in a ballet to work together?

**Think
and
Write**

Prewrite

The author of this selection says that Arthur Mitchell "could move sleekly like a cat . . . rapidly like a fly." Think about and discuss some words that name ways people move—for example, *running, jumping, stretching.*

In the following chart, there are examples of ways people move. Add two more descriptions for the people listed.

1. The athlete jumps like a kangaroo.
2. The dancer stretches like a tree swaying in the wind.
3. The clown ______________________________.
4. The conductor __________________________.

Draft

Think of someone you have seen in person or on television who uses movement as a way of expression. Write a poem describing the way this person moves. Use comparisons such as those you used in the above chart to help make your description clearer.

Revise

Read your poem aloud. How does it sound? Do the words and comparisons you have chosen help you see the movement you described? Make whatever changes and additions are needed to improve your poem.

The Snow Has Come at Last

a Navaho poem selected by Flora Hood

The snow has come at last,
Coming down in soft flakes,
Caressing my face with tenderness
As if it were telling me,
You are the first I've touched.

And as I walk along,
The snowflakes seem to sing
A song that has never been heard,
A song that has never been sung,
Unheard, unsung, except in my heart.

A Central Eskimo Chant

selected by James Houston

Ayii, ayii, ayii,
My arms, they wave high in the air,
My hands, they flutter behind my back,
They wave above my head
Like the wings of a bird.
Let me move my feet.
Let me dance.
Let me shrug my shoulders.
Let me shake my body.
Let me crouch down.
My arms, let me fold them.
Let me hold my hands under my chin.

Canadian Children's Book
Award Author

Being left-handed helped Mike to get on a baseball team. Read to find out how playing baseball leads Mike to join a dance class.

Just Because I'm Left-Handed

by Linda McCollum Brown

This whole mess started just because I'm left-handed.

Last month Tim and Jeff talked me into signing up for Little League. Now, baseball is okay and all, but it isn't my favorite thing to do. Just give me my clarinet or a chemistry set or a tennis racket or a book to read —especially a mystery—and I'm happy. But Tim and Jeff are my best friends. They said that a lefty can really do a right-handed pitcher in, and that I could help their team a whole lot.

So, I figured, why not? The Panthers' coach, Mr. Goodwin, said, "Hey, great—a southpaw!" I can't stand it when people call me a southpaw (I mean, does that make them northpaws?), but other than that he is okay. He is a real strong ballplayer, a super athlete.

Mom said I could ride the bus to practice so I wouldn't have to bother Mrs. Neumerski, our after-school babysitter, for a ride. I never miss supper because we eat late anyhow, since Mom gets home from work late.

Everything was going fine until my sister Kathie (she's only in third grade) saw that article in the newspaper. I wish she didn't like to read so much! What's worse is that she has to tell everyone about what she reads.

I was all set to dive into my cherry pie after supper one night when she said, "Hey, Mom, I just read a really good article in the *Times*. It's about how some football and baseball players take ballet lessons."

"Ballet lessons?" Mom asked, looking up.

"Ballet lessons!" I almost choked on a mouthful of cherries.

"Yes, ballet lessons," Kathie answered, "during the off-season to help them keep in shape. Some of them even do it during the playing season because it helps them be more graceful."

"Oh, next I suppose you'll say that I should take ballet lessons," I said, laughing. "What a joke!"

"Well," she said, looking at Mom and me, "our whole dancing school is going to do *The Nutcracker* for Christmas this year. The only trouble is there aren't enough boys, and I told Mrs. Goodwin that when baseball season ends, Mike would like to stay in shape and that he would come and . . ."

"*You what*?" This time I really did choke. "Me, dancing? No way!"

Mom glared at me. She turned to Kathie. "You know, dear, you mustn't promise something like that unless you ask Mike about it first."

Then she turned to me, and I could tell by the look in her eye that I was doomed. "However, Mike, it might be a good idea. You love music, and you complain that you don't get enough exercise during the winter."

"It's not winter now," I sputtered.

"No, but they really do need some tall boys practicing now to be ready to dance *The Nutcracker* at Christmas. I was talking to Mrs. Goodwin the other day. Why don't you give it a try? If you still don't like it after a month or so, then you can drop it," Mom said. I could tell by her tone of voice there was no use trying to talk her out of it.

So now, there I was. The next day was my first—ugh—ballet lesson. If Jeff or Tim or any of the other guys had found out about it, I think I would have just died.

"Hey, Mom, can you call Jeff and tell him I'm sick or something? I was supposed to go over to his house tomorrow after practice, but now I've got that dumb dancing lesson."

"That won't be necessary, dear," Mom had said, giving me her you-know-we-don't-do-that-kind-of-thing look. "Jeff just called to say his uncle will be visiting him tomorrow, so it wouldn't work out anyway."

The next day Jeff was sure quiet at practice. He didn't even talk about his uncle coming, so I figured maybe he didn't like him or something. After practice Coach Goodwin said to me, "Can I give you a lift to the dancing school?"

"Sh-h-h!" I hissed, looking around quickly to make sure no one had heard him. "You mean *you're* going over there?"

"Sure," he said. "I teach the boys' class."

"You do?" I couldn't believe what I was hearing.

"Right," he answered. "I used to dance with a ballet company full-time until I injured my knee. You know, you've got to be in excellent physical shape to be a good dancer, just like any other athlete."

He might have told me more, but just then we reached his car. And what do you know—Jeff was sitting in the car, looking as miserable as I had felt earlier. Tim and some of the other guys were twirling around on their toes in the dust beside the car. "Jeff's going to dance like this," Tim hooted as he spun around. The rest of the guys were laughing.

Right then I wanted to run the other way, straight home—fast. But Jeff sure looked all alone. Besides, if I had to go to dancing class, it would be a lot more fun

to have one of my friends there, too. So I called out loud, "Hey, Jeff, did you know you have to be in great shape to be a good dancer? Some of the best ballplayers take ballet lessons to stay in shape for the season."

Tim and the other guys just stood there in the dust. I guess they didn't know what to say to that.

Jeff grinned and looked a little better. I never thought that anything Kathie said would make me or my friends feel better, but I'm glad that I remembered her *Times* article.

Then I remembered something else. "Hey, Jeff, what about your uncle?"

He rolled his eyes. "Aw, I just made that up. I couldn't tell you where I was really going."

This may not be so bad after all. I guess we can give it a try.

1. Why did Kathie suggest that Mike take ballet lessons?

2. On the day of Mike's first ballet lesson, what happened at baseball practice?

3. Do you think there was any connection between Mrs. Goodwin, the ballet teacher, and Mr. Goodwin, the coach? Explain your answer.

4. When in the story did you know that Mike's mother would not make excuses for him?

5. Why did Mike feel better about taking ballet lessons after talking with Coach Goodwin?

6. People willing to try new things may discover unexpected rewards. How does this apply to the selection?

Prewrite

Because Mike was left-handed, his friends thought he could help the team as a pitcher. This started a chain of events. Copy and complete the chain of events on the next page showing how one event led to the next one. The flow chart does not have to stop at the fourth step. Think of an activity that could be the result of the dance lessons and add it to the chart.

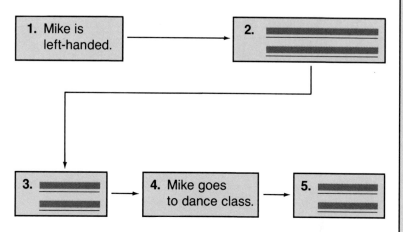

Draft

Now, write a short explanation of how Mike could become involved in this new activity.

Revise

Read your explanation. Have you given enough details to make it clear? Have you given reasons why Mike becomes involved in this new activity? Make whatever changes and additions are needed for your explanation to be clear.

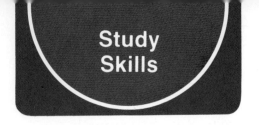
Advertisements

Advertisements have two main purposes. One is to **inform** and the other is to **persuade.** An advertisement that informs tells you facts about a product or service. An advertisement that persuades tries to convince you that you need what is being offered. Many advertisements both inform and persuade.

Advertisements, sometimes called *ads*, can be very helpful. They help people to find jobs and places to live. They can also help people to locate products and services that they need. Ads also give people more choices. If you read several ads from different companies for the same product or service, you may be able to make a better decision about what to buy.

Read the following ad. Notice how the ad has been written.

Ever Wear Is Everywhere!

Ever Wear Ballet Shoes are now available in children's, as well as adults', sizes. These shoes come in a wide variety of colors.

Showstopper Shoe Store
926 West Elm Street

Children—$12.95
Adult—$17.95

310

Through reading the ad for the ballet shoes, what facts did you learn? You were told the name of the product, and you were given a description of it. What else were you told? You were told where you could buy it and how much it costs. This kind of advertisement mainly informs the reader.

Some advertisements do more than give you facts. They also give opinions. They try to persuade you to buy or use the product. This happens especially when there are a number of products in competition with each other.

Read this ad for the Sure-Stop baseball mitt for left-handed persons. Look for the facts and opinions that it gives. Notice how it tries to persuade you.

Sure-Stop baseball mitt, made only for left-handed players, will stop any ball hit your way. The amazing trap pocket closes over a ball like a net. Special leather laces add to its beauty.

Lefty's Sports Shop
1064 Fenton Road   only $**49.98**

This advertisement does give facts. It tells you a little about the mitt. It tells you where you can buy it and how much it costs. However, the ad does more than that. It also tries to persuade you to buy the product by giving you opinions. It tells you that the mitt will stop any ball that is hit your way and that it costs only $49.98.

How Advertisements Persuade

How does an advertisement try to persuade you to buy something? One way is by using descriptive words such as amazing and special as in the Sure-Stop mitt ad. One part of the mitt, the pocket, is said to work like a net in stopping a ball. Do you think that it really can?

The name given to the product is also meant to persuade you. Sure-Stop gives the impression that the mitt will do all the work.

While the ad about the baseball mitt does give facts, it gives more opinions than facts. Now let's look at another way advertisers try to persuade you.

The Bandwagon Approach

You may have heard the old expression "get on the bandwagon." To get on the **bandwagon** means join in with what everyone else is doing. Advertisers know that people want to be in step with things that are going on. That is why they use the bandwagon approach.

Do you need a Robot Pen or a Rocket Recorder? Do you even know what they are? You probably do not, but imagine that you see these headlines on two different ads:

Don't Be the Last One to Get a Robot Pen!

You Mean You Still Don't Have a Rocket Recorder?

If these headlines make you feel as if you are going to be left out of things unless you have a

Robot Pen or a Rocket Recorder, then you are being persuaded by bandwagon advertising.

Advertisers sometimes use bandwagon advertising in another way. Instead of trying to make you feel left out, they suggest that you should have something because everyone else does. An ad with this approach might say: "All your friends have Robot Pens" or "Everybody records with a Rocket!"

Sometimes an ad praises one product at the expense of another. Look at the following example:

In our recent test, 88% of the students in the fourth grade chose Robot Pens over Ever Writers.

This is an example of the bandwagon approach because it tells you that a great number of people have chosen one product over another.

Remember that advertisements are useful and important to people who need products and services. Because many similar products are competing for your dollars, advertisers try to persuade you to buy *their* products or services instead of the others. Read every advertisement carefully to be sure you are getting all the information you need to make a good decision. Notice whether or not you are being persuaded and, if you are, notice how. If you read ads carefully, you will not be persuaded unless you *want* to be.

Children's Choices Author

The Riddle of the Drum

based on a tale from Tizapán, Mexico, translated and retold by Verna Aardema
and adapted as a play by Anne Maley

Spanish Glossary

jacaranda (hä·kä·rän′dä) A tropical tree with blue flowers

olé (ō·lā′) A shout of approval; great

rebozo (rā·bō′sō) A long scarf

señor (sen·yôr′) Mister

sí (sē) Yes

tacos (tä′kōs) Fried tortillas

Tizapán (tē·sä·pän′) A place in central Mexico hundreds of years ago

tortillas (tôr·tē′yəs) Round, flat cakes of cornmeal usually eaten hot with a filling

uf (o͞of) An expression of disgust, like *ugh*

uno, dos, tres, cuatro, cinco (o͞o′nō, dōs, träs, kwä′trō, sēn′kō) One, two, three, four, five

---

CHARACTERS

Narrator

Wizard

King

Guard

Chorus

Prince Tuzán (tōo·sän′)

Corrín Corrán (kôr·rēn′ kôr·rän′), the runner

Voices 1–6

Tirín Tirán (tē·rēn′ tē·rän′), the archer

Oyín Oyán (ō·yēn′ ō·yän′), the hearer

Soplín Soplán (sō·plēn′ sō·plän′), the blower

Comín Comán (kō·mēn′ kō·män′), the eater

Princess Fruela (frōo·ā′lä)

Old Woman

Scene One

Setting: At the king's palace

Narrator: There was a king in Tizapán who had a beautiful daughter named Fruela. The king loved Fruela so much that he decided that whoever married her would have to prove himself worthy. So the king asked a wizard to make a strange drum.

Wizard: (*enters, carrying a drum*) Good day, Your Majesty. (*He bows to the King.*) Here is your drum, at last.

King: (*looking curious*) Ah, Wizard. Tell me its story.

Wizard: (*proudly*) The drum is just as you desired. The drumhead is made from a kind of leather that no one has ever used before. It is as black as jet. (*He strikes the drum.*) Its sound is like thunder on a distant mountain. (*He lowers his voice.*) And only you and I know that the drumhead is made of . . . (*He whispers the words in the king's ear.*)

King: (*smiling*) Well done! Now let us send this drum throughout the land to find a man who is worthy of my daughter Fruela.

Narrator: Everywhere the guard went, the children would fall in line behind him and join in with the song.

Guard, Chorus: (*singing together with the drum*)
　　　　　　Tum-te-dum!
　　The head of the drum-te-dum!
　　Guess what it's from-te-dum!
　　And marry the Princess Fruela.

Scene Two

Setting: On the road toward the palace

Narrator: Now, a handsome prince from a nearby land heard about the riddle of the drum. So he set out to try to win the princess. On the way, he met a man who was running as if a coyote were nipping at his heels.

Prince Tuzán: (*shouting*) Stop! Stop, señor! Why do you run so fast? Is something chasing you?

Corrín Corrán: (*proudly*) No, señor. I run for fun, for I am the runner, Corrín Corrán.

Prince Tuzán: I am Prince Tuzán. I'm on my way to the king, to try to win the princess. If you will help me, I shall reward you.

Corrín Corrán: (*bowing to the prince*) I'll do what I can. Lead the way, and I will follow.

Voice 1: Then on and on went Prince Tuzán,

Voice 2: Behind him the runner, Corrín Corrán.

Chorus: The two marched on toward the palace.

Narrator: Soon they met a man who carried a bow and a quiver of arrows.

Prince Tuzán: Good day, señor. I am Prince Tuzán. What is your name?

Tirín Tirán: (*pulling on his bow*) I am the archer, Tirín Tirán. Let me show you what I can do. (*He draws out an arrow and puts it into his bow.*)

Narrator: Then Tirín Tirán tossed his hat high in the air and shot an arrow through it.

Prince Tuzán: (*surprised*) Olé! Come along and help me win the princess, and I shall reward you.

Voice 1:　Then on and on went Prince Tuzán,

Voice 2:　Behind him the runner, Corrín Corrán,

Voice 3:　Behind him the archer, Tirín Tirán.

Chorus:　They all marched on toward the palace.

Narrator:　Farther on, they came upon a man who had the largest ears Prince Tuzán had ever seen. He was lying under a tree with one huge ear pressed to the ground.

Prince Tuzán:　Hello, señor. What are you doing?

Oyín Oyán:　(*looking up*) I am the hearer, Oyín Oyán. I am listening to the talk at the palace. Another suitor for the princess has just guessed wrong.

Prince Tuzán:　(*eagerly*) Do you know the right answer?

Oyín Oyán:　(*getting up and laughing*) No, but I know all the wrong ones. I know that it isn't (*in a singsong voice*) duck skin or buck skin, goat skin or shoat skin, mule skin or mole skin, mare skin or bear skin—or even armadillo!

Prince Tuzán:　Then come along. If you can keep me from guessing wrong, I shall reward you.

Voice 1:　Then on and on went Prince Tuzán,

Voice 2:　Behind him the runner, Corrín Corrán,

Voice 3:　Behind him the archer, Tirín Tirán,

Voice 4:　Behind him the hearer, Oyín Oyán.

Chorus:　They all marched on toward the palace.

Narrator:　They hadn't gone far when they came upon a man who was running a windmill. With his head held back and his cheeks puffed out, he blew—and the windmill turned faster and faster.

Prince Tuzán: How extraordinary!

Soplín Soplán: (*shrugging*) Quite ordinary for me, señor. I am the blower, Soplín Soplán.

Prince Tuzán: I am Prince Tuzán. Come along with us. Help me win the princess, and I shall reward you.

Voice 1: Then on and on went Prince Tuzán,

Voice 2: Behind him the runner, Corrín Corrán,

Voice 3: Behind him the archer, Tirín Tirán,

Voice 4: Behind him the hearer, Oyín Oyán,

Voice 5: Behind him the blower, Soplín Soplán.

Chorus: They all marched on toward the palace.

Narrator: They were all becoming tired and hungry when they came upon a man who was cooking a whole ox over a fire.

Prince Tuzán: Señor, are you cooking all this meat for yourself?

Comín Comán: (*nodding and smiling*) Sí. I am the eater, Comín Comán. For me, this is just one big piece of meat. But come and share my meal.

Prince Tuzán: Thank you, señor. (*They sit down and begin to eat.*) When we are finished, come and help me win the princess, and I shall reward you.

Voice 1: Then on and on went Prince Tuzán,

Voice 2: Behind him the runner, Corrín Corrán,

Voice 3: Behind him the archer, Tirín Tirán,

Voice 4: Behind him the hearer, Oyín Oyán,

Voice 5: Behind him the blower, Soplín Soplán,

Voice 6: Behind him the eater, Comín Comán.

Chorus: They all marched on toward the palace.

Scene Three

Setting: At the king's palace

Narrator: Soon they rounded the top of a hill and saw the palace on the far hillside. Far away, the princess was on her balcony. She and her father were talking. Oyín Oyán put his ear to the ground and overheard these words.

Princess Fruela: (*pointing*) Papa, look! A prince is coming!

King: (*looking into the distance*) Sí! And he has uno, dos, tres, cuatro, cinco attendants! Too bad he has to die—just because he doesn't know that the drumhead is made from the skin of a . . .

Narrator: That was when the king said the word! Oyín Oyán leaped up so fast, his ears flapped.

Oyín Oyán: (*shouting*) I heard the answer to the riddle! (*He whispers it in the prince's ear.*)

Narrator: Then Prince Tuzán and his men went on to the palace, where they were brought before the king.

Prince Tuzán: (*bowing low*) Your Majesty, I have come to solve the riddle of the drum.

King: (*sternly*) Do you know that if you fail, you will lose your life?

Prince Tuzán: (*calmly*) Sí, I know. Show me the drum.

Guard: (*enters, singing and beating the drum*)
Tum-te-dum!
The head of the drum-te-dum!
Guess what it's from-te-dum!
And marry the Princess Fruela!

Narrator: Prince Tuzán ran his fingers over the thin, black skin of the drum. He tapped out a little rhythm and began to speak.

Prince Tuzán: (*in a sing-song voice as he taps*) It isn't duck skin or buck skin, goat skin or shoat skin, mule skin or mole skin, mare skin or . . .

King: (*shouting*) Don't tell me what it isn't! Tell me what it is!

Prince Tuzán: (*thoughtfully*) It looks to me like this is the skin of a very large flea!

King: (*angrily*) Uf! I can't believe it! You're right! (*He speaks more quietly.*) But there are two more things you must do before you marry my daughter! First, one of your servants and one of my servants will race to the sea and fetch water. If mine returns first, you lose your life!

Narrator: Then Corrín Corrán stepped forward.

Corrín Corrán: Prince Tuzán, allow me to run for you.

Narrator: Then up stepped an old woman in a long, gray dress with a black rebozo around her shoulders.

Old Woman: (*smiling*) And I will run for the king!

Narrator: Corrín Corrán laughed at that. But after they began to run, he discovered that the old woman had magic powers. He had to run with all his might just to keep up with her. Side by side they raced down the valley, past a jacaranda tree, over a hill, and onto the beach. At the sea, they filled their small bottles with water and both turned back at the same moment.

Corrín Corrán: (*to himself*) What is wrong? I cannot seem to beat her! But I must win and save the prince's life!

Narrator: So Corrín Corrán went faster and reached the jacaranda tree just ahead of the old woman. But she was ready with her magic.

Old Woman: *(loudly)* Sleep! Go . . . to . . . sleep!

Corrín Corrán: *(falls under the tree, snoring)* Z-z-z-z!

Narrator: Oyín Oyán heard her words, and he heard the runner snoring. So he spoke to the archer.

Oyín Oyán: *(excitedly)* Tirín Tirán! Shoot the tree! Wake up the runner!

Narrator: The archer sent an arrow into the tree just above the sleeping runner. Zap! Corrín Corrán woke up and leaped into the race, but by now the woman was far ahead.

Old Woman: *(laughing)* I hear you behind me, but you will never catch me!

Narrator: Then Soplín Soplán puffed out his cheeks and aimed a strong wind at her. The wind lifted her up and carried her — kicking and screeching — all the way back to the jacaranda tree. Then Corrín Corrán won the race. The king, of course, was upset.

King: *(protesting)* You cheated, Prince Tuzán! But I will not punish you. You still have one last task to do. Before the sun sets, one of your servants must eat a cartload of food. If he fails, you die!

Narrator: So a cart filled with food was brought in, and Comín Comán set to his task.

Comín Comán: *(licking his lips)* Ah! Tacos, tortillas, meat, puddings! This will be a nice little lunch.

Narrator: Before evening, Comín Comán had eaten everything — even the cart! When the last task was

done, the king finally gave Prince Tuzán the Princess Fruela in marriage. The two lived together happily for many years. But what happened to the five faithful servants?

Voice 2: The faithful runner, Corrín Corrán, (*He bows.*)

Voice 3: The faithful archer, Tirín Tirán, (*He bows.*)

Voice 4: The faithful hearer, Oyín Oyán, (*He bows.*)

Voice 5: The faithful blower, Soplín Soplán, (*He bows.*)

Voice 6: The faithful eater, Comín Comán, (*He bows.*)

Chorus: They all lived well at the palace.

1. How did the prince discover the answer to the riddle of the drum?

2. What three things did Prince Tuzán have to do before he could marry Princess Fruela?

3. When did you first begin to think that each of the five faithful servants would somehow help Prince Tuzán?

4. Which of the servants do you think was the most helpful to the prince? Explain your choice.

5. How were the faithful servants rewarded for helping the prince?

6. How did the five faithful servants working together as a team accomplish what one servant working alone could not do?

Think and Write

Prewrite

In folktales and fairy tales, people often have superhuman powers to help them do things. What would you do if you had the powers of the characters in this play? Copy and complete the chart on the next page.

1. If I could shoot an arrow like Tirín Tirán, I would *shoot the rain out of the clouds.*
2. If I could blow the wind like Soplín Soplán, I would _____.
3. If I could run like Corrín Corrán, I would _____.
4. If I could hear like Oyín Oyán, I would _____.
5. If I could eat like Comín Comán, I would _____.

Draft

Write a folktale in which you are the hero and have one or more of the characteristics of the characters listed above. In the folktale, you will need to solve a problem by using the superhuman power(s). Tell what the problem is and how you solve it. Remember that your folktale is imaginary and that it can be either funny or serious.

Revise

Read your folktale. Is it fun or interesting to read? Is there a surprise in it? Do you like the way you solved the problem? Does the superhuman power fit well in the story? Make whatever changes and additions are needed to improve your folktale.

Lewis Has a Trumpet

by Karla Kuskin

National Council of Teachers of English Award for Excellence in Poetry Poet

A trumpet
A trumpet
Lewis has a trumpet
A bright one that's yellow
A loud proud horn.
He blows it in the evening
When the moon is newly rising
He blows it when it's raining
In the cold and misty morn
It honks and it whistles
It roars like a lion
It rumbles like a lion
With a wheezy huffing hum
His parents say it's awful
Oh really simply awful
But
Lewis says he loves it
It's such a handsome trumpet
And when he's through with trumpets
He's going to buy a drum.

*A pan of gingerbread and a slide trombone
cause problems between the king and queen
in this folktale. Read to find out how the
problems are finally solved.*

The Queen Who Couldn't Bake Gingerbread

by Dorothy Van Woerkom

King Pilaf[1] of Mulligatawny[2] was having a very bad day. To begin with, he bumped his head against the Lord Chamberlain's upon getting out of bed. Then he discovered a hole in the heel of his stocking that was the size of a marble. And he knew without asking that his breakfast gingerbread would be crumbly again.

The King sat on the edge of his bed with his thumb through the hole in his stocking.

---

[1] Pilaf [pē'läf]
[2] Mulligatawny [mul'ə•gä•tô'nē]

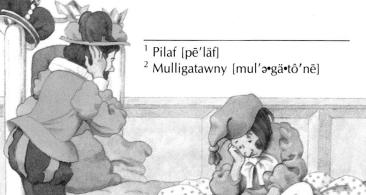

330

"It is time," he said to the Lord Chamberlain, "that Mulligatawny had a Queen and I a wife. She must be beautiful enough to please me. She must be wise enough to help me rule—and to find me a tailor who knows how to *mend*."

The Lord Chamberlain slipped the King's stocking over the Royal foot. "A splendid idea, your Majesty!" he said. "By happy chance I was thinking the very same thing myself. As a matter of fact . . ."

The King wagged his foot under the Lord Chamberlain's nose and sighed loudly. "Not one of your speeches so early in the day, my Lord. Just help me into my boots, and let's have some breakfast."

So they drank their lime juice and ate cheese omelets, with gingerbread that crumbled. The King frowned at the crumbs on his plate and said, "My Queen must be *more* than just wise and beautiful. She must also know how to bake gingerbread."

Now it was the Lord Chamberlain who sighed. For when Pilaf became King, he had turned Mulligatawny inside out to find a gingerbread baker.

"There isn't one in my kingdom who can bake it to a turn," the King was saying. "It should be neither too hard nor too soft, but just properly crisp."

Then the King called for their horses, and away they rode to the kingdom of Ghur,[3] where there lived a princess as wise as she was beautiful. Her name was Madelon.[4]

---

[3] Ghur [gûr]
[4] Madelon [mad'ə•lin]

"No, I cannot bake gingerbread," Princess Madelon said. "But I make perfect little almond cakes."

King Pilaf thought about that: a Queen both wise and beautiful, who could make pretty cakes. But at last he shook his head sadly, and kissed Princess Madelon's hand.

"I'm sorry to say that it must be gingerbread," he said.

Then off he galloped with the Lord Chamberlain to the kingdom of Shoggen.[5]

Here lived a Princess who was not as wise as she was beautiful. Her name was Jebelle.[6]

"No, I cannot bake gingerbread," said Princess Jebelle. "But I can bake the best zwieback that you will ever taste."

Princess Jebelle would make a beautiful Queen. But *zwieback*—no, the King could never like zwieback at all.

"I'm sorry to say that it must be gingerbread," he said.

King Pilaf kissed her hand and rode away with his Chamberlain to the kingdom of Tintinnabulum.[7]

---

[5] Shoggen [shog'ən]
[6] Jebelle [jə•bel']
[7] Tintinnabulum [tin'tə•nab'yə•ləm]

Here lived a Princess who was not as beautiful as she was wise. Her name was Calliope.[8]

"Ah, King Pilaf!" Princess Calliope cried, as the King strode into her chamber. "You are, I suppose, seeking a wife?"

"I am, indeed, your Highness. A wife who can bake gingerbread and who . . ."

"Oh no, I *never* bake gingerbread. But I am seeking a husband. He must be as kind as he is handsome, and he must know how to play the slide trombone."

For a moment the King's mouth made an "O" like the hole in the heel of his stocking.

"I cannot play the slide trombone," he said at last. "But I can shoot an arrow as straight as the tail of a comet." He took a deep breath.

"Then I'm sorry to say," said the Princess, "that the husband for me is the man who can play the slide trombone."

---

[8] Calliope [kə•lī′ə•pē]

Her smile made him wish he could say, "Yes, I can!" But all he could do was bow himself out, and take to his horse once again.

Now, in every single kingdom it was the same: no one at all could bake a proper gingerbread. King Pilaf kissed the hand of the very last Princess. He called for his horse and rode home with his Chamberlain, to brood.

After quite a long while (a hole had now appeared in the heel of his other stocking—and he had never felt so lonely, besides!) he said, "Lord Chamberlain, it is plain to see that I must do without gingerbread. Go back to the kingdom of Ghur and ask the Princess Madelon if she will marry me. She is as wise as she is beautiful, and perhaps in time I can learn to like almond cakes."

When the Lord Chamberlain arrived in Ghur, he found the kingdom prepared for a wedding. The Princess was going to marry the King of Rocky Knob Island!

"Well," said King Pilaf, when he heard about this, "you must go to the kingdom of Shoggen. Princess Jebelle is not as wise as she is beautiful, but perhaps in time I can learn to like zwieback."

The Lord Chamberlain soon returned with news that Princess Jebelle had left a note on her crown for her father. She had run off to marry a sourdough baker and was baking miles of zwieback.

King Pilaf surprised the Lord Chamberlain by dancing a jig when he heard about Princess Jebelle.

"To tell you the truth, my Lord," he said, "I like Princess Calliope best. She is not as beautiful, of course, as she is wise. But then what chance have I, since I cannot play on the slide trombone?"

"As a matter of fact," the Lord Chamberlain said, "I was thinking of Princess Calliope, too. She is, as you say, very wise. Perhaps she knows what can be done."

"Excellent advice!" cried the King. "I shall go to see her at once."

When Princess Calliope heard why King Pilaf had come, she said, "Let me think about this. I am sure we can come to some sort of agreement."

He paced up and down outside of her chamber, until at last she came to the door.

"It seems to me," she said with a bow, "that a husband who is as kind as he is handsome is more to be loved than one who can play on the slide trombone."

"And a wife who is wise," the King said quickly, "as well as—er—beautiful, does not need to know how to bake gingerbread."

They clasped hands together, and Calliope said, "Then let us add this to our marriage vows: We must never again mention *slide trombone* . . ."

"Or *gingerbread*!" he finished, with a laugh that shook the walls of the castle.

They lived happily together for nearly a year, and ruled their kingdom as well as anyone could.

Then one day, everything went wrong. The King dropped the crown on his foot, and the Queen awoke with a headache. The Lord Chamberlain was ill, and the cook slept late. The court painter put his head through their Majesties' new portrait, and the Queen's dog chewed up all the paintbrushes. Outside, it snowed one minute and rained the next.

The King was angry; the Queen was cross. They quarrelled all day.

"I wish," the King shouted, "that you could bake gingerbread! Then *something* would be right about this terrible day."

"And why," cried the Queen, "can't *you* play on the slide trombone? It would certainly help to calm my nerves!"

They glared at each other with anger and spite. The forbidden words had been said, their marriage vows broken.

They both turned around and swept from the room, to the opposite ends of their castle.

They stayed there for days, feeling grumpy and sorry for themselves. Servants left food on trays near their doors, then scampered away before the doors might open.

The citizens of Mulligatawny began to ask each other, "What has gone wrong at the castle?"

At last, Queen Calliope looked at herself in her mirror. "The King married me because I was wise, not beautiful," she said. "Now, was it wise to shout *slide trombone* at him?"

It was not. She sent for the Lord Chamberlain.

At the other end of the castle, King Pilaf was trying to shave himself. "With that nose and those eyes," he said to the King in the mirror, "you are not nearly so handsome as you like to believe."

He wiped blood from the cut on his chin. "Why, the Queen married me because she thought I was kind! Was it kind to shout *gingerbread?*"

He struck off the last whisker and sent for the Lord Chamberlain.

Before very long, from one end of the castle came the odor of scorched pots. From the other came sounds like an elephant blowing its nose. The servants rushed in one direction holding their ears; in the other they rushed holding their breath.

The citizens of Mulligatawny thought the world was coming to an end.

But then, in the middle of one night, the smells grew sweeter. At the very same time, the sounds became more tuneful. The servants hurried about with noses high in the air to smell the delicious smells. They paused in their work to hear the sweet sounds.

The citizens of Mulligatawny began to hope for the future.

At last, the Lord Chamberlain announced that their Majesties would come from their opposite sides of the castle and meet in the Great Hall.

With a blast of trumpets, the door at one end of the Great Hall swung open. In marched the King, with an apron around his middle, a baker's hat on his head, and flour on his nose. He carried a pan of the most perfect gingerbread that had ever been baked in his kingdom— or in any other.

Without any sound at all, the doors at the other end of the Great Hall opened. Through them stepped the Queen. She raised a slide trombone to her lips, and played such a melody that even the nightingales hushed.

From that day, the first sound heard each morning in Mulligatawny was Queen Calliope's slide trombone. The first scent was that of King Pilaf's fresh gingerbread. It became the custom of the citizens to awake at sunrise, to sniff, and to listen. Their noses and their ears would tell them if all was still well in the kingdom.

To the end of their days, they were never disappointed.

1. How did the King and Queen finally solve their problem?

2. What was King Pilaf looking for in a queen?

3. Name three of the things that happened on the day that everything went wrong at the castle.

4. Do you think the Lord Chamberlain was an important character in the story? Explain your answer.

5. When did you first begin to think that Queen Calliope was sorry that she and the King had quarrelled? What did the Queen say to make you think that?

6. What important lesson did the King and Queen have to learn before peace and harmony could be restored in the kingdom?

Think and Write

Prewrite

King Pilaf and Queen Calliope both had a problem. They each found a way to solve their problem. Think of a funny problem and think of some funny ways to solve that problem. What solutions are good choices? Why?

Fill in the chart below, stating the problem and possible solutions.

The problem:

Possible solutions:
1. _____
2. _____
3. _____

Draft

Now, write a paragraph about the problem you listed above. Write an explanation of how you could solve your problem. First, state the problem. Next, tell what the possible solutions are. Finally, explain why you chose the solution you did. Remember that this is a funny problem, so include humor in your description.

Revise

Read your explanation. Is it clear? Does your solution make sense? Will others understand if they read your explanation? Is it humorous? Have you remembered to tell why you chose this solution? Make any changes necessary so your explanation will read more clearly.

Characterization

You know that characters are the people or the animals in a story. Some of the characters are more important than others. The important characters are called **major characters.** The major characters in "The Queen Who Couldn't Bake Gingerbread" are King Pilaf and Queen Calliope. The characters who are not as important as the major characters are the **minor characters.** Lord Chamberlain is a minor character in "The Queen Who Couldn't Bake Gingerbread."

In the story "Just Because I'm Left-Handed," Mike is the major character. Who are the minor characters? Mike's mother, his sister, Jeff, Mr. Goodwin, and the other ballplayers are the minor characters.

The way an author helps you to get to know a character is called **characterization.** Authors use several ways to let you know a character. They may describe the character, they may have the character describe himself or herself, or they may have another character in the story describe that character.

Read the following paragraphs. Who is describing the character Tyro? How do you know?

Tyro thought to himself, "Those engines should not be starting while I am out here.

It's too dangerous. Surely they'll realize that and stop the test immediately."

Later as he tumbled in space, he thought, "Soon they will discover I am missing. Then they will return for me."

You are right if you said that Tyro is describing himself. The words *himself* and *I* are clues. You also know that Tyro is describing himself because the author lets you know what Tyro is thinking.

Authors also let you know about the way most characters feel and act by telling you things that make the characters seem real. They give their characters the same traits that many people have to help you feel that you know the characters. Through the author's words, you discover whether a character is wise or dull, brave or cowardly, happy or sad.

Read the paragraphs about Tyro again. What character traits do you think Tyro has? How does the author help you to know this?

Did you say that Tyro was brave and hopeful? Notice that the author helps you see this when Tyro says, "Surely they'll realize that and stop the test immediately." You get another clue that Tyro is brave because he says these words calmly. We know that he is hopeful because the author uses the word *surely*. These traits are supported further by the author when Tyro says, "Soon, they will discover I am missing. Then they will return for me." Only someone brave and hopeful would say such words.

If the author had wanted Tyro to be excited and afraid, what words would Tyro have said? How would he have said them?

Now read the following story. Use the sidenotes to help you discover who the major character is, how the author helps you to know the character, and what traits that major character has.

In this paragraph, the author is letting you know that Jennie is the major character in the story.

The only thing on Jennie Gray's mind was the big horse show coming up this weekend. If she could win just two more classes, she would have a chance for the High Point Trophy.

It was all because of Mountain Laurel, her new horse. In competition, Laurel's gleaming color and fine training always caught the judges' eyes. Jennie and Laurel had become a good team.

"Hello, beautiful Laurel!" Jennie called as she ran into the barn. In the stall next to Laurel stood a little piebald pony. "Oh, hi, Jingle," said Jennie as she gave him a quick glance. Jingle had been Jennie's first horse. He was a kind and gentle pony and had practically taught Jennie how to ride. Now Jennie had grown too big for him and spent all of her time with Laurel. Jingle spent most of his time alone in the pasture. He had a big grass belly, and his coat was thick and dull and splotched with mud. His mane and tail had grown bushy and wild.

Here you continue to learn about Jennie through the author's description. You know that Jennie's happy to see Laurel and is not thinking about Jingle.

346

Jennie began to groom Laurel. Then she saddled up and rode out to the ring. Later, Jennie and Laurel walked happily back to the barn. As she untacked Laurel, she heard some scuffling noises in Jingle's stall. "Oh, that pony," thought Jennie. "He's rubbing against the feed tub again!" The noises continued. "Stop it, Jingle!" But Jingle didn't stop.

Jennie put Laurel away, then looked angrily in at Jingle. Jingle was down in the stall rolling and kicking and nipping at his sides. He was obviously in pain. Jennie knew that colic was intense pain in a horse's belly. "Oh, no," she whispered. "Oh, poor Jingle!"

Jennie knew the first thing to do was to stop Jingle from rolling. She spoke to him softly and quieted him enough to put on his halter. "Come on, Jingle, come on, boy," she pleaded. "Let's try to get up."

Jingle looked at Jennie and tried to get to his feet. "Good boy!" she said. "Now, we must walk." Jennie led the sick pony to the telephone on the barn wall. She called Dad. "Oh, Dad," Jennie cried, "come quick! I think Jingle has colic!"

The author is giving you more clues to Jennie's character. You know that Jennie is not taking care of the pony. The author has helped you to see that Jennie is self-centered and not loyal to her old friend, Jingle.

The author supports Jennie's selfish and self-centered trait by having Jennie snap at Jingle.

Now the author is beginning to let you see a shift in Jennie's character. Read the rest of the story. What character traits does Jennie have at the end of the story? How does the author help you to know this?

A few minutes later Mr. and Mrs. Gray came running down to the barn. "Dr. Bordwell will come as soon as possible," Dad said. "In the meantime we must do all we can for Jingle." Jennie sponged the pony's lathered sides, for he was sweating heavily. She put a thin sheet over his body to try to cool him. And then she walked him. He faithfully followed Jennie as she walked around the enclosure.

Jennie's throat grew tight and tears spilled down her cheeks. She remembered how she and Jingle used to go galloping through the fields where he would stop to munch on his favorite buttercups. She thought about her first horse shows when Jingle would cover up the mistakes that she made.

Now she looked at his shaggy, dirty coat and dry, cracked feet. Jennie put her arms around the pony's neck. "Oh, Jingle, I am so sorry. I love you, and I couldn't bear to lose you!"

Jennie stayed with Jingle until midnight. "Come to bed now, Jennie," said Dad. "Jingle is going to be all right, and you have to be up early tomorrow for the show."

"And afterwards," Jennie said, "I'm going to take Jingle to play in the big meadow. I hope he still likes to eat buttercups!"

from *Jennie's Horse, Jennie's Pony*
by Deborah Ellison Hocking

The author helped you to see Jennie change from being selfish and self-centered to being kind and caring and to even being ashamed of the way that she had been treating Jingle. Jennie knew that she had treated Jingle poorly and intended to change this. Do you think that Jingle will ever go ungroomed again? Probably not. The author helps you to see this by having Jennie really take a close look at Jingle and notice his "shaggy, dirty coat and dry, cracked feet." Remember that she hugged the pony and said that she was sorry. The author further supports this change in Jennie's character by having Jennie stay with the pony until he was almost better, and by having Jennie promise to take Jingle to the meadow to eat buttercups.

As you read other stories, look for the ways that authors help you to know characters. Look also for the traits that the characters have. Notice whether the author chooses to change the characters' traits as the characters develop in the stories.

This selection tells how a symphony with a surprise ending came to be written. Read to find out what the surprise was.

A Farewell to Music

by David Lasker

KARL

Karl was a young musician who played the horn in an orchestra. The orchestra entertained in the great European castle of Esterhaza,[1] which was owned by a wealthy Prince. The musicians were the servants of the Prince. They had to do whatever the Prince wanted them to do. This was the way it was in the eighteenth century. If they wanted to leave the castle for any reason, they had to get his permission.

One year, the Prince decided to keep his orchestra at the castle longer than usual. This story tells how Karl and the other musicians felt when this happened. Based on a true story, it also tells how Joseph Haydn[2] came to write the *Farewell Symphony*, in 1772.

---

[1] Esterhaza [es′tər•hä•zä]
[2] Haydn [hīd′ən]

Prince Nicolaus Esterhazy,[3] the richest man in Hungary, owned many acres of land and dozens of castles. The largest was Esterhaza, the most beautiful castle in the Austrian Empire. The prince liked it so well that, even though it was a summer palace, he stayed there later and later each year. Summer ended and fall began. Yet the Prince would not return to Vienna, capital city of the Empire.

While the Prince stayed, Esterhaza's musicians, singers, actors, dancers, and painters stayed, too. They were lonely. The Prince did not let them visit their families. Only during those few months when he returned to his winter palace could they see their families.

---

[3] Esterhazy [es'tər•hä•zē]

Joseph Haydn, the famous composer, was the music director at Esterhaza. At a rehearsal one day in October 1772, he spoke to his musicians. "Gentlemen," he said, tapping his violin bow against his music stand, "I know you are all tired and homesick. This time the Prince has kept us here longer than ever before. But you know why: the Empress Maria Theresa will visit Esterhaza for a few days. We must play well for her during her visit. When she returns to Vienna, Prince Nicolaus will surely follow, and then we will go with him. Now, let us tune our instruments and begin the rehearsal."

Xavier,[4] the bass viol player, was a tall man, but his instrument was taller. He winced as he turned the tuning pegs. The long strings were stretched so tightly that the pegs always slipped loose. He took longer to tune than anyone else, and the other musicians liked to joke about it.

"I'll bet you wish you played the piccolo," teased Karl, the young horn player.

Xavier was mad. "I've heard that one before, Karl, at least a hundred times," he said.

Suddenly cannons fired in the distance.

"The Empress! The Empress is coming!" said Haydn. "No time to rehearse now. Quick, gentlemen, to the gate."

The musicians took their instruments and rushed to their places near the gate that led to the Vienna road. Prince Nicolaus, in a golden chair carried by footmen, held a piece of lace cloth in his right hand. When he saw the Empress's party coming, he waved the cloth in the air. The great spectacle began.

The trumpets and drums played a rousing "ta-ran-ta-ra." One hundred and fifty grenadiers fired their muskets into the sky. People from the villages around Esterhaza crowded both sides of the road and cheered.

The royal coach stopped at the gate. Out stepped her Imperial Majesty, the Empress Maria Theresa. Her jewel-laden dress was so wide that she had to turn sideways to fit through the door of the coach.

---

[4] Xavier [zā′vē•ər]

The Prince led his guests to the palace, where they took time to rest from their trip. Later he entertained them with an opera. The musicians, led by Haydn, were placed between the audience and the singers on the stage.

As they played, they thought: Each note brings us closer to the end of another day. Each note brings us closer to Vienna and to our families and friends.

The following morning a servant shook Karl awake. "Get up," he said. "The Prince wants to go on a fox hunt."

"I wish I were home in Vienna instead of chasing a silly fox," Karl said sleepily.

"Don't argue with the Prince's orders," said the servant as he left.

Karl was angry at the Prince for staying at Esterhaza so late into the fall. He was angry at himself for being a horn player.

Karl was the huntmaster, who rode at the head of the pack as it charged out of the castle grounds. He was needed to blow loud horn calls to the hounds, not to make music.

Karl used a small horn for hunting. Unlike his larger orchestral horn, it could sound only a few notes. Like many horn players of his time, Karl was afraid that someday his horse would leap forward, bang the horn's mouthpiece against his teeth, and knock them out. If that happened, he could never play the horn again.

After the hunt, Karl rushed to join the other musicians at lunch. He was dusty, sweaty, and out of breath. Xavier called out, 'I'll bet you wish you played the bass.'' Everyone laughed, but Karl was angry.

"It's not fair!" he yelled, stamping his feet. "Prince Nicolaus has no right to keep us here this long!" The laughing stopped. Everyone felt as Karl did.

"It's late October," said Xavier. "I haven't seen my family for seven months."

Karl sat down and looked out the window. Toward the west was Vienna, where he and his father had played their horns together. There he had sung songs with his sisters and mother. "Oh," he said. "I wish I could say farewell to this place."

The Empress left, and only a few guests remained. After many days of activity, Esterhaza was quiet. A week passed, then two weeks. The days grew shorter and colder. The leaves dropped off the trees. But Prince Nicolaus was still at Esterhaza.

At last Haydn spoke to the Prince. He walked into the Prince's chamber and bowed deeply. "Exalted Prince, I kiss your noble hands. I beg you to hear this plea: When would it please Your Majesty to depart?"

The Prince, himself a musician, liked Haydn very much. When Haydn's house in Vienna had burned down, Prince Nicolaus had built him a large one right away. He had never before kept his musicians away for so long; he knew how they felt. But to leave his lovely Esterhaza now? The peaceful gardens? The splashing fountains? He thought a moment and said quietly, "Haydn may tell our musicians that we shall leave Esterhaza when we wish it."

Haydn answered in the formal way that was expected of him. "Gracious lord and sire, I thank you for your kindness. I am now, and for my whole life will be, your most humble and obedient servant."

Karl met Haydn after Haydn's meeting with the Prince. Karl asked if the Prince was ready to leave. "Ready? I'm afraid we'll never get out of here," replied Haydn.

Then Karl noticed Baron von Scheffstoss, the Prince's secretary, at the head of the staircase. Without thinking, Karl ran up the marble steps.

"Honorable Baron, please ask the Prince to let us go home," Karl said breathlessly.

The Baron became stiff as a statue and red with rage. "How dare you!" he shouted. "Who do you think you are? I'll have you thrown into the dungeon! Now get out!" With that, he pushed Karl, who fell backward down the stairs.

Haydn, trying not to laugh, helped Karl up. "Don't you know better than to approach a nobleman like that?"

Karl brushed himself off. "Just trying to help," he said.

"That's not the way, Karl. Prince Nicolaus won't be won over by rudeness. We've got to do something that will amuse him. He'd like that."

"If all the musicians got up in the middle of your next performance and marched off to Vienna, *I'd* be amused," said Karl.

"Hmm. That's not bad! I like your idea, Karl. Let's give it a try."

A few days later the orchestra performed for Prince
Nicolaus and his few remaining guests. They played the
symphony Haydn had just written. It had a surprise
ending.

Karl played a solo. Then, while the others went on
playing, he blew out the candles alongside his music
stand. He packed up his horn under his arm, and
walked off into the side room. Xavier did the same and
carried off his heavy bass viol. They waited by the door
and watched the Prince's surprised face.

One by one, the musicians left. Only a few violinists and cellists remained. The sound of this small group was much softer than that of the full orchestra. A great stillness settled over the room. The music told the Prince how the musicians felt: homesick and lonely.

More players finished and joined the others. Soon only Haydn and Tomasini, the first violinist, were left. Finally they, too, put out their candles and withdrew. The symphony was over.

Prince Nicolaus stood up. "What a wonderful symphony! Congratulations, Haydn," he said. Then he turned to his guests and announced, "If they all leave, we may as well leave, too."

"Bravo! Hooray for Haydn!" the musicians cheered, shaking hands and slapping backs. Xavier and Tomasini lifted Haydn onto their shoulders.

Karl blew a loud horn call and they happily marched back to their rooms.

They all left for Vienna the next day.

1. What was the surprise ending to the *Farewell* Symphony?

2. Why did the musicians want to leave Esterhaza?

3. Where on page 359 does the author give a clue to how the selection will end?

4. Which did Karl enjoy more, being the huntmaster or playing in the orchestra? Explain your answer.

5. How was Haydn responsible for Prince Nicolaus's decision to return to Vienna?

6. How does the expression "You can catch more flies with sugar than with vinegar" apply to this selection?

Prewrite

In the story, Haydn used a clever idea to tell the Prince to leave Esterhaza. What are some other clever ideas the musicians could have used to tell the Prince that it was time to leave? Discuss your ideas with a classmate.

Draft

Now, imagine that you are one of the
musicians. How could you convince the Prince
that it is time to go back to Vienna? Remember,
the Prince likes clever ideas, and if he likes the
way you tell him to leave Esterhaza, he will
probably go. Write your plan as if you were one
of the musicians trying to get the Prince to
return. Remember, Haydn's plan did not use
words to convince Prince Nicolaus. The plan you
write about does not have to be one that uses
words either.

Revise

Read your plan. Is your idea a good one? Did
you use a clever way to tell the Prince what you
want? If you were the Prince, would you be
convinced by what your musician does? Make
whatever changes and additions are needed for
your plan to be convincing.

Read to find out why audiences especially enjoy performances by this famous musician.

As you read, try to decide what makes this newspaper article different from the other selections in this unit.

Center City Post

Itzhak Perlman: Violinist for All People

by Stephen Wigler

OF THE CENTER CITY POST STAFF

CENTER CITY, MAY 7—Every year Itzhak Perlman travels around the world to play his violin. No matter what country he is in, many people want to hear him play. When Itzhak Perlman appears in concert, every seat in the hall is filled.

This does not surprise anyone who knows the Perlman story. For many years, people have lined up to hear him. After he plays, halls echo with loud cheers. No other violinist in the world gets such cheers.

Part of the reason for the cheers is that people love Itzhak Perlman. When Perlman plays, he makes people think that he's playing just for them. They react to him the way they would to a close friend. He brings joy to his listeners.

Itzhak Perlman first appeared in the United States as a thirteen-year-old prodigy on television's *Ed Sullivan Show.* Millions of people watched that night. They fell in love with the Israeli boy on crutches who played so beautifully. They have never stopped loving him.

Even if people did not love him so much, Itzhak Perlman would still be one of the world's greatest musicians. He plays everything wonderfully. He can play short, crowd-pleasing pieces or long, difficult ones.

It is hard to say why Itzhak Perlman has such extraordinary appeal. Perlman himself says that there are violinists who play as well as he does, or even better. However, no other violinist seems to be as lovable. With his short, rounded build and thick, curly hair, he looks like a teddy bear. He has been a favorite on TV talk shows, and he has appeared in several TV advertisements. Some people think that Perlman is the world's most popular violinist because he appears on TV so much.

However, that is not the real reason. Itzhak Perlman shows something to an audience that other violinists do not: love of playing the instrument.

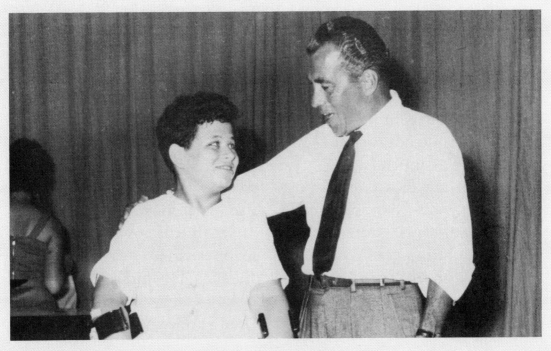

The violin is one of the most difficult instruments to play, yet it does not seem to be hard for Itzhak Perlman. Violinists who may have as much skill as Perlman just do not seem to enjoy playing as much.

Itzhak Perlman seems to be having a good time onstage, and he wants his audience to have a good time, too. When he plays with an orchestra, he always works out a *shtick* with the concertmaster, or head

violinist. A *shtick* is a planned joke.

The joke goes like this:

Perlman hands his violin to the concertmaster before walking offstage. When he returns to play an encore, or extra piece, Perlman asks for his violin. The concertmaster hands Perlman his own violin. He keeps Perlman's priceless Stradivarius for himself. Perlman looks as if he is about to play. Then suddenly he sees that the violin is not his. Perlman makes believe he is angry, and grabs his violin back from the concertmaster. The audience always claps and cheers.

Perlman once explained why he plays jokes on the stage that do not have anything to do with music.

"When I go out to play," Perlman said, "I never say to myself that I have to make this audience love me. I love to play music, and people catch that and enjoy it.

"The thing is this: The minute there is something not normal, like a joke, it makes the audience feel good. And it makes me feel good to make people have a nicer time. I talk to people at concerts; I try to reach them. A lot of people think they are not supposed to have a good time at a concert. I think they should. I like to make people feel, 'Hey, I've gotten to know this man.' "

Even when Perlman gives concerts without an orchestra, he makes his audience feel at home. He makes jokes with his old friend, Samuel Sanders, who accompanies him on the piano. He loves to make people laugh. He even jokes about the problem that makes him walk on crutches.

Once, after agreeing to meet with a newspaper writer, he stood the writer up. When Perlman called the writer the next day, he said he was sorry. Then he joked, "I never really stand anyone up. I *sit* them up."

Perlman developed polio at the age of four. Only in the last few years has he been able to joke, or even talk, about his disability.

The same strong will that kept Itzhak Perlman playing the violin when he was a very sick little boy still shows now when he plays. He walks across the stage leaning on crutches. It is not easy for him. His legs are in braces. When he plays, he does so sitting down.

People wrote about Perlman in the 1960's and 1970's when he first came to this country. They always talked about what a great player he was even though he had a disability. This made Perlman angry.

"All the writers talked about how brave I was," he once said. " 'He walked across the stage barely able to move,' they said." After a while, however, the writers didn't talk about his disability anymore.

"Then I got mad that they had forgotten. I realized that I had become so well-known that I could do some good. Now every time I speak to a writer, I bring up the problems that the disabled face. I've come full circle."

A lot of people, Perlman said, are afraid of disability. "People don't like to look trouble in the face. It's not pretty. But it's human."

Perlman has done a lot more than talk about the problems of the disabled. Everywhere he plays, he tries to make concert halls easier for disabled people to enter and move around in. He doesn't like the halls in which someone has to take his wheelchair up the steps. He talks to friends who are architects about how to make things easier for the disabled. He wants disabled people to be able to take elevators from floor to floor.

Of course, Perlman does not think about these problems when he is onstage. When Perlman sits down to play, his face shows nothing but happiness.

It is hard to believe that any human being could be so happy. "Sure I am," Perlman has said. "You can't fake that. And if I'm very happy, why should I hide it?"

That may be why people love Perlman so much. During the two hours that his concerts last, audiences share his joy in being alive.

There is one thing in his life that most of Perlman's audiences cannot share: his disability. To help them understand disability better, he wishes that they could experience it.

"They should spend a week on crutches or in a wheelchair," he has said, "and try to do their work."

In spite of the difficulties, Itzhak Perlman will keep on working. He loves playing music too much to stop.

369

1. Give three reasons why audiences enjoy Itzhak Perlman's performances.

2. How did Itzhak Perlman begin his career in the United States?

3. How does Perlman help other disabled people to enjoy his concerts?

4. Why do you think Perlman was upset when writers stopped talking about his disability?

5. What did you read that makes you think that Itzhak Perlman might make a good actor?

6. How did Perlman turn his disability into an asset?

Prewrite

What did you find most interesting about Itzhak Perlman? Copy and complete the idea burst on the next page. In the center, name a trait that makes Itzhak Perlman a special person. Then add details that help to explain this trait.

Itzhak is courageous in dealing with his disability.

is not self-conscious about his disability

tries to make concert halls better for disabled

Draft

Pretend that Itzhak Perlman is coming to your school to give a concert, and you have been asked to introduce him. Write a short introductory speech. Use the traits and examples listed in your idea burst to help you with your introduction.

Revise

Read your speech. Does Mr. Perlman sound like someone you would enjoy meeting? Make whatever changes and additions are needed to give Mr. Perlman a good introduction.

David is a composer, a person who writes music. Join him as he takes you through the process of creating a new piece of music.

Making Music

by Arthur K. Paxton

This photojournal tells how David Amram, one of America's best-known composers and musicians, creates a new piece of music. The photographs show the sequence of events and are accompanied by short explanations written in the style of a story.

David is a composer—he makes music. One day he just sat and imagined new sounds. He tried to make them at the piano.

He played one note,
high notes,
quiet notes,
many notes,
low notes,
loud notes.

David kept thinking of other sounds, too. The sounds of musicians who

blew,

plucked,

bowed,

and struck.

If David conducted and they all played together, what a glorious sound they would make!

David knew just when they could do it. He was going to conduct a series of concerts.

374

He would write a new piece for orchestra. The new piece could be played at the concerts along with music by other composers. David got some music paper and started to write down his music.

Sometimes he went to the piano to work out his ideas and to check what he had written. Even then, he always imagined the sound of an orchestra.

When he finished writing his piece, a copyist wrote out the parts for each of the players. All the players got their parts and practiced by themselves.

In the meantime, people found out about the concerts from announcements in the newspaper and on the radio.

The musicians needed to practice together. One by one they showed up at the rehearsal hall and got out their instruments.

They all tuned up—even the tympanist. Then everyone began to play.

David used his baton to show the beat and to keep the musicians together when the music went faster or slower. He used his left hand to give clues. He showed the musicians when to make the music sound sweet or joyful.

When people played too loud, he let them know!

After several rehearsals, everyone played together beautifully. The only thing missing was the kind of excitement that comes from playing for a live audience.

Some people came early to the first concert. The orchestra was just starting to go out onto the stage.

When David gave the downbeat, music filled the hall.

The concerts featured a variety of pieces in different styles and moods. Each concert ended with David's new music.

The audience
   listened
      and listened
         and listened
            and even helped conduct!

The audience clapped and shouted, "Bravo!" Some people stood up. David beamed as he waved for his players to stand and share the applause.

Today it's raining outside, and David is alone with his flute. The rain sounds like drums, then like clapping, and David remembers his concerts and the joy of conducting his own music.

1. What was the first thing David did when he began creating his new piece of music?

2. What had to be done before an orchestra could play David's music?

3. What do you think is the most interesting part of creating a new piece of music?

4. What words in the selection tell you why an audience is important to a performance?

5. Do you think David will want to try writing another piece of music to be performed? Why?

6. Would David have been able to bring his piece of music to life without the orchestra? Without the copyist? Without the audience? Explain your answer.

Prewrite

A photojournal, like the one about David Amram, uses both words and pictures to tell its story. What kinds of stories can best be told as photojournals? List some of them. For each idea you listed, write one or two things that pictures could show especially well.

Draft

Create a photojournal by picking one of the ideas from your list. Decide on five or six pictures you would use to tell your story. Try to find the pictures in magazines, or draw them yourself. For each picture, write one or two sentences that tell what is happening in the picture.

Revise

Read and look at your photojournal. Do your pictures and sentences go well together? Is your story clear? Do you need to add or change any of the pictures or any of the words? Make the changes necessary for your photojournal to be interesting.

Diary, Journal, Letters

Do you write your private thoughts in a book for you *alone* to read? Do you keep a written record of school projects or hobbies? If you do, you are writing in a diary or journal. **Diaries** and **journals** are accounts of writers' experiences. **Diaries** are intended to be read only by the writer because the thoughts recorded may be very personal.

Journals are less private and less personal than diaries. Journals often focus on the progress of a hobby or a project. They are places to record changes observed, to gather materials for a project, or even to collect ideas for writing. Journals often are intended to be read by others.

Throughout history, millions of people have written diaries and journals. Much of what we know about England in the late 1600's comes from the diary of Samuel Pepys (Peeps). It is through this diary that we know about the Great Fire that nearly destroyed London.

Before George Washington became our first president, many important people met in Philadelphia to decide about the kind of government we would have. Much of what we know about those meetings comes from the daily notes of James Madison, who later became the fourth president of the United States. His diary helps us understand an important part of our history that otherwise would be lost.

The diary of Anne Frank was written by a young Jewish girl, forced to hide for two years in Holland in the 1940's. Her diary gives us a look at the thoughts of a young girl growing up in war-torn Europe.

Letters are another kind of personal writing. A correspondence, which is a series of letters between two people, is like a conversation when these people are apart. Letters, like diaries and journals, have also added a great deal to what we know about famous people and the times in which they lived. Abigail Adams, the wife of the second president of the United States, and also the mother of our sixth president, wrote many letters. Her letters were saved, and they help us know about these two presidents, and about what happened during their lives.

Beverly Cleary, the author of the next selection, tells the fictional story of Leigh Botts entirely through letters and diary entries. Leigh's letters are written to Mr. Henshaw, an author. As you read the next selection, notice how the letters and diary entries help you to know Leigh and Mr. Henshaw.

These are characteristics of diaries, journals, and letters to remember.

- Diaries are private accounts of the writer's feelings and reactions to be read only by the writer.
- Journals are records of projects and hobbies or collections of ideas for writing. Sometimes they are read by others.
- Letters are written conversations between two people.

Beverly Cleary

When Beverly Cleary was a child, she wondered why there were no books written about children like her. Most books at that time were about wealthy English children or people on the frontier. When she grew up, she began to write stories about ordinary American children. Children today enjoy reading her stories. More than four million copies of her books have been sold.

Beverly Cleary was born in Oregon. She lived on a farm for the first few years of her life. Her mother had been a teacher, and she would recite stories and poems from memory for Beverly.

They lived near a small town that had no library, so Beverly's mother started one in an unused room over a bank. Beverly Cleary remembers that time well. She says, "My mother arranged for the state library to have crates of books shipped in. I don't remember how often, but I remember hanging over those crates looking for the children's books." It was during this time that Beverly Cleary learned to love books.

After Beverly graduated from college, she entered the School of Librarianship at the University of Washington in Seattle. There she specialized in library work with children. She was a children's librarian in Yakima, Washington, until she married Clarence Cleary and moved to California. The Clearys had twins, a boy and a girl, who are now grown up.

Beverly Cleary's first book, *Henry Huggins*, was published in 1950. She has written several more books about Henry, his friend Beezus, and her little sister Ramona, characters whose realistic adventures are filled with humor. These characters have become the favorites of many readers. In fact, the Clearys have a ten-gallon mailbox to hold all the letters Beverly Cleary receives from children who read her books.

Children often ask Beverly Cleary where she finds the ideas for the books she writes. She answers, "From my own experience and from the world around me." She tells children to read widely while they are growing up, and when the time comes for them to write, they will find their own way of writing. She tells them to read, look, listen, think, and write. She also advises children to keep diaries as a way to practice their writing.

Beverly Cleary has won many prizes for the books she has written, including a Newbery Medal for the book *Dear Mr. Henshaw.* You will be reading a selection from *Dear Mr. Henshaw* next. As you read the selection, think about how Beverly Cleary feels about children and their writing.

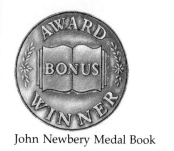
Leigh Botts wants to be a writer. Read to find out how his favorite author helps Leigh to help himself.

Dear Mr. Henshaw

by Beverly Cleary

May 12

Dear Mr. Henshaw,

My teacher read your book about the dog to our class. It was funny. We licked it.

Your freind,
Leigh Botts (boy)

December 3

Dear Mr. Henshaw,

I am the boy who wrote to you last year when I was in the second grade. Maybe you didn't get my letter. This year I read the book I wrote to you about called *Ways to Amuse a Dog*. It is the first thick book with chapters that I have read.

My teacher taught me a trick about the word *friend*. The *i* goes before *e* so that at the end it will spell *end*.
Keep in tutch.

> Your fri*end*,
> Leigh (Lee) Botts

November 13

Dear Mr. Henshaw,

I am in the fourth grade now. I made a diorama of *Ways to Amuse a Dog*, the book I wrote to you about two times before. Now our teacher is making us write to authors for Book Week. I got your answer to my letter last year, but it was only printed. Please would you write to me in your own handwriting? I am a great enjoyer of your books.

> Your best reader,
> Leigh Botts

October 2

Dear Mr. Henshaw,

I am in the fifth grade now. You might like to know that I gave a book report on *Ways to Amuse a Dog*. The class liked it. I got an A−. The minus was because the teacher said I didn't stand on both feet.

> Sincerely,
> Leigh Botts

November 7

Dear Mr. Henshaw,

I got your letter and did what you said. I read a different book by you. I read *Moose on Toast*. I liked it almost as much as *Ways to Amuse a Dog*. It was really funny the way the boy's mother tried to think up ways to cook the moose meat they had in their freezer. One thousand pounds is a lot of moose.

Your number 1 fan,
Leigh Botts

September 20

Dear Mr. Henshaw,

This year I am in the sixth grade in a new school in a different town. Our teacher is making us do author reports to improve our writing skills, so of course I thought of you. Please answer the following questions.

1. How many books have you written?
2. Is Boyd Henshaw your real name or is it fake?
3. Why do you write books for children?
4. Where do you get your ideas?
5. What is your favorite book that you wrote?
6. Do you like to write books?
7. What is the title of your next book?
8. Please give me some tips on how to write a book.

I need your answer by next Friday. This is urgent!

Sincerely,
Leigh Botts

November 15

Dear Mr. Henshaw,

At first I was pretty upset when I didn't get an answer to my letter in time for my report, but I worked it out okay. I read what it said about you on the back of *Ways to Amuse a Dog* and wrote real big on every other line so I filled up the paper.

When your letter finally came I didn't want to read it to the class, because I didn't think Miss Martinez would like silly answers. But she said I had to read it. The class laughed when I came to the part about your favorite animal was a purple monster who ate children who sent authors long lists of questions for reports instead of learning to use the library. Anyway, thank you for answering my questions.

Your writing tips were okay. I could tell you meant what you said. Don't worry. When I write something, I won't send it to you. I understand how busy you are with your own books.

That list of questions you sent for me to answer really made me mad. Nobody else's author put in a list of questions to be answered, and I don't think it's fair to make me do more work when I already wrote a report. I'm not going to answer them, and you can't make me. You're not my teacher.

Yours truly,
Leigh Botts

P.S. Do you really write books because you have read every book in the library and because writing beats mowing the lawn or shoveling snow?

November 16

Dear Mr. Henshaw,

Mom found your letter and your list of questions which I was dumb enough to leave lying around. She says I have to answer your questions because authors are working people like anyone else, and if you took time to answer my questions, I should answer yours. She says I can't go through life expecting everyone to do everything for me.

Well, I got to go now. It's bedtime. Maybe I'll get around to answering your questions, and maybe I won't. There isn't any law that says I have to. Maybe I won't even read any more of your books.

Disgusted reader,
Leigh Botts

November 20

Dear Mr. Henshaw,

Mom is nagging me about your dumb old questions. She says if I really want to be an author, I should follow the tips in your letter. I should read, look, listen, think, and *write*. So here goes.

1. Who are you?

Like I've been telling you, I am Leigh Botts, Leigh Marcus Botts. I don't like Leigh for a name because some people don't know how to say it or think it's a girl's name.

I am just a plain boy. This school doesn't say I am gifted and talented, but I am not stupid either.

2. What do you look like?

I am sort of medium. I don't have red hair or anything like that. In first and second grades kids used to call me Leigh the Flea, but I have grown. Now when the class lines up according to height, I am in the middle. I guess you could call me the mediumest boy in the class.

This is hard work. To be continued, maybe.

Leigh Botts

November 22

Dear Mr. Henshaw,

I wasn't going to answer any more of your questions, but Mom won't get the TV repaired because she says it was rotting my brain.

3. What is your family like?

Since Dad went away, my family is just Mom and me. We used to live in a mobile home outside Bakersfield in California before Mom and Dad got divorced.

Dad drives a big truck, a cab-over job. That means the cab is over the engine. His big rig sure is a beauty, with a bunk in the cab and everything. His rig, which truckers call a tractor but everyone else calls a truck, has ten wheels, two in front and eight in back so he can hitch up to anything—flatbeds, refrigerated vans, a couple of gondolas.

In school they teach you that a gondola is some kind of boat in Italy, but in the U.S. it is a container for hauling loose stuff like carrots.

My hand is all worn out from all this writing, but I try to treat Mom and Dad the same so I'll get to Mom next time.

Your pooped reader,
Leigh Botts

November 23

Mr. Henshaw:

Why should I call you "dear," when you are the reason I'm stuck with all this work? It wouldn't be fair to leave Mom out so here is Question 3 continued.

Mom works part-time for Catering by Katy which is run by a real nice lady Mom knew when she was growing up. Mom and Katy and some other ladies make fancy food for weddings and parties. They also bake for restaurants. Mom is a good cook.

Your ex-friend,
Leigh Botts

November 24

Mr. Henshaw:

Here we go again.

4. *Where do you live?*

After the divorce Mom and I moved from Bakersfield to Pacific Grove, which is on California's Central Coast.

We live in a little house, a *really* little house, that used to be somebody's summer cottage. Now it is what they call a garden cottage.

Next door is a gas station that goes ping-ping, ping-ping every time a car drives in. They turn off the pinger at 10:00 P.M. Most of the time I am asleep by then.

Sometimes when the gas station isn't pinging, I can hear the ocean roaring and the sea lions barking. They sound like dogs.

Two more questions to go. Maybe I won't answer them. So there. Ha-ha.

Still disgusted,
Leigh Botts

November 27

Mr. Henshaw:

Okay, you win, because Mom is still nagging me, and I don't have anything else to do. I'll answer your last two questions.

5. *Do you like school?*
   School is okay, I guess.

6. *Who are your friends?*

I don't have a whole lot of friends in my new school. A new boy in school has to be pretty cautious until he gets to know who's who. Maybe I'm just a boy nobody pays much attention to. The only time anybody paid much attention to me was in my last school when I gave the book report on *Ways to Amuse a Dog.* After my report some people went to the library to get the book.

I wish somebody would ask me over sometime.

There, Mr. Henshaw. That's the end of your crummy questions. I hope you are satisfied for making me do all this extra work.

Fooey on you,
Leigh Botts

December 4

Dear Mr. Henshaw,

I am sorry I was rude in my last letter when I finished answering your questions. Maybe I was mad about some other things.

When you answered my questions, you said the way

to get to be an author was to *write*. You underlined it twice. Well, I sure did a lot of writing, and you know what? Now that I think about it, it wasn't so bad when it wasn't for a book report or a report on some country or anything where I had to look things up in the library. I even sort of miss writing now that I've finished your questions.

Are you writing another book? Please answer my letter so we can be pen pals.

Still your No. 1 fan,
Leigh Botts

December 12

Dear Mr. Henshaw,

I was glad to get your postcard. Don't worry. I get the message. You don't have a lot of time for answering letters. That's okay with me, because I'm glad you are busy writing a book.

Something nice happened today. When I was hanging around at school waiting for the first bell to ring, I was watching Mr. Fridley, the custodian, raise the flags. Maybe I better explain that the state flag of California is white with a brown bear in the middle. When he pulled the flags to the top of the flagpole, the bear was upside down with his feet in the air. I said, "Hey, Mr. Fridley, the bear is upside down."

This is a new paragraph because Miss Martinez says there should be a new paragraph when a different person speaks. Mr. Fridley said, "Well, so it is. How would you like to turn him right side up?"

So I got to pull the flags down, turn the bear flag the right way, and raise both flags again. Mr. Fridley said maybe I should come to school a few minutes early every morning to help him with the flags. It was nice to have somebody notice me.

I've been thinking about what you said on your postcard about keeping a diary. Maybe I'll try it.

Sincerely,
Leigh Botts

December 13

Dear Mr. Henshaw,

I bought a composition book like you said. It is yellow with a spiral binding. On the front I printed

Diary of Leigh Marcus Botts

Private — Keep Out

This Means You!!!!!

When I started to write in it, I didn't know how to begin. I felt as if I should write "Dear Composition Book," but that sounds dumb. So does "Dear Piece of Paper." The first page still looks the way I feel—blank. I don't think I can keep a diary. I don't want to be a nuisance to you, but I wish you could tell me how. I am stuck.

Puzzled reader,
Leigh Botts

December 21

Dear Mr. Henshaw,

I got your postcard with the picture of the bears. Maybe I'll do what you said and pretend my diary is a letter to somebody. Maybe I'll pretend I am writing to you because when I answered all your questions, I got the habit of beginning, "Dear Mr. Henshaw." Don't worry. I won't send it to you.

Thanks for the tip. I know you're busy.

Your grateful friend,
Leigh Botts

FROM THE PRIVATE DIARY OF LEIGH BOTTS

Friday, December 22

Dear Mr. Pretend Henshaw,

This is a diary. I will keep it, not mail it.

I guess I don't have to sign my name to a diary letter the way I sign a real letter that I would mail.

Wednesday, January 3

Dear Mr. Pretend Henshaw,

I got behind in my diary during Christmas vacation because I had a lot of things to do such as go to the dentist for a checkup, get some new shoes, and do a lot of things that don't get done during school.

Wednesday, January 10

Dear Mr. Pretend Henshaw,

I read over the letter you wrote that time answering my questions and thought about your tips on how to write a book. One of the tips was *listen.* I guess you meant to listen and write down the way people talk, sort of like a play.

January 12

Dear Mr. Henshaw,

This is a real letter I am going to mail. Maybe I had better explain that I have written you some other letters that are really my diary which I keep because you said so and because Mom still won't have the TV repaired. She wants my brain to stay in good shape. She says I will need my brain all my life.

Guess what? Today the school librarian stopped me in the hall and said she had something for me. She told me to come to the library. There she handed me your new book and said I could be the first to read it. I must have looked surprised. She said she knew how much I love your books since I check them out so often. Now I know Mr. Fridley isn't the only one who notices me.

I am on page 14 of *Beggar Bears.* It is a good book. I just wanted you to know that I am the first person around here to get to read it.

Your No. 1 fan,
Leigh Botts

January 15

Dear Mr. Henshaw,

I finished *Beggar Bears* in two nights. It is a really good book. At first I was surprised because it wasn't funny like your other books, but then I got to thinking (you said authors should think) and decided a book doesn't have to be funny to be good, although it often helps. This book did not need to be funny.

I hope your book wins a million awards.

Sincerely,
Leigh Botts

January 19

Dear Mr. Henshaw,

Thank you for sending me the postcard with the picture of the lake and mountains and all that snow. Yes, I will continue to write in my diary even if I do have to pretend I am writing to you. You know something? I think I feel better when I write in my diary.

My teacher says my writing skills are improving. Maybe I will be a famous author someday. She said our school, along with some other schools, is going to print a book of work of young authors, and I should write a story for it. The writers of the best work will win a lunch with a Famous Author. I hope the Famous Author is you.

That's all for now. I am going to try to think up a story. Don't worry. I won't send it to you to read. I know you are busy and I don't want to be a nuisance.

Your good friend,
Leigh Botts the First

FROM THE DIARY OF LEIGH BOTTS

Saturday, January 20

Dear Mr. Pretend Henshaw,

Every time I try to think up a story, it turns out to be like something someone else had written, usually you. I want to do what you said in your tips and write like me, not like somebody else. I'll keep trying because I want to be a Young Author with my story printed.

Monday, February 5

~~Dear Mr. Henshaw,~~

I don't have to pretend to write to Mr. Henshaw anymore. I have learned to say what I think on a piece of paper.

Today after school I felt so rotten I decided to go for a walk. I wasn't going any special place, just walking. I had started down the street past some shops when I came to a sign that said "Butterfly Trees." I had heard a lot about those trees where monarch butterflies fly thousands of miles to spend the winter. I followed arrows until I came to a grove of mossy pine and eucalyptus trees with signs saying "Quiet."

The place was so quiet that I tiptoed. The grove was shady. At first I saw only three or four monarchs flitting around. Then I discovered some of the branches looked strange, as if they were covered with little brown sticks.

Then the sun came out from behind a cloud. The sticks began to move, and slowly they opened wings and turned into orange and black butterflies, thousands of them quivering on one tree. Then they began to float off through the trees in the sunshine. Those clouds of butterflies were so beautiful I felt good all over and just stood there watching them until the fog began to roll in, and the butterflies came back and turned into brown sticks again. They made me think of a story Mom used to read me about Cinderella returning from the ball.

I felt so good I ran all the way home.

Thursday, February 8

I started another story which I hope will get printed in the Young Writers' Yearbook. I think I will call it *The Ten-Foot Wax Man*. All the boys in my class are writing weird stories full of monsters, lasers, and creatures from outer space. Girls seem to be writing mostly poems or stories about horses.

February 15

Dear Mr. Henshaw,

I haven't written to you for a long time, because I know you are busy, but I need help with the story I am trying to write for the Young Writer's Yearbook. I got started, but I don't know how to finish it.

My story is about a man ten feet tall who drives a big truck. The man is made of wax, and every time he crosses the desert, he melts a little. He makes so many trips and melts so much he finally can't handle the gears or reach the brakes. That is as far as I can get. What should I do now?

The boys in my class who are writing about monsters just bring in a new monster on the last page to finish off the villains with a laser. That kind of ending doesn't seem right to me. I don't know why.

Please help. Just a postcard will do.

Hopefully,
Leigh Botts

February 28

Dear Mr. Henshaw,

Thank you for answering my letter. I was surprised that you had trouble writing stories when you were my age. I think you are right. Maybe I am not ready to write a story. I understand what you mean. A character in a story should solve a problem or change in some way. I can see that a wax man who melts until he's a puddle wouldn't be there to solve anything and melting isn't the sort of change you mean. I suppose somebody could turn up on the last page and make candles out of him. That would change him all right, but that is not the ending I want.

I asked Miss Martinez if I had to write a story for Young Writers, and she said I could write a poem or a description.

Your grateful friend,
Leigh

FROM THE DIARY OF LEIGH BOTTS
VOL. 2

Thursday, March 1

I am getting behind in this diary for several reasons, including working on my story and writing to Mr. Henshaw (really, not just pretend). I also had to buy a new notebook because I had filled up the first one.

I finally gave up on my story about the ten-foot wax man, which was really pretty dumb. I thought I would write a poem about butterflies for Young Writers because a poem can be short.

Saturday, March 17

Today is Saturday, so this morning I walked to the butterfly trees again. The grove was quiet and peaceful, and because the sun was shining, I stood there a long time, looking at the orange butterflies floating through the gray and green leaves and listening to the sound of the ocean on the rocks. I thought I might write about them in prose instead of poetry, but on the way home I got to thinking about Dad and one time when he took me along when he was hauling grapes and what a great day it had been.

Tuesday, March 20

Yesterday Miss Neely, the librarian, asked if I had written anything for the Young Writers' Yearbook, because all writing had to be turned in by tomorrow. When I told her I hadn't she said I still had twenty-four hours and why didn't I get busy? So I did, because I really would like to meet a Famous Author. My story about the ten-foot wax man went into the wastebasket.

Finally I dashed off a description of the time I rode with my father when he was trucking the load of grapes down Highway 152 through Pacheco Pass. I put in things like the signs that said "Steep Grade, Trucks Use Low Gear," and how Dad down-shifted and how skillful he was handling a long, heavy load on the curves. I put in about the hawks on the telephone wires and about that high peak where Black Bart's lookout used to watch for travelers coming through the pass so he could signal to Black Bart to rob them, and how the leaves on the trees along the stream at the bottom of the pass were turning yellow and how good the grapes smelled in the sun. Then I copied the whole thing over in case neatness counts and gave it to Miss Neely.

Monday, March 26

Today wasn't the greatest day of my life. When our class went to the library, I saw a stack of Yearbooks and could hardly wait for Miss Neely to hand them out. When I finally got mine and opened it to the first page, there was a monster story, and I saw I hadn't won first prize. I kept turning. I didn't win second prize which went to a poem, and I didn't win third or fourth prize, either. Then I turned another page and saw Honorable Mention and under it:

A Day on Dad's Rig
by
Leigh M. Botts

There was my title with my name under it in print. I can't say I wasn't disappointed because I hadn't won a prize, I was. I was really disappointed about not getting to meet the mysterious Famous Author, but I liked seeing my name in print.

Some kids were mad because they didn't win or even get something printed. They said they wouldn't ever try to write again which I think is pretty dumb. I have heard that real authors sometimes have their books turned down. I figure you win some, you lose some.

Friday, March 30

Today turned out to be exciting. In the middle of second period Miss Neely called me out of class and asked if I would like to go have lunch with the famous author, Angela Badger. I said, "Sure, how come?"

Miss Neely explained that the teachers discovered that the winning poem had been copied out of a book and wasn't original so the girl who submitted it would not be allowed to go and would I like to go in her place? Would I!

Miss Neely telephoned Mom at work for permission. Then she drove all the winners in her own car to the hotel, where some other librarians and their winners were waiting in the lobby. Then Angela Badger arrived, and we were all led into the dining room which was pretty crowded. One of the librarians told the winners to sit at a long table with a sign that said Reserved. Angela Badger sat in the middle and some of the girls pushed to sit beside her. I sat across from her.

There I was face to face with a real live author who seemed like a nice lady, plump with wild hair. I couldn't think of a thing to say because I hadn't read her books. Some girls told her how much they loved her books, but some of the boys and girls were too shy to say anything. Nothing seemed to happen until Mrs. Badger said, "Why don't we all go help ourselves to lunch at the salad bar?"

Getting lunch took longer than in a school cafeteria.

I was still trying to think of something interesting to say to Mrs. Badger while I chased garbanzo beans around my plate with a fork. A couple of girls did all the talking, telling Mrs. Badger how they wanted to write books exactly like hers.

Mrs. Badger tried to get some of the shy people to say something, without much luck, and I still couldn't think of anything to say. Finally Mrs. Badger looked straight at me and asked, "What did you write for the Yearbook?"

I felt myself turn red and answered, "Just something about a ride on a truck."

"Oh!" said Mrs. Badger. "So you're the author of *A Day on Dad's Rig*!"

Everyone was quiet. None of us had known the real live author would have read what we had written, but she had and she remembered my title.

"I just got honorable mention," I said, but I was thinking, she called me an author. *A real live author called me an author.*

"What difference does that make?" asked Mrs. Badger. "Judges never agree. I happened to like *A Day on Dad's Rig* because it was written by a boy who wrote honestly about something he knew and had strong feelings about. You made me feel what it was like to ride down a steep grade with tons of grapes behind me."

"But I couldn't make it into a story," I said, feeling a whole lot braver.

"Who cares?" said Mrs. Badger with a wave of her hand. "What do you expect? The ability to write stories comes later, when you have lived longer and have more understanding. *A Day on Dad's Rig* was splendid work for a boy your age. You wrote like you, and you did not try to imitate someone else. This is one mark of a good writer. Keep it up."

I noticed a couple of girls, who had been saying they wanted to write books exactly like Angela Badger, exchange embarrassed looks.

"Gee, thanks," was all I could say. Everyone got over being shy and began to ask Mrs. Badger if she wrote in pencil or on the typewriter and did she ever have books rejected and were her characters real people and what did it feel like to be a famous author?

I didn't think answers to those questions were very important, but I did have one question I wanted to ask which I finally managed to get in at the last minute

when Mrs. Badger was autographing some books people had brought.

"Mrs. Badger," I said, "did you ever meet Boyd Henshaw?"

"Why, yes," she said, scribbling away in someone's book. "I once met him at a meeting."

"What's he like?" I asked over the head of a girl crowding up with her book.

"He's a very nice young man with a wicked twinkle in his eye," she answered. I think I have known that since the time he answered my questions when Miss Martinez made us write to an author.

On the ride home everybody was chattering about Mrs. Badger this, and Mrs. Badger that. I didn't want to talk. I just wanted to think. A real live author had called *me* an author. A real live author had told me to keep it up. Mom was proud of me when I told her.

The gas station stopped pinging a long time ago, but I wanted to write all this down while I remembered.

March 31

Dear Mr. Henshaw,

I'll keep this short to save you time reading it. I had to tell you something. You were right. I wasn't ready to write an imaginary story. But guess what! I wrote a true story which won Honorable Mention in the Yearbook. Maybe next year I'll write something that will win first or second place. Maybe by then I will be able to write an imaginary story.

I just thought you would like to know. Thank you for your help. If it hadn't been for you, I might have handed in that dumb story about the melting wax trucker.

Your friend, the author,
Leigh Botts

P.S. I still write in the diary you started me on.

1. How did Mr. Henshaw help Leigh to become a better writer?

2. Name three people, besides Mr. Henshaw, who encouraged Leigh to write. How did each one encourage him?

3. Why do you think that Mr. Henshaw sent Leigh the list of questions?

4. Look back at the closings of the letters Leigh wrote to Mr. Henshaw. Find three that reflect how Leigh felt about answering Mr. Henshaw's questions.

5. How did Angela Badger give Leigh more confidence in his ability to write?

6. How does the expression "Practice makes perfect" apply to this story?

Thinking About "Symphonies"

In this unit, you learned that in a symphony an orchestra blends the sounds of many instruments to make music. David Amram showed you how. You read about the dedication of other real people: a violinist, an artist, a dancer, and a writer. Their stories are alike in important ways that made this unit a symphony of expressions.

Itzhak Perlman loves to play the violin, Trina Schart Hyman wants only to draw, and Arthur Mitchell is dedicated to dance. Beverly Cleary enjoys telling stories about ordinary children. All these people find joy in their expressions.

This unit also included many fictional characters who found their own special forms of expression. You read about the members of an orchestra who used music to solve a problem. You read about a queen who finally decided to learn to play her favorite instrument, the slide trombone. These fictional characters, too, are somewhat alike. They come from the imaginations of writers. Writers must be blenders, too. They must create a symphony with words. Leigh Botts discovered how difficult—and exciting—this can be.

As you read other stories, watch for more characters who understand the joy of expression.

1. You read some biographical selections and one autobiographical selection in this unit. How was the writing in "Ballet Is for Everyone" different from the writing in "Self-Portrait: Trina Schart Hyman"?

2. The boy in "Just Because I'm Left-Handed" had his own reason for dancing. How was it different from the reason the children had for dancing in "A Central Eskimo Chant"?

3. Arthur Mitchell in "Ballet Is for Everyone" and Mike in "Just Because I'm Left-Handed" both had problems with friends. How were their problems alike? How were they different?

4. Lewis had a trumpet, and the queen had a slide trombone. Compare the sounds Lewis made on his trumpet with the sounds the queen made at first on her slide trombone. How were they alike?

5. In what way is Beverly Cleary's writing like Trina Schart Hyman's illustrations?

6. Which selection in this unit do you think Leigh Botts would have liked the most? Why?

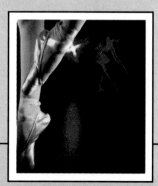

413

Unit 4
Memories

People remember many different events in their lives. They recall good times and bad times. They remember special friends from long ago. They think of special occasions spent with family members. They remember favorite places they have been. They think fondly of objects that have special meaning. People like to talk about their memories and share them with others. Memories are an important link with the past.

In "Memories" you will read about some of the places, persons, and experiences that have been important parts of someone's life. You will read a tall tale—a story that is remembered and retold for years because it is so much fun both to listen to and to read. You will also read about ways to save memories.

As you read, think about why certain memories and objects became important to the characters in the selections.

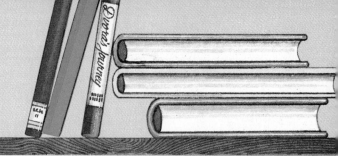

Read on Your Own

My Prairie Year: Based on the Diary of Eleanor Plaisted *by Brett Harvey. Holiday.* With information from an old diary, the author describes the life of a pioneer prairie dweller.

At Grandmother's House *by John Lim. Tundra.* The author takes us back to his childhood visits to his grandmother near Singapore. Paintings and text tell of daily life and special occasions.

When Batistine Made Bread *by Treska Lindsey. Macmillan.* We follow a young girl, in days gone by, as she does her share of the work by making bread. A recipe is included for you.

One Summer at Grandmother's House *by Poupa Montaufier. Carolrhoda Bks.* In words and pictures, the author takes us back to her childhood, on a visit with her grandmother in Alsace.

Tin Lizzie *by Peter Spier. Doubleday.* In 1909, a new Model-T was bought in a midwestern town. Years later, an antique car collector buys and restores it.

Trouble at the Mines *by Doreen Rappaport. Crowell.* In 1898, she was called "the most dangerous woman in America." Mother Jones, a widowed, retired schoolteacher, showed Pennsylvania miners how to work together for better working conditions.

What's the Big Idea, Ben Franklin? *by Jean Fritz. Putnam.* This is a brief biography of the eighteenth-century printer, inventor, and statesman who played an important part in the early history of the United States.

We'll Race You, Henry: A Story About Henry Ford *by Barbara Mitchell. Carolrhoda Bks.* Henry Ford was most instrumental in bringing cars into the lives of the American people. He not only produced the Model-T in 1908 but also showed the world how to run a factory.

Little House in the Big Woods *by Laura Ingalls Wilder. Harper.* This is the first book in a series about the Ingalls family and how they survive in the prairie wilderness.

In this selection, you will read about one woman's memories of "how it used to be" when she was young.

Childtimes

*by Eloise Greenfield
and Lessie Jones Little*

with material by Pattie Ridley Jones

Pattie Frances Ridley was born in Bertie County, North Carolina, in 1884. She grew up in the town of Parmele. *Pomma-lee*, as everyone called it, was a town where two railroads crossed and a lumber company had built a mill. When the lumber company came to Parmele, many people followed, looking for jobs. Pattie Ridley's father was one of them. Here is Pattie's story, as she remembers it.

Papa's Jobs

We were living in a little place called Robersonville, about three miles from Parmele, when Papa heard about the mill going up. He had been down sick with a bad case of rheumatism around that time, and Mama and all of us had been real worried about him, but he was better by then and walking on crutches. So early one morning he took the train to go see about getting a job.

They hired Papa, and that's when we moved to Parmele. Papa got seventy-five cents a day for feeding the horses that pulled the wagonloads of machines—saws and things—from the train station to the mill. And when all the machinery was in, he got the job of cooking at the clubhouse where the company's officers lived, and cleaning up their bedrooms and the dining room. The clubhouse was different from most all the houses around Parmele. It had radiators, and pipes running from the mill, for steam heat in the wintertime. There was even a bathtub, it was in the dining room, and pipes for hot and cold running water, and hardly anybody had that in their houses.

Papa worked at the clubhouse until the mill closed down, and then he stayed on as the night watchman. After all the machines had been taken out and shipped away, Papa spent his nights there, watching those empty buildings.

Water

We didn't have running water. At first we had a well out in the backyard, until it started caving in and Papa had to get rid of it. He filled it in with dirt. Then every time we wanted water for bathing or drinking or washing clothes, we had to go get water from a neighbor's pump. We got so tired of carrying those buckets of water, and we were some kind of glad when Papa finally put a pump on our back porch.

Chores

We had right much work to do, in the house and out in the garden, too. We planted and weeded, and dug up sweet potatoes, and picked butter beans. Papa let us sell the beans and keep the money for ourselves.

We had to keep the yards clean, too, front and back. Most people didn't have grass in their yards. They had dirt yards, and we would sweep our yards every day, get up all the loose dirt, and leave them brushed clean, with the brush strokes the yard broom made looking almost like a design.

My sister Mary and I did the cooking. Some weeks she cooked and some weeks I cooked. We had one of those big iron stoves that you put coal in to make a fire, and that stove would get so hot, not just on the cooking eyes, but all over. When we did the ironing, we'd set the irons on the stove to heat them up. Our irons were heavy. They were made of real iron, even the handles, and we had to use a thick piece of cloth to hold them. We had four or five irons, and we'd iron with one until it got too cool and then we'd pick up another one, and keep on like that until we got the ironing done.

We had feather beds. The mattresses were stuffed with chicken feathers, and we had to turn them over nearly every day, and we couldn't miss a day shaking them up and smoothing out all the lumps. They had to be exactly right, just as smooth and neat, or Mama would make us do them all over again.

We didn't pull our bedspreads all the way up over the pillows the way a lot of people do nowadays. We had pillow shams that Mama had made, white cotton material that she cut in the shape of the pillow and embroidered. Sometimes she put lace around the edges, and she kept them starched so stiff and ironed so pretty. We would tack the top of the sham on to the head of the bedstead with thumbtacks, and after we finished making up the rest of the bed, we'd stand the pillows up and let the shams hang down in front of them. It was a pretty sight. Then at night when we went to bed we'd fold the shams back over the head of the bedstead so they wouldn't get wrinkled.

When you finished making up a bed, you knew better than to sit on it. Wherever you sat, those chicken feathers would mash flat and they'd stay mashed, and then you'd have to take everything off and start all over, shaking and patting to get it right again. We wouldn't ever sit on the bed. We already had enough chores to do, and we sure didn't want to do anything twice.

School

The school we went to was a one-room schoolhouse, a little square building with a big old potbellied stove inside. In the winter, the boys used to take turns going to school early in the morning to start the fire in the stove. That fire would be just blazing when the rest of us got there, and the room would be so warm.

Our seats were long benches, and we didn't have desks. We wrote on slates in our laps with a little piece of chalk. Mr. Highsmith—that was our teacher—he used to walk up and down between the benches, smiling, while we studied our books. Spelling books, reading books, arithmetic books. We had to study, study, study. We'd be some kind of glad when twelve o'clock came and we could go out for recess.

Most of the time we played in the schoolyard, but sometimes when the weather was nice and warm, we'd walk a ways from the school to a road where there were all these mulberry trees with ripe mulberries just waiting to be picked. We'd find some lightwood knots, those little pieces of pine wood you see lying in the woods sometimes, and we'd throw them up at the branches to knock the berries down. We had the best old time eating and getting our faces and hands all purple and sticky.

When recess was over, Mr. Highsmith would ring this little bell like the one Mama rang for us to come in to dinner. But if we were right in the schoolyard, he wouldn't ring the bell. He'd come to the schoolhouse door and call, "Books! Books!" He meant it was time for us to get back to those books and study some more.

The Jones Family

When I was about fourteen, a Mr. and Mrs. Jones moved to Parmele. Edmund and Eliza Knight Jones and their ten children. There were three sons and seven daughters. The Jones family bought two acres of land not far from our house, and they had a one-and-a-half-story house built on it. Two large rooms and a hall were on the first floor, and the second floor was an attic with a real low ceiling. It was so low, a grown person couldn't stand up in it, so it was used for the boys to sleep in.

Mrs. Jones loved to read. She used to teach school sometimes, and she loved books. She wanted all of her children to be able to read, so she taught the big ones and the big ones taught the little ones. Mrs. Jones used to sell chicken eggs for ten cents a dozen to buy books for her children. A book cost fifteen cents, and that was a lot of money back then.

One day there was a big windstorm in Parmele, and I mean that was some storm! It blew the Jones's house over. Nobody got hurt, but Mrs. Jones and two of her daughters had to go to work to save money for a new house. They went to Greenville and worked in the tobacco factory, pulling the stems off the tobacco leaves, until they had enough money. The family did most all the work on the new house themselves. They couldn't afford to buy nails, and their fingers bled from pulling the nails out of the old house to use again.

My favorite person in the Jones family was William, the oldest one of their children. When I got old enough to have a fella, William was my fella. We went to church

together and sang in the choir together. And Sunday
evenings, Mama would let us go for a walk down to
the train station to watch the trains come in and see
the people passing through town. I was old enough to
wear long dresses by then, and I would get all prettied
up on a Sunday, and William would come and get me.

My little sisters, Mary and Leah, always wanted to
go with us on our walks. They kept begging and begging until one day I told them to come on and go. So
William and I were walking along kind of slow, and I
was holding the back of my dress with one hand the
way I'd seen the ladies do, lifting it up just the tiniest
little bit. Well, I happened to look back, and what were
Mary and Leah doing but just switching along, holding
the backs of their dresses, mocking me and giggling to
beat the band!

Well, the Jones family were our neighbors for a good long while. My brother John married Roberta, one of the daughters, and on December 30, 1903, William Jones and I got married.

After we were married, we stayed with his family for a while until he could finish the house he had started building, and then we went to live in our own three-room house. William and I had six children. Four of them lived to grow up—four daughters. One of them was Lessie.

Pattie Ridley Jones is the first of three women in her family who have recorded their memories of growing up. In the book Childtimes, *Mrs. Jones, Lessie Little, and Eloise Greenfield tell the story of three generations of one American family.*

1. Name three ways that life is different today from when Pattie Ridley was a young girl.

2. What were three chores for which the Ridley children were responsible?

3. What did you think was the most interesting part of Pattie's story?

4. What clues helped you to know that Pattie thought the officers' clubhouse was not only *different* from, but *better* than, the other houses in Parmele?

5. Pattie Ridley said that her favorite person in the Jones family was William. How do you know that this was true?

6. People choose different ways to recall experiences from their pasts. How did Pattie Ridley Jones choose to save the memories of her childhood?

Prewrite

"Childtimes" is a story told by the person who lived through the experiences. It is told in the first person, using *I*, *me*, and *my*. Read the sentences on the next page. They tell about

428

experiences that happened to someone else. On a sheet of paper, rewrite each one as if it were something that had happened to you—your personal experience. Add details if you wish.

1. Scott set out on the strangest journey of his life.
2. Just when she had given up all hope, Michele discovered something.
3. In Frank's family, Frank was always the tallest.

Draft

Write a story about one of the sentences you rewrote as your own personal experience. Try to choose an incident that tells something interesting and will be of interest to the reader.

Revise

Read your story. What does it tell the reader? Does it have a clear beginning, middle, and end? Make whatever changes and additions are necessary for the story to be interesting.

Personal Narrative

A **personal narrative** is the story of a personal experience, told from the point of view of the person who lived it. The person telling the story may be real, as in "Childtimes," or fictional, such as Tom in "The Midnight Fox" and Kim in "Those Weird Wagners."

How do you know when you are reading a personal narrative? Several clues may help you. A personal narrative is told from the first-person point of view, using the words *I, me, my, mine, we, our, ours,* or *us.* Another clue is that the writer speaks to the reader and expresses thoughts and feelings about an important experience or event in his or her own life.

Read the following paragraph. Look for clues that tell you that it is part of a personal narrative.

We didn't have running water. Every time we wanted water for bathing or drinking or washing clothes, we had to go get water from a neighbor's pump. We got so tired of carrying those buckets of water, and we were some kind of glad when Papa finally put a pump on our back porch.

The use of the word *we* is one clue that this paragraph is a personal narrative. The writer is telling a personal experience from the first-person point of view. She is speaking directly to the reader and is sharing her feelings.

Read the following groups of sentences. Which group is an example of a personal narrative? Why?

1. I always got scared when I walked across the bridge. Then one day I decided to be brave.
2. Yoshiko was afraid to walk across the bridge. Then one day she decided to be brave.

The first group of sentences is an example of a personal narrative. The sentences are written in the first person. The writer is speaking directly to the reader about feeling afraid.

Read the following paragraphs. Decide which one is an example of a personal narrative and why. Then change the other paragraph to make it an example of a personal narrative.

I had a pen-pal author who suggested I write my thoughts in a diary. I wrote in it all the time. I think all that practice helped me to be a better writer.

Leigh had trouble deciding what he could write about for the Young Writers Yearbook. He started a story called "The Ten-Foot Wax Man," but later turned in a description titled "A Day on Dad's Rig."

When you find the following characteristics in a story, you are reading a personal narrative.

- It is written in the first person.
- It tells about the writer's personal experience.
- It shows the writer's thoughts and feelings.

New Jersey Institute of Technology
Award Author

Every family has memories to share. Families also share other things, such as family traits. Read to find out where family traits come from and how they are passed from one generation to another.

Me and My Family Tree

by Paul Showers

There are many ways to picture your family. One way to show your family is to start with one of your ancestors. You show him and his wife (or her and her husband) and all their children. Then you show the children's children, and so on until it comes to you. This is called your *family tree*.

Here is just a part of my family tree. It starts with my great-great-grandfather, Dan Kelly, who had red hair. He and his wife, Martha, had four sons and three daughters.

One of his daughters was my great-grandmother. She and her husband had three sons and three daughters. One of their sons was my grandfather. He and his wife had two sons and two daughters.

One of their sons had red hair. He is my father. My father's brother is my uncle and my father's sisters are my aunts.

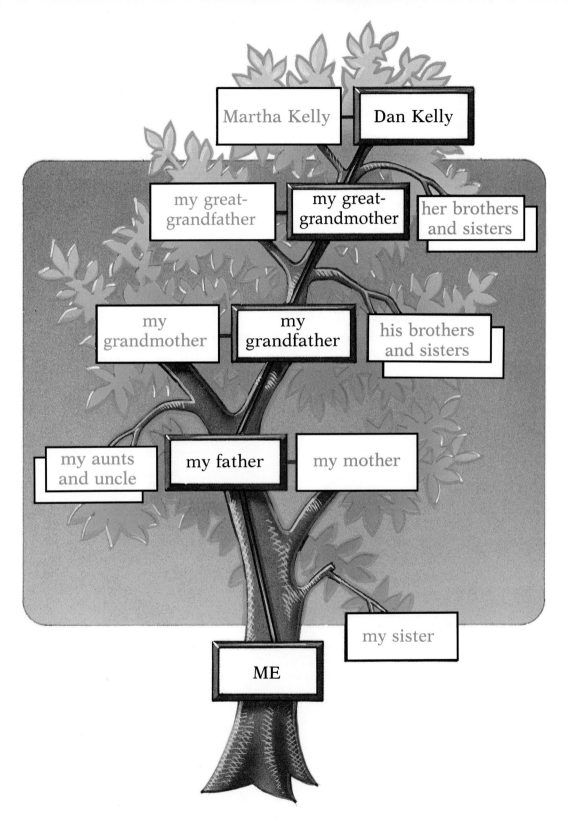

Martha Kelly — Dan Kelly

my great-grandfather

my great-grandmother

her brothers and sisters

my grandmother

my grandfather

his brothers and sisters

my aunts and uncle

my father — my mother

my sister

ME

I don't know many of the people on my family tree. Most of them were dead before I was born, but I have pictures of some of them.

This is my great-great-grandfather, Dan Kelly—one of my ancestors. He had a red beard and red hair. My father says Dan Kelly passed his hair down to us.

Heredity

The things your ancestors pass down to you are called *traits*. Red hair is a trait. Brown hair, straight hair, and curly hair are traits. The shape of your ears and hands, the color of your eyes, the color of your skin—these are all traits people get from their ancestors.

All the traits from all your ancestors are called your *heredity*. Every living thing has heredity. A dog, an elephant, a goldfish—each one gets traits from its ancestors. Even plants have heredity.

For a long time people didn't understand heredity. They didn't know where traits came from. Some people thought they came only from the mother, and others thought traits came only from the father. Over a hundred years ago Gregor Mendel[1] began to study heredity. He started with plants.

Gregor Mendel

Gregor Mendel was a monk. He grew peas in the monastery garden. Some of his pea plants had red flowers. When pollen from a red flower fell on another red flower, seeds were formed. Plants with red flowers grew from these seeds. Mendel also had pea plants with white flowers. Their seeds always grew into plants with white flowers.

Mendel decided to try an experiment. He took a little brush and scraped pollen from the red flowers. He brushed this pollen onto the white flowers. This is called *cross-pollination*.

Mendel cross-pollinated many pea plants in his garden. He carefully saved all the seeds from the cross-pollinated flowers. The next year he planted these seeds and watched them grow into new plants. When flowers came out in these new plants, they were all red. None of these "children" of the red and white plants had white flowers.

---

[1] Mendel [men′dəl]

When these "children" made seeds, Mendel planted the seeds the next year. The plants that grew from these seeds were the "grandchildren" of his red and white pea plants. Most of the "grandchildren" plants had red flowers, but some of them had white flowers. The white trait had been passed down from the ancestors to some of the "grandchildren" plants.

Mendel repeated this experiment many times. He also studied other traits of his pea plants. He cross-pollinated short plants and tall plants. He kept track of the seeds of hundreds of them. Mendel grew peas for nearly ten years, and he found out some important things about heredity.

He learned that traits come from the ancestors of both the mother and the father. Sometimes these traits—like red hair or long legs—are not seen in the children, but they may show up again in the grandchildren or great-grandchildren.

What Mendel learned about pea plants is true of other living things. It is true of some traits in birds and fish, dogs and cats, and other animals. It is true of some traits in people.

People are much harder to study than pea plants, of course. They have many more traits, and their traits are all mixed-up. However, we can still see some traits from the ancestors in the children and grandchildren.

I get my red hair from my father and my great-great-grandfather. My mother is short, like *her* mother. Perhaps I will be like them, or I may be tall like my father and his ancestors. I can't tell yet. I don't know all the traits that will come to me from my ancestors. I am still growing.

1. How did the narrator get his or her color hair and other traits?

2. What kind of experiments did Mendel perform to study heredity?

3. What happened when Mendel cross-pollinated the pea plants?

4. What traits do you think that you might have inherited from one of your ancestors?

5. In the selection, why are the words *traits, heredity,* and *cross-pollination* written in italics?

6. What makes us different from each other?

7. Gregor Mendel had an idea and he tested it. Why were the results of Mendel's experiments important?

Prewrite

Pretend that you are writing a history of your family. Think of something you would like to know more about. Perhaps your great-grandfather came to the United States as a cabin boy on a ship. Do you have a relative who has rescued someone from danger? Think about some questions you might ask family members to find out more about your family history.

Draft

Write a letter to a member of your family, requesting the needed information for your family history. Explain what you want to know and why.

Revise

Read your letter. Have you stated clearly what you need? Have you made your request in such a way that the reader will be willing to help you? Make whatever changes and additions are needed to improve your letter.

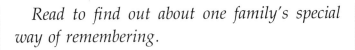

*Read to find out about one family's special
way of remembering.*

The Patchwork Quilt

by Valerie Flournoy

Tanya sat restlessly on her chair by the kitchen
window, watching Mama bake biscuits. She gazed
through the window and saw her two brothers, Ted
and Jim, and Papa building the new backyard fence.

"I'm gonna talk to Grandma," she said.

Grandma was sitting in her favorite spot — the big
soft chair in front of the picture window. In her lap
were scraps of materials of all textures and colors.
Tanya recognized some of them. The plaid was from
Papa's old work shirt, and the red scraps were from
the shirt Ted had torn that winter.

"Watcha gonna do with all that stuff?" Tanya
asked.

"Stuff? These aren't stuff. These little pieces are
gonna make me a quilt, a patchwork quilt."

Tanya tilted her head. "I know what a quilt is,
Grandma. There's one on your bed, but it's old and
dirty and Mama can never get it clean."

Grandma sighed. "It isn't dirty, honey. It's worn,
the way it's supposed to be."

440

Grandma flexed her fingers to keep them from stiffening. She sucked in some air and said, "My mother made me a quilt when I wasn't any older than you. But sometimes the old ways are forgotten."

Tanya leaned against the chair and rested her head on her grandmother's shoulder.

Just then Mama walked in with two glasses of milk and some biscuits. Mama looked at the scraps of material that were scattered all over. "Grandma," she said, "I just cleaned this room, and now it's a mess."

"It's not a mess, Mama," Tanya said through a mouthful of biscuit. "It's a quilt."

"A quilt! You don't need these scraps. I can get you a quilt," Mama said.

Grandma looked at her daughter and then turned to her grandchild. "Yes, your mama can get you a quilt from any department store. But it won't be like my patchwork quilt, and it won't last as long either."

Grandma's eyes grew dark and distant. She turned away from Tanya and gazed out the window, absent-mindedly rubbing the pieces of material through her fingers.

"Grandma, I'll help you make your quilt," Tanya said.

"Thank you, honey."

"Let's start right now. We'll be finished in no time."

Grandma held Tanya close and patted her head. "It's gonna take quite a while to make this quilt, not a couple of days or a week—not even a month. A good quilt, a masterpiece . . ." Grandma's eyes shone at the thought. "Why, I need more material. More gold and blue, some red and green. And I'll need the time to do it right. It'll take me a year at least."

"A year!" shouted Tanya. "That's too long. I can't wait that long, Grandma."

Grandma laughed. "A year isn't that long, honey. Makin' this quilt is gonna be a joy. Now run along and let Grandma rest." Grandma turned her head toward the sunlight and closed her eyes.

"I'm gonna make a masterpiece," she murmured, clutching a scrap of cloth in her hand, just before she fell asleep.

One August afternoon, Mama told Jim that his favorite blue corduroy pants were worn out. "We'll have to get you a new pair and use these old ones for rags," Mama said.

Jim was miserable. His favorite pants had been held together with patches; now they were beyond repair.

"Bring them here," Grandma said.

Grandma took part of the pant leg and cut a few blue squares. Jim gave her a hug and watched her add his patches to the others. "A quilt won't forget. It can tell your life story," she said.

The arrival of autumn meant school and Halloween. This year Tanya would be an African princess. She danced around in the long, flowing robes Mama had made from several yards of colorful material. The old bracelets and earrings Tanya had found in a trunk in the attic jingled noisily as she moved. Grandma cut some squares out of the leftover scraps and added Tanya to the quilt, too!

The days grew colder, but Tanya and her brothers didn't mind. They knew snow wasn't far away, but it was the end of November when Ted, Jim, and Tanya got their wish. They awoke one morning to find everything in sight covered with snow.

Tanya got dressed and flew down the stairs. Ted and Jim, and even Mama and Papa, were already outside.

"I don't like leaving Grandma in that house by herself," Mama said. "I know she's lonely."

Tanya pulled herself out of the snow, being careful not to ruin her snow angel. "Grandma isn't lonely," Tanya said happily. "She and the quilt are telling each other stories."

Mama glanced questioningly at Tanya. "Telling each other stories?"

"Yes, Grandma says a quilt never forgets!"

The family spent the morning and most of the afternoon sledding down the hill. Finally, when they were all numb from the cold, they went inside for milk and sandwiches.

"I think I'll go sit and talk to Grandma," Mama said.

"Then she can explain to you about our quilt—our very own family quilt," Tanya said.

Mama saw the mischievous glint in her youngest child's eyes.

"Why, I may just have her do that, young lady," Mama said as she walked out of the kitchen.

Tanya leaned over the table to see into the living room. Grandma was hunched over, her eyes close to the fabric as she made tiny stitches. Mama sat at the old woman's feet. Tanya couldn't hear what was said, but she knew Grandma was telling Mama all about quilts and how *this* quilt would be very special. Tanya sipped her milk slowly; then she saw Mama pick up a

piece of fabric, rub it with her fingers, and smile.

From that moment on both women spent their winter evenings working on the quilt. Mama did the sewing while Grandma cut the fabrics and placed the scraps in a pattern of colors. Even while they were cooking and baking all their holiday specialties during the day, at night they still worked on the quilt. Only once did Mama put it aside. She wanted to wear something special for the holidays, so she bought some gold material and made a beautiful dress. Tanya knew without asking that the gold scraps would be in the quilt, too.

When Tanya got downstairs one December morning, she found Papa fixing pancakes.

"Where's Mama?" asked Tanya.

"Grandma doesn't feel well this morning," Papa said. "Your mother is with her now till the doctor gets here."

"Will Grandma be all right?" Ted asked.

Papa rubbed his son's head and smiled. "There's nothing for you to worry about. We'll take care of Grandma."

Tanya looked into the living room. There on the back of the big chair rested the patchwork quilt. It was folded neatly, just as Grandma had left it.

"Grandma didn't want us to know she wasn't feeling well. She thought it would spoil our holidays," Mama told them later, her face drawn and tired, her eyes a puffy red. "Now it's up to all of us to be quiet and make her as comfortable as possible." Papa put an arm around Mama's shoulder.

"Can we see Grandma?" Tanya asked.

"No, not tonight," Papa said. "Grandma needs plenty of rest."

It was nearly a week later, the day before New Year's, when the children were permitted to see their grandmother. She looked tired and spoke in whispers.

"We miss you, Grandma," Ted said.

"And your muffins and biscuits," added Jim. Grandma smiled.

"Your quilt misses you, too, Grandma," Tanya said. Grandma's smile faded from her lips. Her eyes grew cloudy.

"My masterpiece," Grandma sighed. "It would have been beautiful. Almost half finished." The old woman closed her eyes and turned away from her grandchildren. Papa whispered it was time to leave. Ted, Jim, and Tanya crept from the room.

Tanya walked slowly to where the quilt lay. She had seen Grandma and Mama work on it. Tanya thought very hard. She knew how to cut the scraps, but she wasn't certain of the rest. Just then Tanya felt a hand resting on her shoulder. She looked up and saw Mama.

"Tomorrow," Mama said.

New Year's Day was the beginning. After the dishes were washed and put away, Tanya and Mama examined the quilt.

"You cut more squares, Tanya, while I stitch some patches together," Mama said.

Tanya snipped and trimmed the scraps of material till her hands hurt from the scissors. Mama watched her carefully, making sure the squares were all the same size. The next day was the same as the last—more snipping and cutting. But Mama couldn't always be around to watch Tanya work. Grandma had to be looked after. So Tanya worked by herself.

Then one night, as Papa read them stories, Jim walked over and looked at the quilt. In it he saw patches of blue—his blue. Without saying a word, Jim picked up the scissors and some scraps and started to make squares. Ted helped Jim put the squares in piles while Mama showed Tanya how to join them.

Every day, as soon as she got home from school, Tanya worked on the quilt. Ted and Jim were too busy with sports, and Mama was looking after Grandma, so Tanya worked alone. But after a few weeks she stopped. Something was wrong—something was missing, Tanya thought. For days the quilt lay on the back of the chair. No one knew why Tanya had stopped working. Tanya would sit and look at the quilt. Finally she knew. Some*thing* wasn't missing. Some*one* was missing from the quilt.

That evening before she went to bed Tanya tiptoed into Grandma's room, a pair of scissors in her hand.

She quietly lifted the end of Grandma's old quilt and carefully removed a few squares.

February and March came and went as Mama proudly watched her daughter work on the last few rows of patches. Tanya always found time for the quilt. Grandma had been watching, too. The old woman had been getting stronger and stronger as the months passed. Once she was able, Papa would carry Grandma to her chair by the window. Then she would sit and hum softly to herself and watch Tanya work.

"Yes, honey, this quilt is nothin' but a joy," Grandma said.

Summer vacation was almost here. One June day Tanya came home to find Grandma working on the quilt again! She had finished sewing the last few squares together; the stuffing was in place, and she was already pinning on the backing.

"Grandma!" Tanya shouted.

Grandma looked up. "Hush, child. It's almost time to do the quilting on these patches. But first I have some special finishing touches. . . ."

The next night Grandma cut the final thread with her teeth. "There. It's done," she said. Mama helped Grandma spread the quilt full length.

Nobody had realized how big it had gotten or how beautiful. Reds, greens, blues, and golds, light shades and dark, blended in and out throughout the quilt. "It's beautiful," Papa said. He touched the gold patch, looked at Mama, and remembered.

Jim remembered, too. There was his blue and the red from Ted's shirt. There was Tanya's Halloween costume. And there was Grandma. Even though her patch was old, it fit right in.

They all remembered the past year. They especially remembered Tanya and all her work. So it had been decided. In the right-hand corner of the last row of patches was delicately stitched, "For Tanya from Your Mama and Grandma."

1. What was the special way that Grandma saved memories?

2. How did Tanya help complete the quilt?

3. Why do you think Grandma called the quilt her "masterpiece"?

4. About how long did it take to finish the quilt? What time clues help you to know this?

5. What happened when the family looked at the finished quilt?

6. What do you think that Grandma meant by the expression "A quilt never forgets"?

Prewrite

There are many ways of remembering the things that have happened to us. Collect a variety of objects that remind you of special occasions you have shared with family and friends. You might include photographs, pictures you have drawn or cut from magazines, scraps of material or wallpaper, ticket stubs, leaves, or flowers. Arrange all these items in an interesting pattern and paste them down to make a collage. Think about what events these items help you remember.

Draft

Select one item in your collage that has special meaning to you. Write a story that explains why you chose this particular item. First, tell what the item helps you remember. Then, tell why this event was important to you.

Revise

Read your story. Have you clearly stated why the item has special meaning? What event does the item in your collage help you to remember? Does your story help to explain why the item is important to you? Make whatever changes and additions are needed to improve your story.

In this tall tale, Josh McBroom sets matters straight by recalling how his "wonderful one-acre farm" got started. Read to find out how Josh turned his one-acre disaster into a success.

McBroom Tells the Truth

by Sid Fleischman

One summer day, Josh McBroom, his dear wife Melissa, and their eleven children left their Connecticut farm. They piled everything into their old car and headed West, where the land is good and the sun shines all winter. On the way through Iowa, they met up with farmer Hector (Heck) Jones, who had some neighboring farmland to sell. Quick as a wink, Heck Jones had sold them eighty acres—for only ten dollars. The McBrooms thought they had made a good deal. Then Heck Jones took them out to see their new land.

We gazed with delight at our new farm. It was broad and sunny, with an oak tree on a gentle hill. There was one defect, to be sure. A boggy-looking pond spread across an acre beside the road. You could lose a cow in a place like that, but we had got a bargain—no doubt about it.

"Mama," I said to my dear Melissa. "See that fine old oak on the hill? That's where we'll build our farmhouse."

"No you won't," said Mr. Heck Jones. "That oak is not on your property."

"But, sir—"

"All that's yours is what you see under water. Not a rock or a tree stump in it."

I thought he must be having his little joke, except that there wasn't a smile to be found on his face. "But, *sir*!" I said. "You clearly stated that the farm was eighty acres."

"That's right."

"That marshy pond hardly covers an acre."

"That's wrong," he said. "There are a full eighty acres—one piled on the other, like griddle cakes. I didn't say your farm was all on the surface. It's eighty acres deep, McBroom. Read the deed."

I read the deed. It was true.

"Hee-haw! Hee-haw!" he snorted. "I got the best of you, McBroom! Good day, neighbor."

He scurried away, laughing up his sleeve all the way home. I soon learned that Mr. Heck was always laughing up his sleeve. Folks told me that when he'd hang up his coat and go to bed, all the stored-up laughter would pour out his sleeve and keep him awake nights. But there's no truth to that.

I'll tell you about the watermelons in a minute.

Well, there we stood gazing at our one-acre farm that wasn't good for anything but jumping into on a hot day. And that day was the hottest I could remember. The hottest on record, as it turned out. That was the day, three minutes before noon, when the cornfields all over Iowa exploded into popcorn. That's history. You must have read about that. There are pictures to prove it.

I turned to our children. "Will*jill*hester*chester*peter*polly*tim*tom*mary*larry*andlittle*clarinda*," I said. "There's always a bright side to things. That pond we bought is a mite muddy, but it's wet. Let's jump in and cool off."

That idea met with favor, and we were soon in our

swimming togs. I gave the signal, and we took a running jump. At that moment such a dry spell struck that we landed in an acre of dry earth. The pond had evaporated. It was very surprising.

My boys had jumped in headfirst, and there was nothing to be seen of them but their legs kicking in the air. I had to pluck them out of the earth like carrots. Some of my girls were still holding their noses. Of course, they were sorely disappointed to have that swimming hole pulled out from under them.

But the moment I ran the topsoil through my fingers, my farmer's heart skipped a beat. That pond bottom felt as soft and rich as black silk. "My dear Melissa!" I called. "Come look! This topsoil is so rich it ought to be kept in a bank."

I was in a sudden fever of excitement. That glorious topsoil seemed to cry out for seed. My dear Melissa had a sack of dried beans along, and I sent Will and Chester to fetch it. I saw no need to bother plowing the field. I directed Polly to draw a straight furrow with a stick and Tim to follow her, poking holes in the ground. Then I came along. I dropped a bean in each hole and stamped on it with my heel.

Well, I had hardly gone a couple of yards when something green and leafy tangled my foot. I looked behind me. There was a beanstalk traveling along in a hurry and looking for a pole to climb on.

"Glory be!" I exclaimed. That soil was *rich*! The stalks were spreading out all over. I had to rush along to keep ahead of them.

By the time I got to the end of the furrow, the first stalks had blossomed, and the pods had formed, and they were ready for picking.

You can imagine our excitement. Will's ears wiggled. Jill's eyes blinked. Chester's nose twitched. Hester's arms flapped. Peter's missing front teeth whistled. Tom stood on his head.

"Will*jill*hester*chester*peter*polly*tim*tom*mary*larry*and-little*clarinda*," I shouted. "Harvest those beans!"

Within an hour we had planted and harvested that entire crop of beans. Was it hot working in the sun! I sent Larry to find a good acorn along the road. We planted it, but it didn't grow near as fast as I had expected. We had to wait an entire three hours for a shade tree.

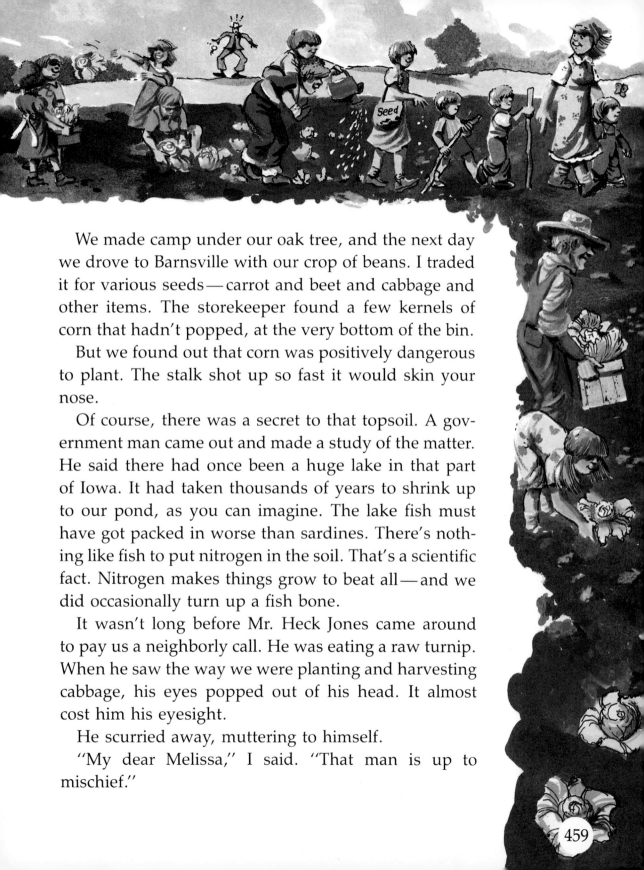

We made camp under our oak tree, and the next day we drove to Barnsville with our crop of beans. I traded it for various seeds—carrot and beet and cabbage and other items. The storekeeper found a few kernels of corn that hadn't popped, at the very bottom of the bin.

But we found out that corn was positively dangerous to plant. The stalk shot up so fast it would skin your nose.

Of course, there was a secret to that topsoil. A government man came out and made a study of the matter. He said there had once been a huge lake in that part of Iowa. It had taken thousands of years to shrink up to our pond, as you can imagine. The lake fish must have got packed in worse than sardines. There's nothing like fish to put nitrogen in the soil. That's a scientific fact. Nitrogen makes things grow to beat all—and we did occasionally turn up a fish bone.

It wasn't long before Mr. Heck Jones came around to pay us a neighborly call. He was eating a raw turnip. When he saw the way we were planting and harvesting cabbage, his eyes popped out of his head. It almost cost him his eyesight.

He scurried away, muttering to himself.

"My dear Melissa," I said. "That man is up to mischief."

Meanwhile, we went about our business on the farm. I don't mind saying that before long we were showing a handsome profit. Back in Connecticut we had been lucky to harvest one crop a year. Now we were planting and harvesting three, four crops a *day*.

There were things we had to be careful about—weeds, for one thing. My youngsters took turns standing weed guard. The instant a weed popped out of the ground, they'd race to it and hoe it to death. You can imagine what would happen if weeds ever got going in rich soil like ours.

We also had to be careful about planting time. Once we planted lettuce just before my dear Melissa rang the noon bell for dinner. While we ate, the lettuce headed up and went to seed. We lost the whole crop.

One day, back came Mr. Heck Jones with a grin on his face. He had figured out a loophole in the deed that had made the farm ours.

"*Hee-haw!*" he laughed. He was munching a radish. "I got the best of you now, Neighbor McBroom. The deed says you were to pay me *everything* in your purse, and you *didn't*."

"On the contrary, sir," I answered. "Ten dollars. There wasn't another cent in my purse."

"There were *moths* in the purse. I seen 'em flutter out. Three milky white moths, McBroom. I want three moths by three o'clock this afternoon, or I aim to take back the farm. *Hee-haw!*"

Off he went, laughing up his sleeve.

Mama was just ringing the noon bell, so we didn't

have much time. Confound that man! He did have his legal point.

"Will*jill*hester*chester*peter*polly*tim*tom*mary*larry*and-little*clarinda*!" I said. "We've got to catch three milky white moths! Hurry!"

We hurried in all directions. But moths are next to impossible to locate in the daytime. Try it yourself. Each of us came back empty-handed.

My dear Melissa began to cry, for we were sure to lose our farm. I don't mind telling you that things looked dark. Dark! That was it! I sent the youngsters running down the road to a lonely old pine tree and told them to rush back with a bushel of pine cones.

Didn't we get busy though! We planted a pine cone every three feet. They began to grow. We stood around anxiously, and I kept looking at my pocket watch. I'll tell you about the watermelons in a moment.

Sure enough, by ten minutes to three, those cones had grown into a thick pine forest.

It was dark inside, too! Not a ray of sunlight slipped through the green pine boughs. Deep in the forest I lit a lantern. Hardly a minute passed before I was surrounded by milky white moths—they thought it was night. I caught three on the wing and rushed out of the forest.

There stood Mr. Heck Jones waiting with the sheriff to foreclose.

"*Hee-haw! Hee-haw!*" old Heck laughed. He was eating a quince apple. "It's almost three o'clock, and you can't catch moths in the daytime. The farm is mine!"

"Not so fast, Neighbor Jones," said I, with my hands cupped together. "Here are the three moths. Now, skedaddle, sir, before your feet take root and poison ivy grows out of your ears!"

He scurried away, muttering to himself.

"My dear Melissa," I said. "That man is up to mischief. He'll be back."

It took a good bit of work to clear the timber, I'll tell you. We had some of the pine milled and built ourselves a house on the corner of the farm. What was left we gave away to our neighbors. We were weeks blasting the roots out of the ground.

We'd see Mr. Heck Jones standing on the hill in the distance, watching. He wasn't going to rest until he had pried us off our land.

Then, late one night, I was awakened by a hee-hawing outside the house. I went to the window and saw old Heck in the moonlight. He was cackling and chuckling and heeing and hawing and sprinkling seed every which way.

I pulled off my sleeping cap and rushed outside.

"What mischief are you up to, Neighbor Jones!" I shouted.

"Hee-haw!" he answered, and scurried away, laughing up his sleeve.

I had a sleepless night, as you can imagine. The next morning, as soon as the sun came up, that farm of ours broke out in weeds. You never saw such weeds! They heaved out of the ground and tumbled madly over each other—chickweed and milkweed, thistles and wild morning glory. In no time at all the weeds were in a tangle several feet thick and still rising.

We had a fight on our hands, I tell you! "Will*jill*hester*chester*peter*polly*tim*tom*mary*larry*andlittle*clarinda*!" I shouted. "There's work to do!"

We started hoeing and hacking away. For every weed we uprooted, another reseeded itself. We were a solid month battling those weeds. If our neighbors hadn't pitched in to help, we'd still be there burning weeds.

The day finally came when the farm was cleared, and up popped old Heck Jones. He was eating a big slice of watermelon. That's what I was going to tell you about.

"Howdy, Neighbor McBroom," he said. "I came to say good-bye."

"Are you leaving, sir?" I asked.

"No, but *you* are."

I looked him squarely in the eye. "And if I don't, sir?"

"Why, *hee-haw*, McBroom! There's heaps more of weed seed where that came from!"

As my youngsters gathered around, Mr. Heck Jones made the mistake of spitting out a mouthful of watermelon seeds.

Things did happen fast!

Before I had quite realized what he had done, a watermelon vine whipped up around old Heck's scrawny legs and jerked him off his feet. He went whizzing every which way over the farm. Watermelon seeds were flying. Soon he came zipping back and collided with a melon. In no time watermelons went galloping all over the place, and they were knocking him about something wild. He streaked here and there. Melons crashed and exploded. Old Heck was so covered with melon pulp he looked as if he had been shot out of a ketchup bottle.

It was something to see. Will stood there wiggling his ears. Jill blinked her eyes. Chester twitched his nose. Hester flapped her arms like a bird. Peter whistled through his front teeth, which had grown in. Tom

stood on his head. Little Clarinda took her first step.

By then the watermelons began to play themselves out. I figured Mr. Heck Jones would like to get home as fast as possible. So I asked Larry to fetch me the seed of a large banana squash.

"Hee-haw! Neighbor Jones," I said, and pitched the seed at his feet. I hardly had time to say good-bye before the vine had him. A long banana squash gave him a fast ride all the way home. I wish you could have been there to see it. He never came back.

That's the entire truth of the matter. Anything else you hear about McBroom's wonderful one-acre farm is an outright fib.

1. What was the one-acre disaster, and how did the McBrooms turn it into a success?

2. Describe two different ways that Heck Jones tried to cheat or trick the McBrooms.

3. Do you think that the McBrooms' neighbors liked them? Explain your answer.

4. What did Josh McBroom say that made you think that watermelons would play an important part in the story?

5. How do you know that Heck Jones did not cause the McBrooms any more trouble after he rode a banana squash home?

6. How does the saying "Treat others as you would like to be treated" apply to this selection?

Prewrite

Josh McBroom's story does not seem possible. This is because he uses exaggerations when he tells about everyday events. For example, how would Josh McBroom exaggerate the sentence *My dog eats a lot*? One way would be to say this: *My dog eats a ton of food every day.* Write three more sentences that Josh McBroom might say to describe how much his dog eats. Now read this sentence: *That tree is very tall.* Could you use exaggeration to make that sentence funny? Write a sentence that says the same thing but uses exaggeration for humor.

Draft

Think of something that you do every day, like walking to school or making yourself a snack. Then, write it as a story using exaggeration for humor. Use enough exaggerated details to make the everyday event you are writing about seem unusual and humorous.

Revise

Read your story. Is it exaggerated enough to be unusual? Does the exaggeration add humor? Did you make the everyday event seem unusual? Change whatever needs to be changed to make your story a good example of exaggeration.

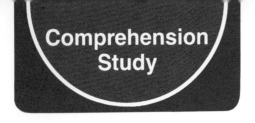

Author's Purpose and Viewpoint

The **author's purpose** is the reason why an author writes a selection. An author may write *to entertain* the reader. Stories such as "McBroom Tells the Truth" and "The Patchwork Quilt" probably were written for you to enjoy. Whether authors are writing funny stories, scary stories, or adventure stories, they intend to entertain you in their own special ways. Read the following paragraphs. See if you can figure out their purpose.

> **A.** My friend Adam was playing dominoes with his dog Topper. I'd never seen a dog play dominoes. "Topper is a very smart dog!" I said.
>
> "Not really," Adam replied. "I've already beaten him in three out of five games."

Did the paragraphs make you laugh? If they did, the author succeeded in his or her purpose, which was probably also to entertain you.

An author may also write to give information—*to inform* the reader. In the paragraph that follows, the author introduces some basic ideas about dominoes.

B. People all over the world have played with dominoes for hundreds of years. The game was played in China so long ago that no one knows when it started.

Did you learn something about dominoes from this paragraph? If you did, the author succeeded in his or her purpose, which was probably to inform you.

Sometimes a writer may want to convince you to believe something or to think a certain way about something. Or, the writer may want to convince you to take a specific action. When any of these is the purpose, the author is writing *to persuade* you.

The attitudes and opinions a person has about a specific subject determine how the person looks at that subject. A writer may want others to accept these same attitudes or opinions. A writer's attitude or opinion is the **author's viewpoint.** Sometimes writers seem to write to persuade you to accept their viewpoint. Read the following paragraph.

C. Dominoes is the most interesting game in the world. It teaches you how to think and plan. Everyone should learn how to play the game.

Can you guess what the writer's viewpoint or opinion about dominoes is? The author thinks it is the most interesting game in the world and states that opinion as a fact. Then the author gives you some information to support opinion. What is the author trying to persuade you to do? The author is probably trying to convince you to learn to play dominoes. The word *should* in the last sentence is a clue that the writer wants you to do something.

Did paragraph **C** make you want to learn how to play dominoes or make you want to tell people that you already know how to play the game? If so, the author succeeded in the purpose of persuading you. Now read the following paragraph. See if you can figure out the author's purpose.

D. Today, the current world domino champion walked out and forfeited the first game of the world championship match. He gave the victory to the challenger. I agree with those who said the champion should have played the match. I think he could have won and kept the championship. Many are convinced he could have won because he had beaten the challenger in three earlier matches.

The writer of this paragraph, Don Martin, expressed an opinion of the current champion's actions. What is his opinion of the champion's actions? What do you think was the writer's purpose for writing this paragraph?

It is clear that the writer wants you to know that he has a negative opinion of how the champion acted. First he tells you that "He gave the victory to the challenger." Then he supports his opinion by telling you that many people also feel the same way and have the same viewpoint. He further supports his opinion with the fact that the challenger has lost many times. After you had read the paragraph, did you think that the champion should have stayed and played the match? If you agree, then the writer has succeeded in his purpose, to convince or persuade you to think the same way that he does.

You know that authors write to entertain, to inform, and to try to persuade readers. It is important to be able to identify the author's purpose when you read, especially if the author is trying to persuade you to think or act in a certain way. Before you let the writer convince you to accept his or her viewpoint, you must think about what the writer is trying to have you think, believe, or do and what supporting information the writer is using.

Paragraph **D** is a good example of the fact that the stronger the argument, the more effective the writer's attempt to convince the reader will be.

Now read the following article by Elizabeth Terry, who probably wants to persuade readers to accept her viewpoint. Notice how she states her viewpoint and what she does to support it.

Did you know that the next time you become sick, the best medicine may be to laugh? When most of us have colds or other illnesses, we lie in bed feeling miserable. But researchers are finding that people who laugh and have a good time when they are sick get better faster. Even if we don't feel like laughing when we are sick, they suggest faking it, because eventually we *will* feel like laughing. That sounds like pretty easy medicine to swallow, doesn't it?

Research studies are also suggesting that laughing can help keep us healthy. And, there is also research supporting the theory that negative feeings like

The author uses this question to tell you what she wants you to believe. What is her viewpoint?

Here the author is telling you about research that supports her viewpoint. Someone has supported her opinion or viewpoint.

What is the author doing in this paragraph?

fear, anger, and hate can weaken our bodies and may cause us to become ill more often.

For example, Ted and Alex found out that they would have to change schools in the fall. They both loved their old school and hated to leave it. But, Ted thought that he could make more friends at the new school. He was friendly with his new classmates. Before he knew it, he was invited to various friends' homes to play. Often he could be found joking and talking with his new friends. He continued to make good grades and maintain a good attendance record.

Alex, on the other hand, was having a difficult time adjusting to his new school. He kept thinking about how happy he had been. He was angry that he had to go to a new school. He dreaded making new friends and having a new teacher. Alex was afraid that the new children and teacher might not like him, so he didn't try to be friendly, and he stayed mostly to himself. He didn't like to participate in class because he was afraid that he'd have the wrong answer. Alex grew more and more unhappy and began having more and more sick days. Often he would get bad stomachaches just before going to school. His colds would last longer.

In these two paragraphs, the author is telling you about two boys who had a similar problem. How do these examples support her viewpoint?

We all have problems. Some of us, however, tend to focus on the negative feelings. Instead, it might be healthier to focus on the good feelings. We all have the ability to laugh. But laughter comes easily to some of us. Like most things, however, practice makes perfect or, at least, almost perfect. If you decide to be healthy, happy, and hopeful, more than likely that's just what you'll be!

from *Laugh Yourself Healthy*
by Elizabeth Terry

In this paragraph the author is summarizing her argument and is making one last attempt to convince you her viewpoint is right. How does she support her viewpoint here?

The author states her opinion about laughter in the title and the opening question. Then she uses some research results to support this viewpoint. Later she quotes even more research. Then, she uses the example of Ted and Alex. Everything works out well for Ted; hardly anything works out for Alex. Ted's actions support her viewpoint; Alex's do not. Therefore, you are supposed to be convinced that if you accept her viewpoint everything will turn out well for you. Finally, she tries to show how easy it is for anyone to try what she is suggesting. The author has expressed her viewpoint and used unspecified research, examples, and an emotional appeal to try to persuade you to "laugh yourself happy."

When you read, look for the author's purpose. If the author is trying to persuade you to believe something or do something, be sure you read carefully and critically. Sometimes opinions or suggested actions may not be good ideas.

It was just an old desk—or was it? Read to discover why there was so much interest in the mysterious rolltop desk.

The Mystery of the Rolltop Desk

by Evelyn Witter

Jenny watched her mother pull the red pickup truck into the driveway. A large canvas-covered object was tied up in the back.

"What do you suppose Mom's bringing home this time?" her brother, Roger, asked.

At that moment Mrs. Marsh breezed through the door and turned to face them. Her face was pale. Her hands trembled.

"What did you buy?" Jenny asked.

"I was helping Mr. Sloan get ready for the auction, as I do every Friday. I saw a rolltop desk. I asked Mr. Sloan if I could buy it before the Saturday auction, and he said 'yes,' and so I did. Then a man came in and insisted on buying it. I said 'no,' but he kept insisting. Finally, I just left with the desk."

"That shouldn't make you nervous, Mom."

"Well, he followed me home!"

Now Jenny began to feel nervous. She parted the kitchen curtains and looked out the window. Clouds floated over the blue sky, and the sun shone brightly. Everything seemed peaceful. Then Jenny saw a man getting out of a small green car. He was neatly dressed in navy blue and had a bushy moustache. He was looking at their house.

"I see him!" Jenny exclaimed.

Mrs. Marsh looked out the window as the man turned to leave. "He's odd," she said. "He even grabbed me by the arm when I refused to sell the desk. He kept saying he just had to have that desk."

"What is so special about the desk?" Roger asked.

"Let's unload it. You can see for yourself," Mrs. Marsh suggested.

"I'll get Al to help," Jenny said as she hurried out. She was back in a few minutes with Alfred Miller, the boy who lived next door and who was her best friend.

Roger soon had the ropes untied and the canvas peeled away from the desk. Al had his father's moving helper—a platform on a roller that his father called a dolly. The boys carried the desk up the stairs and wheeled it into the living room.

When the desk was in place, Jenny told Al about the odd man who said he just had to have it.

"Why does he have to have this particular one?" Al asked.

"It's a good desk," Mrs. Marsh said. "It dates back to 1860."

Jenny studied the desk. It had eight big drawers, twenty pigeon holes, and sixteen little drawers.

"It would hold a lot of stuff," Jenny said.

"Why this desk?" Al asked again.

Jenny was about to give her opinion when she noticed the green car again. She grabbed a pencil and began writing.

"What are you writing?" her mother asked.

"His license number," Jenny replied.

"It really scares me to have that man hanging around like that," Mrs. Marsh said with a shudder.

That night Jenny helped her mother check all the windows and doors to see that they were locked. But Jenny had a strange feeling. Even though the house was locked up, if anyone really wanted to get in, she felt he would somehow be able to do it. She woke several times during the night.

Finally, since she couldn't sleep, she crept downstairs. She walked over to the desk and turned on the light near it. She kept asking herself what there was about the desk that made the man want it so much.

With nimble fingers Jenny touched every drawer and every pigeon hole. As far as she could see, there was nothing unusual about them.

Then Jenny gradually pulled the big desk away from the wall. She looked at the back of the desk and ran her fingers all around the back. The oak boards were smooth, but she found one spot where the varnish felt thicker than the rest. Jenny ran her fingers over that spot again. Then she thumped the spot with her fist. It sounded hollow!

She kept tapping the same spot. She could see a square crack beginning to form as she tapped.

Quickly she ran next door. She threw pebbles at Al's window to wake him. She wanted to share her discovery with Al.

After three throws, Al came to his window. "What's the matter?" he asked with a yawn.

"Hurry!" Jenny told him.

A few minutes later Al was in the Marsh's living room. As soon as he saw the square crack and thumped the back of the desk himself, he ran to the carriage house and got a chisel and hammer.

He worked quickly and quietly, and he and Jenny soon had the square pried loose.

There, lying in the circle of light from the lamp, was a piece of yellowed paper. It had some old-fashioned writing on it. In places the writing was almost all faded away. There were three ink blots between two of the lines.

The writing was hard to read, but Jenny and Al finally figured it out. It read:

Howe's fleet in Chesapeake Bay. Plans to attack Philadelphia. G. Washington.

"George Washington!" exclaimed Al.

"Written by George Washington!" echoed Jenny. "That's what the man really wants!"

"Keep it locked in your dresser," whispered Al as they moved the desk back into place. "I'll be back in the morning, and we'll tell your mom."

The next morning Jenny was awakened by her mother's call. "Jenny! Roger! Come down!"

Jenny threw on her robe and hurried downstairs. She saw desk drawers piled on the sofa and stacked on the floor. The desk was lying on its side, and the hole in the back was plain to see.

Jenny tried to draw her mother aside and tell her about the paper she and Al had found, but the police had already arrived.

"May we check this place out?" one officer asked.

While the police checked for fingerprints, Jenny told Roger about the paper. Then they met with Al in the carriage house at the back of the Marsh property.

"Should we tell them about the paper we found?" Al asked.

"We should," Jenny said.

"I don't believe the man in the green car was the one who broke in last night," Roger said thoughtfully. "He would know that Mom could identify him."

"Maybe," said Al, "but he sure looked suspicious yesterday when he parked his car around here."

"Let's go back to the house," Jenny said.

Back in the house they listened carefully to the questions the police asked and watched the shorter officer check for fingerprints. The tall police officer explained:

"We're checking these fingerprints against those of two men we apprehended last night. We're certain that these are the men who ransacked the rolltop desk. We know that these men have been convicted of break-ins in which valuable documents have been stolen. If these fingerprints match theirs, then we're certain that a valuable document is involved."

Just then the doorbell rang. When Jenny opened the door, she gasped and took three steps backward.

There stood the neatly dressed man who had been watching their house.

"I beg your pardon," he said in a low voice. "My name is Darrell Young. May I please speak with Mrs. Marsh?"

"My mother doesn't want to sell her desk," Jenny told him. She tried to be calm, but she knew the quiver in her voice told how frightened she was.

"I know," said the young man. "I must speak to her and explain about the desk."

Jenny hurried into the living room. "Mom! That man is here—that man in the green car—he's at the front door asking for you!"

"Show him in," ordered the tall police officer.

The man followed Jenny into the living room. He stopped short when he saw the police. He seemed to lose his dignified manner for a moment. A blush covered his neck, went up into his face, and reached the roots of his hair.

"I'm Darrell Young," he stammered. "I seem to have bungled this whole mission."

"What mission?" asked the police officer.

"I represent the Farley Museum," said Mr. Young. He drew out papers and gave them to the officer.

"These papers appear to be in order, Mr. Young," said the officer. "What is your business here?"

"This is my first assignment," explained Mr. Young. "I was to buy the rolltop desk. The museum traced this desk back to a man who was a Virginian. He bought the desk in 1860. The Virginian was the owner of a document signed by George Washington that dated back to the Revolutionary War. The museum had reason to believe that when the Virginian bought the desk, he transferred all the papers to it."

"The Revolutionary War document, too?" asked Jenny.

"Yes," nodded Mr. Young. "Well, I tried several times to get Mrs. Marsh to sell the desk, but she just wouldn't."

"Do you have any knowledge of two men who make a specialty of stealing documents?" one police officer asked.

"I do know of several rare documents that have been stolen in burglaries. It's possible that these thieves could have known about the Washington document and broken in here and stolen it," said Mr. Young.

"No they didn't!" cried Jenny. "I have it."

All eyes were on Jenny and Al as they told how they had found the secret hiding place before the thieves had broken into the house.

Jenny ran upstairs and brought the yellowed paper to Mr. Young.

"That's it!" cried Mr. Young, trembling with excitement. "And George Washington's signature is clear. This is indeed a great find!"

Everyone gathered around Mr. Young.

"We'll have to hold those men," said the tall police officer. "They didn't get what they were looking for, but these prints will probably prove that they did the breaking and entering."

"The museum will pay you handsomely for this document, Mrs. Marsh," Mr. Young cut in. "And of course, Jenny and Al will receive a citation for protecting a valuable historic document."

"They solved the mystery of the rolltop desk before any of us," Mrs. Marsh added proudly.

Jenny and Al smiled happily at each other.

1. What was so special about the rolltop desk?

2. What did Jenny find when she examined the desk?

3. Was Al's suggestion about locking the document in Jenny's dresser a good one? Why?

4. How did the author try to fool the reader?

5. Who solved the mystery of the rolltop desk?

6. How does the saying "Things are not always as they seem" apply to this story?

Think and Write

Prewrite

The actions of a number of people added twists and turns to the plot of this story. What development in the plot was each character responsible for? Copy the chart on the next page and complete it by writing what each person did.

484

1. Man in Virginia in 1860 *put the paper signed by George Washington in the desk.*
2. Mrs. Marsh ▬▬▬▬▬▬▬▬▬▬▬▬▬.
3. Jenny and Al ▬▬▬▬▬▬▬▬▬▬▬.
4. The burglars ▬▬▬▬▬▬▬▬▬▬▬.
5. Darrell Young ▬▬▬▬▬▬▬▬▬▬.

Draft

Pretend you are one of the police officers called to the Marsh house. Write a report on what happened in this case. Start at the beginning of the history of the desk and tell each event in the order in which it occurred.

Revise

Read your report. Did you describe the events in order? Would someone else understand what happened? Make any necessary changes or additions to improve your report.

National Council of Teachers
of English Award For
Excellence in Poetry Poet

Which Washington?

by Eve Merriam

There are many Washingtons:
Which one do you like best?
The rich man with his powdered wig
And silk brocaded vest?

The sportsman from Virginia
Riding with his hounds,
Sounding a silver trumpet
On the green resplendent grounds?

The President with his tricorne hat
And polished leather boots,
With scarlet capes and ruffled shirts
And fine brass-buttoned suits?

Or the patchwork man with ragged feet,
Freezing at Valley Forge,
Richer in courage than all of them—
Though all of them were George.

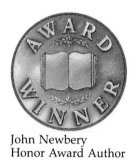

John Newbery
Honor Award Author

In this historical biography, read to find out about the things that went well and the things that did not go so well on Paul Revere's midnight ride.

And Then What Happened, Paul Revere?

by Jean Fritz

Paul Revere lived in Boston, Massachusetts, over two hundred years ago. He was a man of many talents, who crafted things from silver and even made false teeth. Beginning in 1765, however, Paul devoted his talents to helping America win its independence from England. Paul became a leader of the Sons of Liberty, a secret club that wanted freedom from British rule. He was also an express rider who rode his horse between towns carrying secret messages and news. Paul carried many messages on many rides, but only one ride is remembered in history. This is the story of Paul's Big Ride to Lexington.

In the winter of 1774, Paul Revere became Massachusetts's Number One express rider. He also became a secret agent. It looked more and more as if the English soldiers in Boston meant to make war on America, and Paul's job was to try to find out the English plans. So he patrolled the streets of Boston at night, delivered messages, and kept himself ready at all times to warn the countryside.

He was far too busy now to write in his Day Book. He was too busy to make many silver teapots or whittle many teeth.

Sometimes on his missions things went just right. He got past the sentries, got through the snow, kept his horse on the road, and kept himself on his horse.

Sometimes things went poorly. Once the English found him in a rowboat snooping around Castle Island in Boston Harbor. So they stopped him, questioned him, and locked him up. He stayed locked up for two days and three nights.

Paul knew that all his rides were small compared with the Big Ride that lay ahead. Nothing should go wrong with this one. In the spring, everyone agreed, the English would march into the countryside and really start fighting. When they did, Paul Revere would have to be ahead of them.

On Saturday, April 15, it seemed that spring had arrived. Boats for moving troops had been seen on the Charles River. English scouts had been observed on the road to Lexington and Concord. A stableboy had overheard two officers making plans.

Dr. Joseph Warren was directing Patriot activities in Boston. At 10:45 on Tuesday night, April 18, he sent for Paul Revere. Other messengers had been dispatched for Lexington and Concord by longer routes. Paul was to go, as planned, the same way the English were going—across the Charles River. He was to alarm the citizens so that they could arm themselves, and he was to inform John Hancock and Samuel Adams, Boston's two Patriot leaders who were staying in Lexington. Paul was to leave now.

He had already arranged a quick way of warning the people of Charlestown across the river. Two lanterns were to be hung in the steeple of the North Church if the English were coming by water; one lantern if they were coming by land.

So Paul rushed to the North Church and gave directions. "Two lanterns," he said. "Now."

Then he ran home, flung open the door, pulled on his boots, grabbed his coat, kissed his wife, told the children to be good, and off he went—his hat clapped to his head, his coattails flying. He was in such a hurry that he left the door open, and his dog got out.

On the way to the river Paul picked up two friends, who had promised to row him to the other side. Then all three ran to a dock near the Charlestown ferry where Paul had kept a boat hidden during the winter. Paul's dog ran with them.

The night was pleasant, and the moon was bright. Too bright. In the path of moonlight across the river lay an armed English transport. Paul and his friends would have to row past it.

Then Paul realized his first mistake. He had meant to bring cloth to wrap around the oars so the sound would be muffled. He had left the cloth at home.

That wasn't all he had left behind. Paul Revere had started out for his Big Ride without his spurs.

What could be done?

Luckily, one of Paul's friends knew a lady who lived nearby. He ran to her house, called at her window, and asked for some cloth. This lady was not a time waster. She stepped out of the flannel petticoat she was wearing and threw it out the window.

Then all he needed were his spurs. Luckily, Paul's dog was there, and luckily, he was well trained. Paul wrote a note to his wife, tied it around the dog's neck, and told the dog to go home. By the time Paul and his friends had ripped the petticoat in two, wrapped each half around an oar, and launched the boat, the dog was back with Paul's spurs around his neck.

Paul and his two friends rowed softly across the Charles River, slipped carefully past the English transport with its sixty-four guns, and landed in the shadows on the other side — safely. There a group of men from Charlestown who had seen the signal in the church steeple had a horse waiting for Paul.

Off Paul Revere rode on his Big Ride.

He kept his horse on the road and himself on his horse, and all went well until suddenly he saw two men on horseback under a tree. They were English officers. One officer sprang out and tried to get ahead of Paul. The other tried to overtake him from behind, but Paul turned his horse quickly and galloped across country, past a muddy pond, toward another road to Lexington.

And what happened to the officers?

One of them galloped into the mud and got stuck; the other gave up the chase. Paul continued to Lexington, beating on doors as he went, arousing the citizens. At Lexington he woke up John Hancock and Samuel Adams and advised them to leave town. Paul had a quick bite to eat, and then, in the company of two other riders, he continued to Concord, warning farmers along the way.

For a while all went well. Then suddenly from out of the shadows appeared six English officers. They rode up with their pistols in their hands and ordered Paul to stop. But Paul did not stop immediately.

"Stop!" one of the officers shouted. "If you go an inch farther, you are a dead man."

Paul and his companions tried to ride through the group, but they were surrounded and ordered into a pasture at one side of the road. In the pasture six other officers appeared with pistols in their hands.

One of them spoke like a gentleman. He took Paul's horse by the reins and asked Paul where he came from.

Paul told him, "Boston."

The officer asked what time he had left Boston.

Paul told him.

The officer said, "Sir, may I ask your name?"

Paul answered that his name was Revere.

"What! *Paul* Revere?"

Paul said, "Yes."

Now the English officers certainly did not want to let Paul Revere loose, so they put him, along with other prisoners, at the center of their group, and they rode off toward Lexington. As they approached town, they heard a volley of gunfire.

"What was that?" the officer asked.

Paul said it was a signal to alarm the countryside.

With this piece of news, the English decided they'd like to get back to their own troops in a hurry. Indeed, they were in such a hurry that they no longer wanted to be bothered with prisoners. So after taking away the prisoners' horses, they set the prisoners free.

And then what happened?

Paul Revere felt bad, of course, to be on his Big Ride without a horse. He felt uneasy to be on a moonlit road on foot. So he struck out through the country, across stone walls, through pastures, over graveyards, back into Lexington to see if John Hancock and Samuel Adams were still there.

They were. They were just preparing to leave town in John Hancock's carriage. Paul and Hancock's clerk, John Lowell, went with them.

All went well. They rode about two miles into the countryside, and then suddenly John Hancock remembered that he had left a trunk full of important papers back in a Lexington inn. This was a mistake. He didn't want the English to find those papers.

So what happened?

Paul Revere and John Lowell got out of the carriage and walked back to Lexington.

It was morning now. From all over the area, farmers were gathering on Lexington Green. As Paul crossed the green to the inn, there were between fifty and sixty armed men preparing to take a stand against the English. The English troops were said to be near.

Paul went into the inn, had a bite to eat, found the trunk, and carried it out, holding one end while John Lowell held the other. As they stepped on the green, the troops appeared.

And then what happened?

Paul and John held on to the trunk. They walked right through the American lines, holding on to the trunk. They were still holding on when a gun was fired. Then there were two guns, then a succession of guns firing back and forth. Paul did not pay any attention to who was firing or who fired first. He did not stop to think that this might be the first battle of a war. His job was to move a trunk to safety, and that's what he did.

The battles of Lexington and Concord did, of course, begin the Revolutionary War. They were victories for the Americans, who have talked about Paul Revere's ride ever since. Some things went well on Paul's ride. Some things went poorly, but people have always agreed that Paul's ride was a success.

1. On the night of Paul Revere's ride, what happened that he hadn't planned?

2. What was Paul Revere supposed to do on his Big Ride to Lexington?

3. What three things happened on April 15 to suggest the English planned to march?

4. What do you think was the most dangerous thing that happened during the Big Ride?

5. Why did the author use questions such as "And then what happened?" throughout the story?

6. How did the battles at Concord and Lexington prove that the ride was successful?

7. How does the saying "Haste makes waste" apply to this story? Explain your answer.

Think and Write

Prewrite

The chart on the next page lists some moments in the story when Paul Revere ran into trouble. On a separate sheet of paper, write his solution for each problem. Look back at the story to help you write the solutions.

Problems	Solutions
1. forgot cloth to muffle oars	
2. forgot spurs	
3. chased by English officers	
4. had his horse taken away	
5. John Hancock forgot trunk	

Draft

Imagine you are Paul Revere. Write an entry in your Day Book. Describe one of the difficult or tense moments in your trip. Use an incident from the selection, but tell it from the first-person point of view. Include what happened, how you felt, and what you did to solve the problem.

Revise

Read your Day Book entry. Is it in the first person? Does it sound as if Paul Revere wrote it? Is it exciting? Add or change whatever you can to make your Day Book entry interesting for the reader.

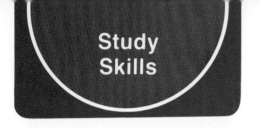
Organize Information

Understanding how an article is organized can help you remember what you have read. The writer of an article usually discusses one *general topic*. This general topic is often the title of the article. The general topic might be a person, place, or thing. To explain the general topic, the writer organizes the article into main ideas or *main topics*. In turn, the main topics are organized by important details that support the main ideas. These important details are called *subtopics*.

For example, suppose that you decide, after reading about Paul Revere's crossing of the Charles River in Boston, to find more information about rivers and to write a report. Before you can write your report, you may want to organize the information you found into certain categories. The title of your report, or the general topic, might be "Rivers." Each of your main topics might be a different important idea about rivers. The subtopics might add more information to these important ideas.

Making an Outline

An **outline** is one way to organize ideas about a general topic. An outline also helps to organize information when you want to write a report.

Below is part of an outline for a report on "Rivers." On the right is the framework for this outline. A framework shows how an outline is organized.

Rivers	General Topic, or Title
I. Rivers, land, and people	Main topic 1
A. Why rivers are important	Subtopic 1
B. How rivers are formed	Subtopic 2
II. Change in rivers	Main topic 2
A. What erosion does to rivers	Subtopic 1
B. What floods do to rivers	Subtopic 2
C. What people do to rivers	Subtopic 3
III. Important rivers in the U.S.	Main topic 3
A. The Mississippi River	Subtopic 1
B. The Ohio River	Subtopic 2
C. The St. Lawrence River	Subtopic 3
D. The Rio Grande	Subtopic 4

The main topics and subtopics are the important pieces of information needed to write your report. Notice how the outline shows the information. Which are the main topics? Which are the subtopics?

The main topics follow Roman numerals. Each subtopic follows a capital letter. Did you notice, too, that each different part of the outline is indented, or moved to the right a certain amount of space?

Textbook Application:
Outlining in Social Studies

Read the following article. Look for the main topic and subtopics. The sidenotes will help you.

The title of the article usually tells you what the general topic is.

AMERICANS COME FROM MANY PLACES

The First Americans

The headings identify three types of American immigrants: the first Americans, the first European explorers, and the French and the English. These three types of immigrants are the main topics.

Thousands of years ago, a piece of land joined Asia to North America. People walked across this land from Asia. They were the first people to come to North America. These people were the **ancestors** (AN·ses·tuhrz), or early families, of the American Indians.

The paragraphs tell more about the main topics. The subtopics and details come from these paragraphs.

The First European Explorers

People from Europe reached North America much later. About 1,000 years ago, the **Vikings** reached North America. These explorers from Northern Europe only stayed a few years. In 1492 **Christopher Columbus** sailed here from Spain. He was trying to reach China. There he hoped to trade for gold, spices, and silk. Columbus thought he could reach China by sailing west from

These sentences are important subtopics under the main topic: The First European Explorers.

Europe. Instead he found North America. He gave the name "Indians" to the people he met. Columbus believed he had reached the islands south of China called the Indies.

Columbus returned to Spain with gold. Hearing his stories, other Spanish explorers crossed the Atlantic Ocean. Among these explorers was an Italian living in Spain, **Amerigo Vespucci** (veh·SPYOO·chee). Vespucci said that he had explored parts of what is now North and South America. He believed he had reached a "new world," not Asia. A German mapmaker thought the new land should be named after Vespucci. Soon all of Europe was calling the new land America.

The French and the English

Because of these early explorers, the Spanish later settled in southern and western North America. They were not the only ones interested in America, though. Columbus's discovery also brought the French and the English.

Traveling by river, the French explored the north and the center of our country. They saw beaver and other animals with valuable furs. Soon the French were buying furs from the Indians to sell in Europe.

These sentences are important subtopics for The French and The English.

> In the 1600's groups of English people settled in the eastern part of America. Some groups, like the **Pilgrims,** came here to find freedom. They wanted to have their own religion. In Europe they were not free to do so.
>
> Many other people from Europe came to America. They wanted to find better lives for themselves. They wanted a chance to own land. They were willing to work hard to keep what they earned.
>
> —*States and Regions*, Harcourt Brace Jovanovich

These sentences are important subtopics for The French and The English.

In the article, notice that each main topic supported the general topic: Americans Come from Many Places.

In an outline, the main topics would follow Roman numerals as shown below.

  I. The First Americans
 II. The First European Explorers
III. The French and the English

The article explains who the people were, and how and why they came to this country. In an outline, this information would be the subtopics. Each subtopic would follow a capital letter.

Look back at the paragraph about the first Americans. Find the subtopics that tell more about these people. The subtopics are shown on the following outline.

I. The First Americans
   A. Where they came from
   B. Who they were
   C. How they got here

Look back at the paragraph about the first European explorers. What do you think the first subtopic would be for this section of the outline?

If you thought that the subtopic should be *Where they came from*, you are right. Now look at the outline for the first European explorers.

II. The First European Explorers
   A. Where they came from
   B. Who they were
   C. How they got here
   D. Why they came

Compare the outline of subtopics for the first Americans and the first European explorers. Notice that one of the subtopics is different because more information was provided about the European explorers than about the first Americans.

Now work with a friend to make an outline for the French and the English. The framework for the outline would be similar to the ones before. The differences might be in the number of subtopics you decide to include. Then, compare your outline for the French and the English with those of other students. Are there any differences in the outlines?

Many times the same information can be outlined and organized in different ways. How the information is organized is up to you, as long as it reflects the information in the article.

One way to "save time" is to save memories. Read to discover one way you can save memories now and enjoy them later.

Saving Time

by Linda Beech

There is an old saying that goes something like this: *If you want to find out how far you have come, then look at where you have been.* Maybe this saying helps explain why people remember and study the past. By looking at the past and trying to understand it, people can learn more about themselves in the present.

Because the past is so important, scientists and historians study it in many ways. For example, scientists often dig deep into the earth, hoping to uncover some evidence of life from long ago. Sometimes they discover whole cities that have been buried for centuries. At other times, they find only a few tools, bits of clothing, and other objects. Yet scientists can sometimes fit these objects together, like pieces of a puzzle. These pieces may then tell the story of a whole civilization.

Time Capsules

Not too long ago, people invented another way to save pieces of time for future generations to study. This invention is called a *time capsule*. A time capsule is a sealed container that holds many objects. These objects will tell people of the future what life was like in the past. A time capsule may hold such objects as pictures of cities and buildings, movies of people and events, and things that people use every day. When a capsule is sealed, it is sometimes placed in a special room or in the cornerstone of a building. A time capsule may also be buried deep in the earth, like objects from long ago.

The first time capsule was made in 1938. It was buried over fifteen meters underground at Flushing Meadows, on the spot at which the New York World's Fair of 1939 was to be held. The capsule is 2.3 meters long. It will be opened in the year 6939, almost five thousand years from now.

In 1940 a huge time capsule was placed in an underground room at Oglethorpe University in Atlanta, Georgia. In it there are films, small models of cars and buildings, and other objects that tell what life was like in 1940. This time capsule is to be opened in the year 8113! Its location has been recorded in libraries and universities in different countries. This should improve its chances of being found. Other time capsules are buried in California, Canada, and Japan.

Hearst Hall, Oglethorpe University

THIS CRYPT

CONTAINS MEMORIALS OF THE CIVILIZATION WHICH EXISTED IN THE UNITED STATES AND IN THE WORLD AT LARGE DURING THE FIRST HALF OF THE TWENTIETH CENTURY. IN RECEPTACLES OF STAINLESS STEEL, IN WHICH THE AIR HAS BEEN REPLACED BY INERT GASES ARE ENCYCLOPEDIAS, HISTORIES, SCIENTIFIC WORKS, SPECIAL EDITIONS OF NEWSPAPERS, TRAVELOGUES, TRAVEL TALKS, CINEMAS REELS, MODELS, PHONOGRAPH RECORDS, AND SIMILAR MATERIALS FROM WHICH AN ADEQUATE IDEA OF THE STATE AND NATURE OF THE CIVILIZATION OF 1900 TO 1950 CAN BE ASCERTAINED. NO JEWELS OR PRECIOUS METALS ARE INCLUDED.

WE DEPEND UPON THE LAWS OF THE COUNTY OF DEKALB, THE STATE OF GEORGIA AND THE GOVERNMENT OF THE UNITED STATES, AND OF THEIR HEIRS, ASSIGNS AND SUCCESSORS, AND UPON THE SENSE OF SPORTSMANSHIP OF POSTERITY FOR THE CONTINUED PRESERVATION OF THIS VAULT UNTIL THE YEAR 8113, AT WHICH TIME WE DIRECT THAT IT SHALL BE OPENED BY AUTHORITIES REPRESENTING THE ABOVE GOVERNMENTAL AGENCIES AND THE ADMINISTRATION OF OGLETHORPE UNIVERSITY. UNTIL THAT TIME, WE BEG OF ALL PERSONS THAT THIS SEALED DOOR AND THE CONTENTS OF THE CRYPT WITHIN MAY REMAIN INVIOLATE.

FRANKLIN DELANO ROOSEVELT   OGLETHORPE UNIVERSITY
PRESIDENT OF THE UNITED STATES   BY THORNWELL JACOBS, PRESIDENT

EUGENE TALMADGE   ANNO DOMINI, 1936
GOVERNOR OF GEORGIA   ARMCO STAINLESS STEEL

Making Time Capsules

Not all time capsules must be opened so far in the future. Nor do time capsules have to be made with people of future generations in mind. A time capsule can be of use to anyone, even if it is put away for only a short time.

Suppose, for example, that you want to remember some details of your life now, this year. You could make a simple time capsule that would help you record what you want to remember.

You might decide to make one time capsule for a whole year or one time capsule for each month of the year. You might make a time capsule for one of your interests, such as sports or music. You might make a time capsule on your birthday, to be opened on your birthday the following year. When you opened the capsule, you could see how much you had changed in that year's time.

When you are ready to make a time capsule, follow these steps:

1. Collect things that tell about you and what you are like now. You might want to include: photographs of you, your family, and your friends; samples of school work; a TV or movie guide with your favorite shows underlined; and even letters and postcards from friends and family. You could select greeting cards you have received, cards or papers that show your activities and the clubs to which you belong, and samples of your hobbies. You might like to include party invitations and ticket stubs or programs from special events you have attended. Don't forget labels from containers of your favorite foods or from anything else you can think of.

2. Find a container for your time capsule items. A shoebox or a large envelope could make a good time capsule. A metal coffee can could be used, too. Be sure that your capsule has a lid or can be sealed.

3. Look through the items that you have collected. Then decide how many will fit in your capsule.

You might want to label some things to help you re-member dates or names when you open your capsule. You might also want to make a list of the items in your capsule. This list can serve as a table of contents.

4. Place the items in your capsule and seal it.

5. Label and date the outside of the capsule. On the outside, also write: *To be opened on* ___. Add the date when the capsule should be opened.

6. Store your time capsule somewhere in your home, in a safe place—and don't forget to open it when the time comes!

Now use your imagination. Suppose you never did open your time capsule. It is the year 3000 A.D. Some-one your age has found the time capsule you sealed and left behind. The person opens the capsule and begins to study the objects inside. Very slowly, this person learns what your life was like, a thousand years before. Can you imagine that? Could it really happen? Only time will tell.

1. According to this selection, what is one way that you can "save time"?

2. What types of things can be put into a time capsule?

3. Why do you think a time capsule sealed in the year 2000 would be important in the year 3000?

4. Why is it important to label and date items in a time capsule?

5. Why did the author number the steps for making a time capsule and leave space between the paragraphs?

6. How does the saying "If you want to find out how far you have come, then look at where you have been" help explain why people remember and study the past?

Prewrite

The selection you have just read tells how to make a time capsule. Imagine that you are part of a committee choosing objects for a time capsule to be opened 300 years from now. The purpose of the time capsule is to tell someone in the future what life is like now. Write a list of things that could be put into this time capsule.

Draft

Choose three objects for the time capsule from your list. Remember, the capsule will not be opened for 300 years. Many things will have changed by then. Select objects that will show people in the future how we live today. Then write a memo to the committee, explaining why you think each item should be put into the time capsule. What will each item tell future generations?

Revise

Read your memo. Have you clearly described each item? Have you explained why it should be included? Did you use words that will convince the rest of the committee? Make changes that are needed for your memo to be convincing.

Telling Time

by *Lilian Moore*

Time ticks,
whispers,
rings,
sounds a chime,
a ping,
a tock,
or the long slow
bong
of a grandfather clock.

Time
on the sundial
is a
shadow,
making its rounds,
moving
till day is done
in secret
understanding
with the sun.

National Council of Teachers
of English Award for
Excellence in Poetry Poet

AWARD WINNER

Sometimes we save time by working together to reach a common goal. Read this Mexican folktale to find out how a lazy bee learned that lesson.

The Lazy Bee

by Horacio Quiroga

Once there lived a bee who did not like to work. Every morning, as soon as the air had been warmed by the sun, the bee would look out of the beehive to make sure the weather was fine. Then she would set off, contentedly buzzing from one flower to the next. She would collect nectar, but instead of keeping it to make honey, she would drink it all. The other bees that worked hard to fill the beehive with honey soon became annoyed with their sister's laziness.

Two older and experienced bees stood guard at the entrance to the beehive. Their job was to protect the beehive from other insects. One day, as the lazy bee was attempting to fly into the beehive, the bees standing guard stopped her.

"Sister," one guard said, "you must begin to work. Every other bee works very hard."

The lazy bee answered, "I do spend the whole day flying, you know, and I get terribly tired."

"It's not a matter of whether you get very tired," the other guard replied, "but of whether you do any work. Let it be our first warning." With that, they let her pass through the opening of the hive.

The next day the lazy bee did not mend her ways. When she returned to the hive the following evening, the bees standing guard warned her again.

"You must work, sister," one guard said.

She immediately replied, "I will. One of these days, I will."

"The important thing is what you are going to do tomorrow. Remember what we've told you," replied the other guard. Then they let her pass through.

The next evening when the lazy bee approached the beehive, she spoke before the guard bees had a chance to say anything.

"Yes, sisters, I know, I know. I remember the promise I made."

"Today is April 19th, little bee. Tomorrow will be April 20th. Just try to bring in enough nectar to make at least one drop of honey," one guard said. Once again the guard bees let her inside for the night.

On April 20th, when the sun set, the weather changed and a cold wind started to blow. The lazy bee hurried toward the beehive, thinking of the cozy warmth inside. However, when she tried to get in, the bees standing guard wouldn't let her through.

"You can't come in," one guard said coldly.

"Please let me in," cried the lazy bee. "This is my beehive."

"This beehive belongs to bees who work very hard," the other bee replied. "We won't let any lazy bees inside."

"I'll work tomorrow, I promise," the lazy bee insisted.

"There's no tomorrow for those who don't work," replied the older bees, and they pushed her out of the beehive.

The lazy bee didn't know what to do, so she flew around for a while. Soon it became very dark outside. She tried to settle on a leaf but fell off. Her body was numb from the cold wind, and she knew she could no longer fly.

She dragged herself across the ground and climbed over sticks and stones that seemed as high as mountains. Then the lazy bee went back to the beehive as the cold raindrops started to fall.

"Oh, no, it's raining and I'm going to freeze to death!" she cried helplessly.

She tried to get into the beehive, but once again the bees standing guard blocked the way.

"Please," moaned the lazy bee, "let me in."

"Too late," one of the older bees replied.

"Sisters, please! I'm sleepy!"

"Too late!" the other guard bee cried.

"Sisters, I beg you. I'm cold!"

"It's no use," they said.

"Just this one time, please, or else I'll die!"

Then one of the guard bees said to her, "No, you won't. You'll learn, in a single night, what it's like to earn some rest after a lot of hard work. Now go away!" They threw the lazy bee out the door.

The lazy bee, shivering with cold, dragged herself along the ground until she fell down a dark hole. She rolled to the bottom of a cave where she found herself face to face with a red snake. The snake was coiled and ready to strike. The lazy bee closed her eyes and waited for her life to end. To her surprise, the snake spoke to her.

"Hello, little bee, how are you?" the snake asked. "You can't be much of a hard worker if you're out at this hour."

"You're right," mumbled the lazy bee. "I don't work, and it's my own fault."

"In that case," said the snake, making fun of the bee, "I'll be doing the world a great service by getting rid of a useless insect like you."

The lazy bee began shaking all over. "That's not fair! I should not have to die just because you're bigger and stronger than I am."

"Ha, ha," laughed the red snake, uncoiling slightly. "Well, whether or not it's fair, I'm going to have you for my dinner." The snake moved her head back, ready to strike.

Just then the lazy bee cried out, "You're only doing this because you're not as clever as I am."

"What do you mean that I'm not as clever as you?" hissed the snake.

"That's just what I said," the lazy bee replied.

"Let's see about that. We will each do a trick. The one that performs the most astonishing trick will be the winner. If I win, you will become my dinner."

"What will happen if I win?" asked the lazy bee.

"If you win," answered her enemy, "you will get to spend the night here. Do you agree?"

"Yes," replied the lazy bee.

The snake began to laugh again because she thought of something no bee could possibly do. First the snake slid out of the cave at such a rapid speed that the bee had no time even to realize what had happened. When the snake came back, she was carrying a capsule of seeds she'd taken from a nearby eucalyptus tree. The snake knew young boys play Spin-the-Top with these tiny capsules.

"Here's my astonishing trick," said the red snake. "Watch carefully now."

As she said this, she wrapped her tail around the little seed pod and then unwound it at such great speed that the top started spinning and humming. The snake laughed because she knew the bee had never spun a top like that. The snake also knew that the lazy bee could never do a trick as great as the one she had just performed.

The lazy bee then said, "That was a fine trick. I could never do that."

"I guess you'll be my dinner then," hissed the snake.

"Wait a minute!" cried the lazy bee. "I can't do what you've done, but I can do something no one else can do."

"What is that?" asked the red snake.

"I can disappear."

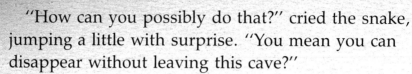

"How can you possibly do that?" cried the snake, jumping a little with surprise. "You mean you can disappear without leaving this cave?"

"That's right, without leaving this cave."

"Can you disappear without hiding in the earth?"

"Without hiding in the earth," the bee responded.

"Well, let's see you do that. Remember, if you don't disappear, you will be my dinner," said the snake.

While the top had been spinning, the bee had had a chance to look around the cave and had seen a little plant growing there. It was a small plant with big leaves the size of coins.

The bee moved closer to the little plant but was very careful not to touch it. Then she told the snake, "Now it's my turn. Will you please turn around and count to three? Then you can start looking for me."

The snake quickly counted to three. When she turned around, she opened her mouth wide with surprise. The lazy bee had disappeared!

The red snake searched the entire cave, looking into every corner and crevice, but she could not locate the bee.

"All right," said the snake at last. "I give up. Where are you?"

A tiny voice from somewhere inside the cave said, "Will you promise you won't have me for dinner? Can I count on you keeping your promise?"

"Yes, of course I will keep my promise. Where are you?"

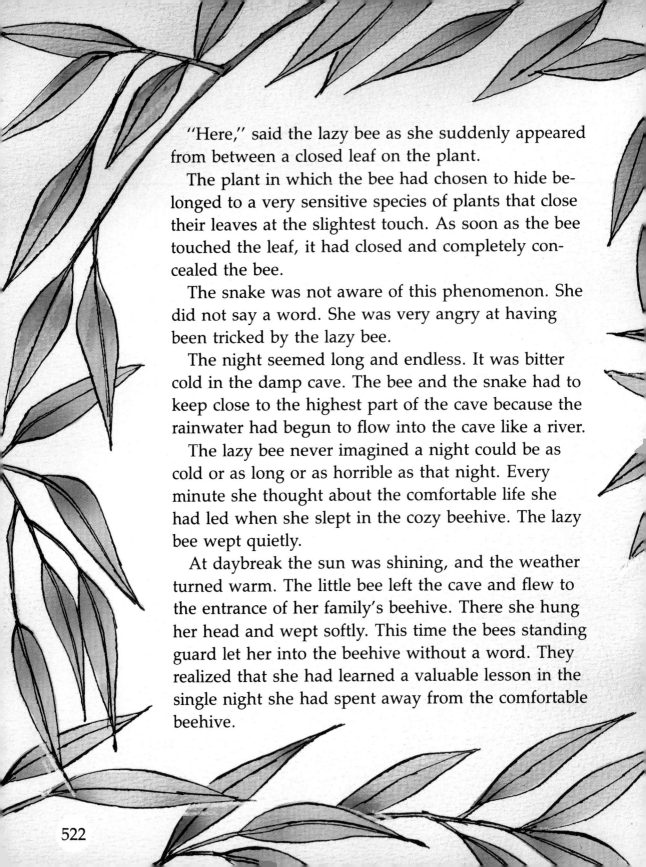

"Here," said the lazy bee as she suddenly appeared from between a closed leaf on the plant.

The plant in which the bee had chosen to hide belonged to a very sensitive species of plants that close their leaves at the slightest touch. As soon as the bee touched the leaf, it had closed and completely concealed the bee.

The snake was not aware of this phenomenon. She did not say a word. She was very angry at having been tricked by the lazy bee.

The night seemed long and endless. It was bitter cold in the damp cave. The bee and the snake had to keep close to the highest part of the cave because the rainwater had begun to flow into the cave like a river.

The lazy bee never imagined a night could be as cold or as long or as horrible as that night. Every minute she thought about the comfortable life she had led when she slept in the cozy beehive. The lazy bee wept quietly.

At daybreak the sun was shining, and the weather turned warm. The little bee left the cave and flew to the entrance of her family's beehive. There she hung her head and wept softly. This time the bees standing guard let her into the beehive without a word. They realized that she had learned a valuable lesson in the single night she had spent away from the comfortable beehive.

They were right. From then on, no other bee collected as much pollen or made as much honey as she did. When fall arrived and her life was almost at an end, this bee spoke to the younger bees. This is what she told them:

"It is hard work that makes us strong. Once I did nothing but fly around all day. I became very tired at night. If I had worked like the other bees, I would have had a sense of responsibility toward my family, and I would not have been as foolish. You see, sisters, as you work, you must always be aware of the final goal you are trying to attain. This is what it means to have an ideal to work toward."

1. What lesson did the lazy bee learn?

2. Why didn't the lazy bee want to spend the night outside?

3. How did the lazy bee escape from the snake?

4. What made you think the snake was an honest snake?

5. What let you know that the bee was very sorry for being lazy?

6. The lazy bee told her sisters that "as you work, you must always be aware of the final goal you are trying to attain. This is what it means to have an ideal to work toward." How does this statement apply to the selection?

Prewrite

The lazy bee had a difficult time when she had to spend the night outside. What were some of the things that happened to her? If you were a cartoonist, how would you draw one of these scenes?

Draft

Pretend that you are a cartoonist and your job is to help turn one part of the story of the lazy bee into a comic strip. Choose one of the scenes, such as the meeting of the snake and the bee, and retell it in three or four cartoon panels. Remember to put the characters' conversations in balloons above their heads.

Revise

Look at your drawings and read the characters' conversations. Have you shown the setting? Have you shown what action took place? Do the characters' conversations make sense? Make whatever changes and additions are needed to improve your comic strip.

Map Coordinates

You may remember how information is given on a map. A compass rose tells direction. It shows where north, south, east, and west are on the map. A scale helps you figure out how far it is from one place to another. A legend uses symbols to show interesting or important places on a map.

Street Maps

On a map of a city, street names help you find places. Look at the section of a street map on the next page. The two avenues run east and west. The three streets run north and south. Find the X on the map. If you wanted some friends to meet you on that corner, how would you tell them its location?

You would probably say, "Meet me at the corner of Ocean Avenue and Main Street." However, there are four corners there. How would you tell them which one to go to?

Using the compass rose, you can see that the X is on the northeast corner. You could tell your friends to meet you at the northeast corner of Ocean Avenue and Main Street. Anyone looking at a map could then tell where to go.

Find the *Y* on the street map. If you were at corner *X*, how would you get to corner *Y*? Tell how you would go, using street and avenue names. Also use the compass rose to tell in which directions you would go.

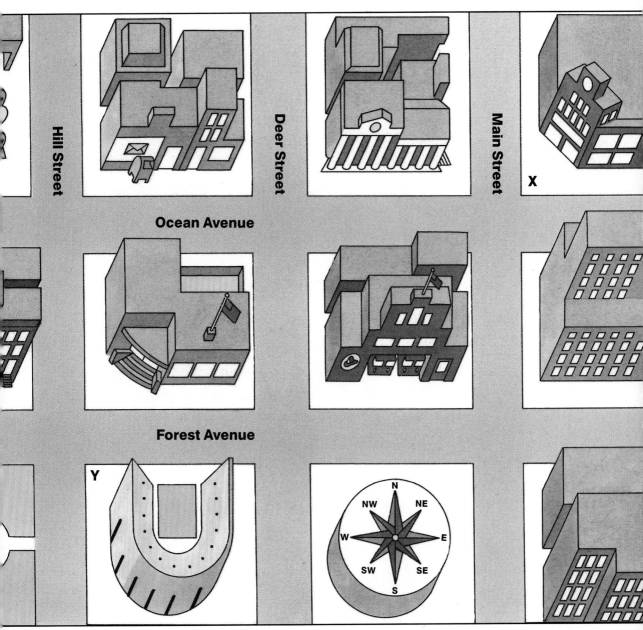

Hill Street

Deer Street

Main Street

Ocean Avenue

Forest Avenue

X

Y

Road Maps

Look at the following road map of Florida.

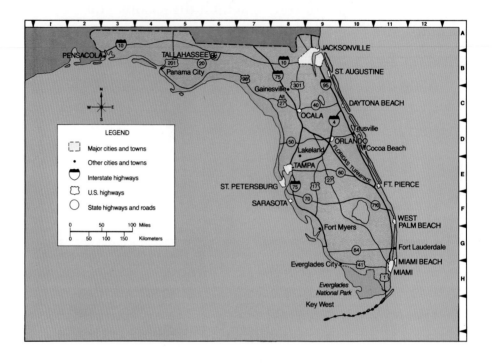

This map has a compass rose, a scale, and a legend. Use the legend to find out what the road map shows. Each highway and main road in the state has its own route number. Most cities and towns are marked with a small circle. The larger cities are shown as yellow areas.

You read a road map to learn which roads to take when you want to go from one place to another. Find Daytona Beach on the east coast of the state. Now find Tampa on the west coast. Which route would you take to go from Daytona Beach to Tampa? You would probably take Route 4. Why? Is there any other route you could take?

Coordinates

A map can also be used to help you find where a place is located. Look at the numbers across the top and the letters along the side of the road map. These are called *map coordinates*. You can use these coordinates to find cities and towns on the map.

Hold a piece of paper straight west from the letter *F* at the side of the map. Put another piece of paper straight south from the number *8* at the top of the map. You will find the city of Sarasota where the two pieces of paper meet.

Now look again at the letter *F*. Above and below the letter are arrows pointing west. The coordinate *F* covers all the area between these two arrows all the way across the map. In the same way, the coordinate *8* covers all the area between its arrows all the way down the map. The *F* and the *8* areas meet to form a square around Sarasota. This entire square is covered by the coordinates *F8*. All cities and towns inside this square have the coordinates *F8*.

Most road maps have a list of cities and towns and their coordinates, and these can help you find any city or town on the map. Next to Sarasota on the list for this map, you would find the coordinates *F8*.

The coordinates for St. Augustine are *B9*. Use the coordinates to find St. Augustine on the map.

Now find the area on the map covered by each of these coordinates: *B6, H11, D10*. Name at least one city or town in each area.

Knowing how to use maps will help you find places that you want to visit. It will also help you find your way around those places once you get there.

Byrd Baylor

When Byrd Baylor was eight years old, she had already made a plan for her life. She wrote these words in her diary: "I will be a riter. I will rite in Europe every winter and at the ranch every summer."

When Byrd grew up, she carried out her plan, at least in part. She became a writer, and she traveled to different places to write. However, she always writes about the same place — the southwestern United States. This is the place she calls home.

Byrd Baylor's first southwestern home was in San Antonio, Texas, where she was born. She grew up, however, in different places. She recalls childhood summers living on a west Texas ranch. She also remembers riding burros around the hills in Sonora, Mexico, where her father worked in a gold mine. She attended school in Arizona, where she still lives in an adobe house she helped to build.

Byrd Baylor's family taught her very early to know and to take pride in the southwestern mountains and deserts. She recalls that her grandfather, a Texas farmer, "looked at the stars every night before he went to sleep and could tell time by the sun." She remembers taking family walks every evening and learning from her father, who "knew all the mountains and the wildflowers." Byrd Baylor also remembers how her mother read books to her and how her father told her stories.

These early experiences helped Byrd to choose writing as her career. They also gave her many ideas for her writing. Her children's books say something special about the Southwest—its land, its animal life, its people, and its history.

Byrd Baylor says, "I try to learn from the land and the people. That's what my books are about." She also says that she writes only for one person—herself. She always sends herself the same message: "Don't forget what's important to you."

Her children's books clearly say what Byrd Baylor feels is important. The books *When Clay Sings* and *If You Are a Hunter of Fossils* came from her experiences of finding very old American Indian pottery and fossils in the desert. *Desert Voices*, *The Desert Is Theirs*, and *Hawk, I'm Your Brother* celebrate the people and animals who live in the southwestern deserts.

The Best Town in the World, however, is a book that records some special family memories. Byrd Baylor says that this book is "made of things I remember my father telling me about the little canyon town where he grew up. . . .At first I thought I'd write it as a present to my own family, but after it was finished I decided maybe other people would like it, too."

As you read *The Best Town in the World*, think about Byrd Baylor's message to herself: "Don't forget what is important to you."

In this selection, a father remembers his hometown in Texas as "the best town in the world." Read to find out what made that town so special.

The Best Town in the World

by Byrd Baylor

All my life I've heard
about
a little, dirt-road,
one-store,
country town
not far from a rocky canyon
way back
in the Texas hills.

This town had lots of space
around it
with caves to find
and honey trees
and giant rocks to climb.

It had a creek
and there were
panther tracks
to follow
and you could swing
on the wild grapevines.
My father said it was
the best town in the world
and he just happened
to be born there.
How's that for being
lucky?

We always liked
to hear about
that town
where everything was
perfect.

Of course it had a name
but people called the town
and all the ranches
and the farms around it
just *The Canyon*,
and they called each other
Canyon People.
The way my father said it,
you could tell
it was a special thing
to be
one of those people.

All the best cooks
in the world lived there.
My father said
if you were walking down the road,
just hunting arrowheads
or maybe coming home from school,
they'd call you in
and give you
sweet potato pie
or gingerbread
and stand there
by the big wood stove
and smile at you
while you were eating.

It was that kind
of town.

The best blackberries
in the world
grew wild.

My father says
the ones in stores
don't taste a thing
like those
he used to pick.
Those tasted just like
a blackberry should.

He'd crawl into
a tangle
of blackberry thicket
and eat all he wanted
and finally
walk home
swinging his bucket
(with enough for four pies)
and his hands
and his face
and his hard bare feet
would be stained
that beautiful color.

All plants
liked
to grow there.
The town was famous for
red chiles
and for melons
and for sweet corn, too.

And it's a well-known fact
that chickens in that canyon
laid prettier brown eggs
than chickens
twenty miles
on down the road.

My father says
no scientist
has figured out
why.

The dogs
were smarter there.
They helped you
herd the goats
and growled at rattlesnakes
before you even saw them.
And if you stopped
to climb a tree
your dogs stopped, too.
They curled up and waited
for you to come down.
They didn't run off
by themselves.

Summer days
were longer there
than they are
in other places,
and wildflowers grew taller
and thicker on the hills—
not just the yellow ones.
There were all shades of
lavender and purple
and orange and red
and blue
and the palest kind of pink.
They all had butterflies
to match.

Fireflies lit up
the whole place
at night,
and in the distance
you could hear
somebody's fiddle
or banjo
or harp.

My father says
no city water
ever tasted half as good
as water that he carried
in a bucket from the well
by their back door.

And there isn't
any water
anywhere
as clear
as the water
in that ice-cold creek
where all the children swam.
You could look down
and see the white sand
and watch the minnows
flashing by.

But
when my father came to the
part
about that ice-cold water
we would always say,

"It doesn't sound
so perfect
if the water was
ice-cold."

He'd look surprised
and say,
"But that's the way
creek water
is supposed to be—
ice-cold."

So we learned that
however
things were
in that town
is just exactly how
things *ought* to be.

People there
did things
in their own way.

Maybe that's part of the reason
it was the best town
in the world.
You could do things
whatever way
seemed good
to you.

For instance, in the summertime
when the air was full of bird song
and cicadas,[1]
my father
(when he was little
and even when he was big)
liked to take his supper
and climb up in a tree
and eat it there
alone.

He did it almost every night.
He had thick slices
of his mother's homemade bread
in a bowl of milk,
fresh from the evening milking.

---

[1] cicadas [si·kā′dəz]

538

No one ever said,
"Eat something else,"
and no one ever said,
"Don't eat it in a tree."
If someone, walking by,
glanced up and saw him
with his bowl and spoon,
they wouldn't say a thing
except,
"Good evening, George."

Of course you knew
everyone's name
and everyone
knew
yours.

People in that town
liked any kind of
celebration.

The best speeches
in the world
were made right there
on Texas Independence Day
and July Fourth.

And every Sunday
people from the farms
and ranches
came to town
with wagons full of children
and baskets full of food.

The whole town gathered
at long tables
underneath the tall shade trees
where all those famous cooks
were bringing out
their famous food.

You could count on fried chicken
and chile con carne[2]
and black-eyed peas
and corn on the cob
and corn bread sticks
and biscuits
and frijoles[3]
and squash and turnip greens
and watermelon pickles
and dumplings
and fritters
and stews.

There was another whole table
just for desserts.
Sometimes you'd see
five different kinds of
chocolate cake.

---

[2] chile con carne [chil'ē kon kär'nē]
[3] frijoles [frē·hō'lēz]

My father said
he thought that if
he took just one
he'd hurt the feelings of
four other
chocolate cake cooks—
so he took one
of each.
But then he thought
that if they saw him
eating cake
he'd hurt the feelings of
the pie cooks,
so he ate pie, too—
to be polite.

He said
he was famous
for being polite
to the cooks.

It seemed like
everybody
in that town
was famous.
My father said
it was because
the smartest people
in the world
were
all right there.

We asked him
what they did
that was so smart.
He said,
"They all had sense enough
to know the best town
in the world
when they saw it.
That's smart."

And they were smart
in other ways.

For instance,
they could tell time
without wearing a watch.
They just glanced
at the sun
and they *knew*.
They wouldn't be more
than ten minutes off . . .
and ten minutes off
doesn't matter.

They could tell
by the stars
what the weather would be.
They could tell
by the moon
when to plant.

If they needed
a house
or corral
or a barn,
they didn't pay someone
to come build it for them.
They cut their own trees
and found their own rocks
and dug their own earth.

Then,
whatever it was,
they built it to last
for a hundred years—
and it did.

Suppose
their children
wanted
kites
or jump ropes
or whistles
or stilts . . .

They didn't have to
go to stores
and buy just what
was there.

They knew how to make
the best toys
in the world.

On winter nights
when they were
sitting by the fire,
by lamplight,
talking,
you'd see them
making
bows and arrows
or soft rag dolls
or blocks
or tops
or bamboo flutes
or even a checkerboard
carved out of oak.

My father said
sometimes
they'd let you
paint the checkers
red
or black
and you'd be
proud.

We liked everything
we ever heard
about those people
and that town,
but we always
had to ask:
"If it really was
the best town
in the world,
why weren't
more people
there?"

And he would say,
"Because
if a lot
of people
lived there,
it wouldn't be
the best town
anymore.
The best town
can't be crowded."

We always wished
that we could live there
and be
Canyon People, too.

543

Still,
we used to wonder
if possibly,
just *possibly*,
there might be
another
perfect town
somewhere.

To find out,
I guess
you'd have to follow
a lot of
dirt roads
past
a whole lot of
wildflower hills.

I guess
you'd have to
try
a lot of
ice-cold
swimming holes
and eat
a lot of
chocolate cake
and pat
a lot of dogs.

It seems
like a good thing
to do.

1. Why was The Canyon the best town in the world?

2. What did the author mean when she said, "So we learned that however things were in that town is just exactly how things *ought* to be"?

3. Name three things found in The Canyon that were supposed to be the very best in the world.

4. Which description of the town do you like the best? Explain your choice.

5. What does the author think that you would have to do to find another town like The Canyon?

6. What sentences in the selection suggest that the narrator might have thought that her father exaggerated his stories a little?

7. Sometimes when people think about something that happened in the past, they remember only the good things. How does this apply to the selection?

Thinking About "Memories"

The first selection in this unit took place in a small town in North Carolina called Parmele. The last selection took place in another wonderful small town in the state of Texas. Both of these selections show that the memories people have of their families and homes are very important to them. People share their memories and pass them on.

There are different ways of sharing memories and remembering. You read about one in "The Patchwork Quilt." Quilts are often passed from one generation to the next. Family memories are passed with them. You found another way of remembering in "Saving Time." There you discovered how a time capsule can help you remember what *you* were like at some time in the past.

The study of history involves remembering the past, too. You read about the memorable midnight ride of Paul Revere. Another Revolutionary War hero was George Washington. You read a poem that spoke of the different images in our minds we have of George Washington. A paper Washington signed was part of "The Mystery of the Rolltop Desk."

Now that you are at the end of *Crossroads*, think about all the selections you have read. Which ones do you remember most clearly? Why?

1. "Childtimes" and "Me and My Family Tree" are both examples of personal narrative. How else are they alike? How are they different?

2. How is the exaggeration in "The Best Town in the World" different from the exaggeration in "McBroom Tells the Truth"?

3. The poem "Which Washington?" suggests that there are many George Washingtons. This means that George Washington is remembered in many different ways. Think about Paul Revere. How many Paul Reveres can you think of? Describe each one.

4. How is a patchwork quilt similar to a time capsule? How is a patchwork quilt like a family tree?

5. Think about the many ways to save memories that you have read about in this unit. Which ways do you like best? Why?

6. You have shared memories and experiences of both real people and fictional characters in this unit. Which one did you enjoy reading about most? Why?

Glossary

The glossary is a special dictionary for this book. The glossary tells you how to spell a word, how to pronounce it, and what the word means. Often the word is used in a sentence. Different forms of the word may also be given. If one of the different forms is used in the book, then that form may be defined or used in a sentence.

A blue box ■ at the end of the entry tells you that an illustration is given for that word.

The following abbreviations are used throughout the glossary: *n.,* noun; *v.,* verb; *adj.,* adjective; *adv.,* adverb; *interj.,* interjection; *prep.,* preposition; *conj.,* conjunction; *pl.,* plural; *sing.,* singular; *syn.,* synonym; *syns.,* synonyms.

An accent mark (′) is used to show which syllable receives the most stress. For example, in the word *granite* [gran′it], the first syllable receives more stress. Sometimes in words of two or more syllables, there is also a lighter mark to show that a syllable receives a lighter stress. For example, in the word *helicopter* [hel′ə·kop′tər], the first syllable has the most stress, and the third syllable has lighter stress.

The symbols used to show how each word is pronounced are explained in the "Pronunciation Key" on the next page.

Pronunciation Key*

a	add, map	m	move, seem	u	up, done
ā	ace, rate	n	nice, tin	û(r)	burn, term
â(r)	care, air	ng	ring, song	yōō	fuse, few
ä	palm, father	o	odd, hot	v	vain, eve
b	bat, rub	ō	open, so	w	win, away
ch	check, catch	ô	order, jaw	y	yet, yearn
d	dog, rod	oi	oil, boy	z	zest, muse
e	end, pet	ou	pout, now	zh	vision, pleasure
ē	equal, tree	ŏŏ	took, full	ə	the schwa,
f	fit, half	ōō	pool, food		an unstressed
g	go, log	p	pit, stop		vowel representing
h	hope, hate	r	run, poor		the sound spelled
i	it, give	s	see, pass	a	in *above*
ī	ice, write	sh	sure, rush	e	in *sicken*
j	joy, ledge	t	talk, sit	i	in *possible*
k	cool, take	th	thin, both	o	in *melon*
l	look, rule	t̶h̶	this, bathe	u	in *circus*

*Adapted entries, the Pronunciation Key, and the Short Key that appear on the following pages are reprinted from *HBJ School Dictionary*. Copyright ©1985 by Harcourt Brace Jovanovich, Inc. Reprinted by permission of Harcourt Brace Jovanovich, Inc.

A

abruptly [ə'brupt'ly] *adv.* Suddenly: The bus ride ended *abruptly. syn.* hastily

absentminded [ab'sənt·mīn'did] *adj.* **absentmindedly** *adv.* Unattentive to what is happening or what is being done: Grandpa was *absentmindedly* walking right past our house. *syn.* forgetful

absorb [ab·sôrb'] *v.* To take in and hold; suck in: Sponges *absorb* spilled liquids. *syn.* hold

accompany [a·kum'pə·nē] *v.* To play a musical instrument along with or for someone: Jan *accompanies* Rick on the guitar when he sings.

adjust [ə·just'] *v.* To become accustomed to: After flying from New York to California, you have *adjusted* very well to the time change. *syn.* adapt

administration [ad·min'is·trā'shən] *n.* A governing group: The school *administration* met to plan the school's activities. *syn.* management

adobe [ə·dō'bē] *n.* A block of clay that is dried in the sun: The Indians constructed many buildings with *adobe. syn.* brick ■

advertisement [ad'vûr·tīz'mənt] *n.* A public notice that brings attention to something for the purpose of selling it: The store put *advertisements* in the newspaper about its special sale. *syn.* ad

aeronautics [âr'ə·nô'tiks] *n.* The art of planning, making, and flying aircraft: Jim studied *aeronautics* in college.

alcove [al'kōv] *n.* A small part of a room that is tucked away from the main area: Maria has a small library in the *alcove. syn.* nook ■

alien [ā'lē·ən] *adj.* Strange; of another place: The *alien* being came out of the spaceship.

alloy [al'oi] *n.* A combination of two or more metals: Two copper *alloys* are brass and bronze.

altitude [al'tə·t(y)ood] *n.* The elevation above a given point: Airplanes can fly at a high *altitude.*

anchor [ang'kər] *v.* **anchored, anchoring** To lower a metal hook from a ship to keep the ship from drifting: We *anchored* the boat for the night.

ancient [ān'shənt] *adj.* Very old; existing very long ago: We read about an *ancient* civilization and how the people lived. *syn.* aged

annoyance [ə·noi′əns] *n.* The mad feeling caused by being upset: The barking dog is a great *annoyance*. *syn.* irritation

anticipation [an·tis′ə·pā′shən] *n.* The looking forward to something to come: The children are waiting with great *anticipation*.

apartment [ə·pärt′mənt] *n.* One or more rooms in which people live: My family lives in an *apartment* in a large building. *syn.* flat

appreciate [ə·prē′shē·āt] *v.* To be thankful for: I really *appreciate* that you took the time to help me. *syn.* value

apprehend [ap′rə·hend′] *v.* **apprehended, apprehending** To seize, arrest: The police *apprehended* the burglar. *syn.* capture

archaeologist [är′kē·ol′ə·jist] *n.* An expert in the study of past times and cultures: The *archaeologist* dug in the ruins, looking for artifacts.

architect [är′kə·tekt] *n.* A person who designs buildings and other structures and sees them through to completion: The *architect* showed the plans for a new building.

assemble [ə·sem′bəl] *v.* **assembled, assembling** To put together all the parts of: Mom *assembled* the bicycle for me. *syns.* combine, unite

astonishment [ə·ston′ish·mənt] *n.* Surprise: José is filled with *astonishment*. *syn.* amazement

athlete [ath′lēt] *n.* A person who is skilled in one or more sports: Greg is a great *athlete*.

atmosphere [at′məs·fir] *n.* The air that surrounds the earth: Our *atmosphere* is very polluted.

attain [ə·tān′] *v.* To reach a goal by hard work: I wish to *attain* stardom in Hollywood. *syns.* achieve, gain

attempt [ə·tempt′] *v.* **attempted, attempting** To make an effort: Bob is *attempting* to swim across the river. *syn.* try

audition [ô·dish′ən] *n.* A meeting to test or choose the best people for a job: Maria went to the *audition* to try out for a part in the play. *syns.* hearing, tryout

---

B

balcony [bal′kə·nē] *n.* A floor surrounded by a fence and attached to the outside of a building: She watched the sunset from her *balcony*. *syn.* terrace

a	add	o	odd	oi	oil
ā	ace	ō	open	ou	pout
â	care	ô	order	ng	ring
ä	palm	o͝o	took	th	thin
e	end	o͞o	pool	th	this
ē	equal	u	up	zh	vision
i	it	û	burn		
ī	ice	yo͞o	fuse		

ə = { a in *above*, e in *sicken*, i in *possible*, o in *melon*, u in *circus* }

bamboo [bam·bōō'] *n.* A tropical grass whose long, slender stems are used in building and making things: I have a chair made of *bamboo*. ■

banister [ban'is·tər] *n.* The railing along the side of a staircase: John held the *banister* tightly as he climbed the stairs. *syn.* handrail

barre [bär] *n.* A handrail used by ballet dancers to maintain balance while exercising: The ballerina practices at the *barre* for six hours each day. ■

barren [bar'ən] *adj.* Without plant life: The *barren* desert sand was all that I could see. *syn.* empty

barrier [bar'ē·ər] *n.* Something that hinders motion, such as a wall or fence: Many *barriers* separate the President from the crowds. *syn.* barricade

bat¹ [bat] *v.* To take a turn hitting the ball in a baseball game: It was Wally's turn to *bat*.

bat² [bat] *n.* A wooden or aluminum stick used for hitting a ball: Don hit a home run using his favorite *bat*.

baton [bə·ton'] *n.* A thin stick used by a conductor in leading an orchestra: The *baton* waved wildly in her hands as she led the musicians.

berth [bûrth] *n.* A place to sleep while traveling: Our cabin on the ship has three *berths*. *syn.* bed

biography [bī·og'rə·fē] *n.* A written story of someone's life: We read a *biography* of Abraham Lincoln for history class.

bleachers [blē'chərz] *n. pl.* Outdoor seats not covered by a roof: There were many people watching the game from the *bleachers*. *syn.* stands ■

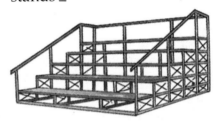

block¹ [blok] *n.* A rectangular area enclosed by streets: My friend's house is up the *block*.

block² [blok] *n.* A solid piece of material usually having a flat surface: The little boy found his missing building *block*. *syn.* slab

bluff [bluf] *n. pl.* **bluffs** High areas of land overlooking a low area: From the *bluffs* we can look down and see the river. *syn.* cliff

bob [bob] *v.* **bobbed, bobbing** To move up and down with a short, sudden motion: The pickles *bobbed* in the barrel. *syn.* teeter

boggy [bog′ē] *adj.* Spongy, wet-looking, such as the ground: The land surrounding the lake was *boggy.* *syns.* swampy, marshy

bomb [bom] *n.* An explosive device that goes off when detonated: Many *bombs* were dropped on Pearl Harbor.

border [bôr′dər] *n.* The dividing line between different counties, states, or countries: We crossed the *border* between the United States and Canada.

bristly [bris′lē] *adj.* Of or like bristles; covered with bristles: The *bristly* cat protected its food from being eaten by the dog.

brocade [brō·kād′] *n.* **brocaded** *adj.* A rich silk fabric woven with a raised design usually in gold or silver: The queen wore a *brocaded* cape.

brood [brood] *v.* To think gloomily about a subject: Chris began to *brood* about his bad luck.

bruise [brooz] *v.* **bruised, bruising** To hurt the body, causing a black-and-blue mark: Gary's body was *bruised* from the fall.

bully [bool′ē] *n.* A person who enjoys annoying or upsetting others: That *bully* is always fighting with smaller people.

bungle [bung′gəl] *v.* **bungled, bungling** To do something badly: Denise *bungled* her chemistry experiment. *syns.* botch, mishandle

burst [bûrst] *v.* To give way to a sudden, strong emotion: Sue was so excited that she *burst* into song. *syn.* break

byte [bīt] *n.* A unit of memory in a computer, standing for a number or letter: Lottie programmed several *bytes* of information into her computer.

C

---

calm [käm] *adj.* Tranquil; at rest, quiet: The principal remained *calm* when speaking to the students. *syn.* peaceful

capsule [kap′səl] *n.* A container filled with objects of current interest, sealed and stored for discovery in the future: The students put a class picture into the time *capsule.*

carriage [kar′ij] *n.* A horse-drawn vehicle for carrying people: The girls went for a ride in the *carriage.* *syn.* coach ■

a	add	o	odd	oi	oil
ā	ace	ō	open	ou	pout
â	care	ô	order	ng	ring
ä	palm	oŏ	took	th	thin
e	end	oō	pool	th	this
ē	equal	u	up	zh	vision
i	it	û	burn		
ī	ice	yoō	fuse		

ə = { a in *above*　e in *sicken*　i in *possible*　o in *melon*　u in *circus* }

cater [kā'tər] *v.* **catered, catering** To supply ready-made food, beverages, and services: The health food store will be *catering* my party.

cautious [kô'shəs] *adj.* **cautiously** *adv.* Careful: The firefighter moved *cautiously* toward the burning house. *syn.* watchful

century [sen'chə·rē] *n.* A one-hundred-year period: The United States became a country in the eighteenth *century.*

challenge [chal'ənj] *n.* A temptation or offer to attempt something difficult or unsafe: NASA encounters many *challenges* in the space program. *syn.* dare

chamberlain [chām'bər·lin] *n.* A person who runs the household of a king or other noble person: The *chamberlain* ordered the cooks to prepare dinner for the queen. *syn.* attendant

characterization [kar'ik·tə·ri·zā'shən] *n.* The act of describing the qualities, habits, and traits of a real or fictional person: Learning about a character through his or her actions is one kind of *characterization.*

charity [char'ə·tē] *n.* The donating of money or volunteer work to the needy: The poor family received *charity* from the local church. *syn.* gift

chemistry [kem'is·trē] *n.* The scientific study of substances and how they react or interact under differ-ent conditions: Maxine got an "A" in *chemistry.*

chime¹ [chīm] *v.* **chimed in** To break into a conversation to express an opinion: My brothers *chimed in* when I started to talk. *syn.* interrupt

chime² [chīm] *n.* The sounds produced by a set of bells, each of which has a different pitch: I heard a *chime* coming from the grandfather clock.

chip [chip] *n.* A tiny, thin, square piece of semiconductor (with thousands of circuits and wires) that runs a computer: Joan wondered how many *chips* were in her home computer.

chisel [chiz'əl] *n.* A sharp tool used to cut or chip away at wood, stone, or marble: The carpenter used a *chisel* to cut the wood. ■

chorus [kôr'əs] *n.* Voices of people or animals speaking or singing together: The class answered in a *chorus.*

cider [sī'dər] *n.* The juice of apples: We made fresh *cider* on the farm.

citation [sī·tā'shən] *n.* A public award: The police officer received a *citation* for her bravery. *syn.* commendation.

civilization [siv′ə·lə·zā′shən] *n.* The culture and society of a specific time or place: Ancient Egyptian *civilization* was very advanced for its time.

clarinet [klar′ə·net′] *n.* A woodwind musical instrument with a single reeded mouthpiece and cylindrical body: Benny Goodman played the *clarinet.* ■

classical [klas′i·kəl] *adj.* Following an established, strict form: Fran is interested in *classical* music.

clerk [klûrk] *n.* An office worker: The *clerk* filed the papers in the filing cabinet.

climate [klī′mit] *n.* The kind of weather that is typical of a place over a lengthy time period: Florida has a warm *climate. syn.* environment

collapse [kə·laps′] *v.* To fall down: The chair began to *collapse* when I sat down. *syn.* give way

collect [kə·lekt′] *v.* To assemble, bring together: We will *collect* butterflies for our science project. *syn.* gather

collide [kə·līd′] *v.* **collided, colliding** To unite with a strong impact: The two cars *collided* on the road. *syn.* crash

comet [kom′it] *n.* A heavenly body that moves around the sun in an elliptical orbit and has a tail of light: The *comet* moved across the sky.

companion [kəm·pan′yən] *n.* Someone who travels with another person: Judy is my friend and *companion.*

compete [kəm·pēt′] *v.* **competed, competing** To try to win a contest: Five students *competed* in the spelling bee. *syn.* contend

complicated [kom′plə·kā′tid] *adj.* Difficult to understand: This math problem is *complicated.*

composer [kəm·pō′zər] *n.* A person who creates an original work, usually musical: Beethoven was a great *composer.*

computer [kəm·pyo͞o′tər] *n.* An electronic instrument which is used to calculate, process, store, and recall various information: My father uses a *computer* in his business. ■

a	add	o	odd	oi	oil
ā	ace	ō	open	ou	pout
â	care	ô	order	ng	ring
ä	palm	o͝o	took	th	thin
e	end	o͞o	pool	th	this
ē	equal	u	up	zh	vision
i	it	û	burn		
ī	ice	yo͞o	fuse		

ə = { a in *above*   e in *sicken*   i in *possible*
      o in *melon*   u in *circus* }

comrade [kom′rad] *n.* A friend or buddy: Stu and I were *comrades* all through summer camp. *syns.* pal, friend

conceal [kən·sēl′] *v.* **concealed, concealing** To keep out of view: The curtains *concealed* her from the audience. *syn.* hide

concentrate [kon′sən·trāt] *v.* To pay close attention: Keith tried to *concentrate* on his homework assignment. *syn.* focus

concertmaster [kon′sûrt·mas′tər] *n.* The leader of the violin section of an orchestra: The *concertmaster* sits near the conductor.

conduct [kən·dukt′] *v.* **conducted, conducting** To lead or direct: Kyle *conducted* a tour of the zoo. *syns.* guide, manage

confidence [kon′fə·dəns] *n.* Self-assurance; trust: She performed her dance routine with *confidence*. *syn.* faith

conquer [kong′kər] *v.* **conquered, conquering** To overcome by force or effort: She has *conquered* her fear of heights.

contented [kən·ten′tid] *adj.* **contentedly** *adv.* Happy with the way things are: Mother sat *contentedly* in the rocking chair. *syn.* satisfied

contrary [kon′trer·ē] *adj.* Opposite, totally different: He and I have *contrary* thoughts on the subject. *syn.* conflicting

coordinate [*v.* kō·ôr′də·nāt′, *n.* kō·ôr′də·nit] **1** *v.* To arrange into the correct relationship for working together: The director *coordinates* the actors, music, and lights on a stage. *syn.* arrange **2** *n.* The numbers and letters used to locate a point on a map: Dave used map *coordinates* to track the path of the hurricane.

cope [kōp] *v.* To manage successfully; to deal with: I can *cope* with all the homework I have to do today. *syn.* handle

copyist [kop′ē·əst] *n.* A person who makes handwritten duplicates: The *copyist* made five copies of the deed.

cornerstone [kôr′nər·stōn′] *n.* A special stone placed at the corner of a building: This *cornerstone* shows the date construction began on the building. ■

cower [kou′ər] *v.* **cowered, cowering** To tremble or stoop in fear: The children were *cowering* near the wall as the storm raged. *syn.* crouch

crevice [krev′is] *n.* A small opening resulting from a split or crack: The mountain climber put his foot into a *crevice* to regain his balance. *syn.* crack

crisis [krī′sis] *n.* A significant moment during an event: The president was quite worried during the nuclear *crisis. syn.* emergency

critic [krit′ik] *n.* An individual who determines the importance or quality of art, books, etc.: Many *critics* attended the opening of the movie. *syn.* judge

criticize [krit′ə·sīz] *v.* **criticized, criticizing** To view harshly: The class *criticized* my work in the play. *syns.* review, judge

crouch [krouch] *v.* **crouched, crouching** To bend or lower to the ground: He *crouched* behind the bushes and hid from his friends. *syn.* squat

custodian [kus·tō′dē·ən] *n.* A person who cares for a building: Mr. Jones is the *custodian* of our church. *syns.* caretaker, guardian

custom [kus′təm] *n.* The ordinary way of doing things or behaving: It's a *custom* to sing before you blow out the candles! *syns.* habit, practice

customer [kus′tə·mər] *n. pl.* **customers** People who purchase things in a store: The store had many *customers* because of the sale. *syn.* patron

---

D

data [dā′tə] *n. pl.* Information: We learned how to feed *data* into the machine. *syn.* facts

defect [dē′fekt] *n.* An imperfection: We had to return our new car because it had a *defect. syns.* flaw, fault

depression [di·presh′ən] *n.* A period when business is drastically down and many people are out of jobs: The Great *Depression* began in 1929.

derisive [di·rī′siv] *adj.* Contemptuous: The girl's *derisive* smile means she doesn't believe me. *syn.* scornful

descent [di·sent′] *n.* The act of moving from a higher to a lower place: The submarine began its *descent* to the ocean floor. *syn.* fall

description [di·skrip′shən] *n.* The act of telling what a person or thing is like: The police needed a *description* of the robber.

desire [di·zīr′] *v.* **desired, desiring** To request or ask for something: Kristy received the toy that she had *desired* for her birthday. *syns.* wish, want

desperate [des′pər·it] *adj.* **desperately** *adv.* Extreme, very great: Roger *desperately* wanted to get off of the roller coaster. *syn.* despairingly

a	add	o	odd	oi	oil
ā	ace	ō	open	ou	pout
â	care	ô	order	ng	ring
ä	palm	o͝o	took	th	thin
e	end	o͞o	pool	th	this
ē	equal	u	up	zh	vision
i	it	û	burn		
ī	ice	yo͞o	fuse		

ə = { a in *above* e in *sicken* i in *possible*
     o in *melon* u in *circus* }

determined [di·tûr′mind] *adj.* Strongly decided: My sister is *determined* to be a pilot. *syn.* sure

diary [dī′ə·rē] *n.* A daily personal record of events and thoughts: Ann wrote in her *diary* daily. *syn.* journal

dignity [dig′nə·tē] *n.* Having character that demands respect: The woman stood with *dignity* before the crowd. *syns.* honor, pride

diorama [dī′ə·rä′mə] *n.* A display with lifelike figures in front that blend with a scene in the background: I made a *diorama* for my school project. ■

disaster [di·zas′tər] *n.* Something terrible that happens: Yesterday's earthquake was a *disaster* for the whole city. *syn.* tragedy

discourage [dis·kûr′ij] *v.* To make someone lose confidence: I do not want to *discourage* you before the big football game. *syn.* deter

disk [disk] *n.* A round, flat plate with magnetic coating on which information for a computer is stored: José needed a new *disk* for the computer.

dispatch [dis·pach′] *v.* **dispatched, dispatching** To send away to a certain place: He *dispatched* the taxi to pick up a passenger.

distant [dis′tənt] *adj.* Far away: My grandmother lives in a *distant* state. *syn.* remote

documents [dok′yə·mənts] *n. pl.* Official papers that serve as proof of something: There are many important *documents* filed at Town Hall. *syn.* records

dome [dōm] *n.* A circular roof that looks like half of a ball: The Capitol building has a *dome* on it. ■

doom [do͞om] *v.* **doomed, dooming** To sentence to a horrible fate: When our bus broke down, we realized our trip was *doomed*. *syn.* condemn

downbeat [doun′bēt′] *n.* The downward stroke made by a conductor to signal the first beat in each measure of music: The orchestra waited for the *downbeat* before they began to play. *syn.* signal

Down's syndrome [dounz sin′drōm] *n.* A condition that causes slow mental and physical growth. The eyes and nose may appear flattened on people who have this condition: My friend Dwight has *Down's syndrome*.

draft [draft] *n.* An outline or plan of something to be written: She brought the first *drafts* of her stories to the publisher. *syn.* rough copy

drench [drench] *v.* **drenched, drenching** To soak totally with water or other liquid: We were *drenched* by the heavy rainfall. *syn.* wet

dumpling [dump′ling] *n.* A round piece of dough cooked in stew or soup: My grandmother made chicken and *dumplings* for dinner.

dune [d(y)o͞on] *n.* A ridge or hill of sand piled up by the wind: We walked over a big *dune* to reach the beach. ■

dusk [dusk] *n.* The time just before night: Mother told us to be home at *dusk. syn.* twilight

---

E

education [ej′o͞o·kā′shən] *n.* Training in a specific field: Matt has a high school *education. syns.* knowledge, schooling

efficient [i·fish′ənt] *adj.* Operating with little or no waste: Our new refrigerator is *efficient. syn.* capable

effort [ef′ərt] *n.* A serious attempt: He made an *effort* to swim 50 laps across the pool. *syns.* endeavor, attempt, try

eighteenth [ā′tēnth′] *adj.* Following the seventeenth: That is the *eighteenth* red car to drive past us.

electronic [i·lek′tron′ik] *adj.* Having to do with the use or control of charged particles: The robot is an *electronic* device.

energy [en′ər·jē] *n.* Power: Electricity provides the *energy* to light up the whole city. *syn.* force

enormous [i·nôr′məs] *adj.* Extremely big, or immense: It took a long time to cross the *enormous* field. *syns.* massive, great

enthusiasm [in·tho͞o′zē·az′əm] *n.* Great interest and excitement: The nurse showed *enthusiasm* for her new job. *syn.* zeal

environment [in·vī′rən·mənt] *n.* The conditions that affect the development of a living thing: Our school provides a good *environment* for learning. *syn.* climate

eucalyptus [yo͞o′kə·lip′təs] *n.* An evergreen tree used for its wood and oil, found mainly in Australia: We saw a koala eating some *eucalyptus* at the zoo. ■

a	add	o	odd	oi	oil
ā	ace	ō	open	ou	pout
â	care	ô	order	ng	ring
ä	palm	o͝o	took	th	thin
e	end	o͞o	pool	th	this
ē	equal	u	up	zh	vision
i	it	û	burn		
ī	ice	yo͞o	fuse		

ə = { a in *above*   e in *sicken*   i in *possible*
{ o in *melon*   u in *circus*

evidence [ev′ə·dens] *n.* Something that shows whether something is true or false, or has happened: There is *evidence* that Mark stole my bicycle. *syn.* proof

exalted [ig·zôl′tid] *adj.* High in rank or position; noble: The *exalted* ruler is respected by his subjects. *syn.* glorified

excellent [ek′sə·lənt] *adj.* Very good: This movie is *excellent. syns.* terrific, great

exceptional [ik·sep′shən·əl] *adj.* Unusual, extraordinary: He is an *exceptional* singer. *syn.* different

extraordinary [ik·strôr′də·ner′ē] *adj.* Exceptional, unusual: The way she won the contest was *extraordinary. syn.* remarkable

---

F

fabric [fab′rik] *n.* A cloth made of knitted fibers: Mother chose a bright *fabric* to cover the new chair. *syn.* cloth

fact [fakt] *n.* Some act or thing known to be real or true, to exist, or to have occurred: A *fact* is something that can be proved. *syn.* truth

fantasy [fan′tə·sē] *n.* A form of literature in which characters and events are imaginary, magical, and unreal: Fairy tales are an example of *fantasy.*

fend [fend] *v.* To repel something or someone: The soldiers had to *fend* off the enemy. *syn.* keep away

ferry [fer′ē] *n.* A craft used to carry people and things across a body of water: We took a *ferry* across the river. ■

fervent [fûr′vənt] *adj.* **fervently** *adv.* Anxious and determined: The boy *fervently* wished to win the game for his team. *syn.* earnest

flex [fleks] *v.* **flexed, flexing** To bend something: She *flexed* her legs to warm up for the race.

flicker [flik′ər] *v.* **flickered, flickering** To burn or glow with a shaky, uneven light: The candle *flickered* in the wind. *syn.* flutter

focus [fō′kəs] *v.* **focuses** Directs to a point: The mirror *focuses* the light into my microscope. *syn.* concentrate

formal [fôr′məl] *adj.* Rigid; strictly complying to rules: They came to a *formal* agreement to sell the car. *syn.* official

fray [frā] *v.* To become worn away due to constant friction; to become threadbare: The collar on my old shirt has begun to *fray. syn.* tear

frenzy [fren′zē] *n.* A hysterical condition like madness: The prisoner was in a *frenzy* while trying to escape. *syns.* hysteria, madness

fritter [frit′ər] *n.* A little cake of batter that is fried and often filled with another food: We ate corn *fritters* at the party.

furrow [fûr′ō] *n.* A deep, long trench on the ground, made by a plow: We planted a different vegetable in each *furrow* in the garden. *syns.* groove, trench

G

galaxy [gal′ək·sē] *n.* An extensive system of planets, stars, and other heavenly bodies: The earth is just a small part of our *galaxy.*

generation [jen′ə·rā′shən] *n.* A step in the line of descent from an ancestor to offspring: The grandmother, daughter, and grandson represented three *generations.*

geography [jē·og′rə·fē] *n.* The study of the earth and its climate: One of my favorite courses is *geography.*

gingerbread [jin′jər·bred′] *n.* A ginger-flavored dessert that is sweetened with molasses and cut into shapes: Grandma makes *gingerbread* for me every Christmas.

glare [glâr] *v.* **glared, glaring** To stare angrily: Howard *glared* at the fan who was booing.

gnarled [närld] *adj.* Twisted or maimed: The boy's fingers were *gnarled* after the accident. *syn.* deformed

grade [grād] *n.* The upward or downward slant in a road: This road has a very steep, downward *grade* just around the next corner. *syn.* slope

graduate [graj′ōō·āt′] *v.* **graduated, graduating** To finish required courses at school: The students *graduated* in June.

graph [graf] *n.* A diagram that shows the relation between two sets of information by lines or bars of different lengths, or with pictures or circles: Our class made bar and circle *graphs* that showed our favorite colors.

gravity [grav′ə·tē] *n.* The force which pulls objects toward the center of the earth: *Gravity* makes things fall down when you let go of them.

grenadier [gren′ə·dir′] *n.* A soldier who carries and throws grenades: The *grenadiers* marched ahead of the other troops.

H

handicapped [han′dē·kapd′] *adj.* Disadvantaged: The *handicapped* man needs a wheelchair. *syn.* disabled

a	add	o	odd	oi	oil
ā	ace	ō	open	ou	pout
â	care	ô	order	ng	ring
ä	palm	o͝o	took	th	thin
e	end	o͞o	pool	th	this
ē	equal	u	up	zh	vision
i	it	û	burn		
ī	ice	yo͞o	fuse		

ə = { a in *above*   e in *sicken*   i in *possible*
      o in *melon*   u in *circus*

hardship [härd′ship] *n. pl.* **hardships** Things that are difficult to live through: My parents told us about the *hardships* they encountered when they were young. *syn.* difficulty

harness [här′nis] *n.* A strap or straps used to hold one in place: I use the shoulder *harness* along with my seat belt whenever I am in the car. *syn.* restraint ■

hazy [hā′zē] *adj.* Unclear: I have *hazy* memories of my childhood. *syns.* confused, unclear

hobby [hob′ē] *n.* An enjoyable activity to do during spare time: George's *hobbies* include stamp collecting and painting. *syns.* pastime, recreation

holiday [hol′ə·dā′] *n. Brit.* A period of time to relax or travel: The family went on *holiday* to the mountains. *syn.* vacation

horizon [hə·rī′zən] *n.* The line in the distance where the sky and the earth come together: The blue sky meets the ocean at the *horizon.*

horsemanship [hôrs′mən·ship′] *n.* The talent of handling or riding horses: The woman displayed her excellent *horsemanship* at the parade.

huddle [hud′(ə)l] *v.* **huddled, huddling** To move close together: They *huddled* in the doorway to escape the rain. *syn.* nestle

hull [hul] *n.* The outer covering or frame of a ship: The *hull* of the boat was mostly under water.

hutch [huch] *n.* A cage or pen that holds small animals: I keep my pet chicken in a *hutch* behind the garage. *syn.* coop

I

ignore [ig·nôr′] *v.* **ignored, ignoring** To not notice: Tom is *ignoring* his sisters. *syns.* neglect, disregard

image [im′ij] *n.* A picture like those shaped by a lens or in a mirror: She saw *images* of a big forest on the movie screen. *syn.* likeness

immediate [i·mē′dē·it] *adj.* Occurring without delay; now: Joe had an *immediate* response to my question. *syn.* instantaneous

industrial [in·dus′trē·əl] *adj.* Having to do with manufacturing or business: All the factories are on the *industrial* side of town.

injure [in′jər] *v.* **injured, injuring** Hurt: When Mary fell, she *injured* her leg. *syn.* damage

instance [in′stəns] *n.* An example: For *instance,* a dog is a mammal. *syns.* illustration, sample

instinctive [in·stingk′tiv] *adj.* **instinctively** *adv.* Proceeding from natural aptitude: The cat *instinctively* knew how to take care of its kittens. *syn.* inborn

instruct [in·strukt′] *v.* **instructed, instructing** To order or direct: She *instructed* the pupils to read two stories that night. *syn.* command

instruction [in·struk′shən] *n.* Direction: Colleen learned how to put the desk together by reading the *instructions. syn.* directive

insulation [in′sə·lā′shən] *n.* Material that is used to keep heat from moving from place to place: My parents put new *insulation* in our attic.

intense [in·tens′] *adj.* Very strong: She gave an *intense* reading of the poem. *syns.* fervent, vivid

interfere [in′tər·fir′] *v.* To get in the way: My brother will not *interfere* with my party plans. *syn.* intervene

invader [in·vād′ər] *n.* Someone who comes with force to conquer. The *invaders* attacked from three sides. *syn.* intruder

invisible [in·viz′ə·bəl] *adj.* Unable to be seen: Molecules are *invisible* to the naked eye.

J

jaunty [jôn′tē] *adj.* Possessing a spirited and active manner: Daniel took quick, *jaunty* steps. *syns.* lively, perky

journal [jûr′nəl] *n.* A timely log of events, business dealings, or ideas: The explorer kept a *journal* of her experiences.

jumble [jum′bəl] *v.* **jumbled, jumbling** To mix together in a confused mass: The toys were *jumbled* together in the toy box. *syns.* disorganize, muddle

K

kernel [kûr′nəl] *n.* A seed or grain: A half cup of corn *kernels* makes a quart of popcorn.

keyboard [kē′bôrd′] *n.* A systematic arrangement of keys by which a machine is operated: We have to learn where each letter is on the computer *keyboard.* ■

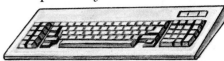

kilogram [kil′ə·gram′] *n.* A unit of weight in the metric system, equal to 2.2 pounds or 1,000 grams: My father weighs 80 *kilograms.*

a	add	o	odd	oi	oil
ā	ace	ō	open	ou	pout
â	care	ô	order	ng	ring
ä	palm	ŏŏ	took	th	thin
e	end	ōō	pool	th	this
ē	equal	u	up	zh	vision
i	it	û	burn		
ī	ice	yōō	fuse		

ə = { a in *above* e in *sicken* i in *possible*
o in *melon* u in *circus*

kilometer [kil'ə·mē'tər *or* ki·lom'-ə·tər] *n.* A measure of length in the metric system, equal to 5/8 of a mile or 1,000 meters: The school is 2 *kilometers* from my house.

kingdom [king'dəm] *n.* A territory or country ruled by a king or queen: He was the best horseman in the *kingdom.*

knowledge [nol'ij] *n.* What is known: Each day we gain new *knowledge* about the world. *syn.* information

L

lander [lan'dər] *n.* A vehicle used to explore planets: A *lander* was sent to Jupiter to learn more about that planet.

landing [lan'ding] *n.* A surface between staircases, or at the top of stairs: The boys were tired after they ran up to the fourth *landing.*

laser [lā'zər] *n.* A machine that makes a strong beam of light whose waves are parallel and equal in length: The doctor used a *laser* to do the delicate eye surgery.

launch [lônch] *v.* **launched, launching** To send into the air or onto the water: We *launched* the boat onto the lake. *syn.* start

lavender [lav'ən·dər] *adj.* A light purple color: Karen's sweater is pink and *lavender. syn.* violet

legal [lē'gəl] *adj.* Having to do with the law: My mother is a *legal* secretary.

lens [lenz] *n.* A piece of glass that helps people see: Mother was angry when I broke both of the *lenses* in my eyeglasses.

lever [lev'ər] *n.* A bar used to control, move, or turn something: The cockpit of the airplane has many buttons and *levers.*

loophole [loop'hōl'] *n.* A way to get out of an agreement or contract: The government lost money because of a *loophole* in the tax law.

M

magazine [mag'ə·zēn' *or* mag'ə·zēn'] *n.* A periodical that contains various articles and stories and is published at regular intervals: *Sports Illustrated* and *Time* are my two favorite *magazines.*

magnetic [mag·net'ik] *adj.* Able to be made into a magnet or drawn toward a magnet: The reactor has a *magnetic* core.

magnify [mag'nə·fī] *v.* To make something appear bigger than it is: We used binoculars to *magnify* the boats on the lake. *syn.* enlarge

major [mā'jər] *v.* **majored, majoring** To study a specific subject to the greatest extent: My mother *majored* in business in college. *syn.* specialize

marriage [mar′ij] *n.* The condition of being closely united: My parents have a happy *marriage.*

mass [mas] *n.* A form with no specific size or shape: The pile of clothes lay in a large *mass* upon the floor. *syn.* heap

masterpiece [mas′tər·pēs′] *n.* A work done with great skill: The painting was a *masterpiece. syn.* great achievement

mattress [mat′rəs] *n.* A strong fabric case, filled with foam rubber, cotton, or springs, used on a bed: Our bunk bed has two *mattresses.*

mechanical [mə·kan′i·kəl] *adj.* Produced or operated by a machine: The engineer looked at the *mechanical* drawing.

melody [mel′ə·dē] *n.* A succession of rhythmically arranged musical tones in a single voice: That song has a lovely *melody. syn.* tune

mentally retarded [men′tə·lē ri·tär′ did] *adj.* Slow in learning and developing: The *mentally retarded* man cannot read as well as I do.

meteorite [mē′tē·ə·rīt′] *n.* A small fragment of matter from space which reaches the earth without burning up: We saw a *meteorite* on display at the museum.

milliner [mil′ə·nər] *n.* A person who makes or sells hats: My grandmother used to own a *milliner's* shop.

minnow [min′ō] *n.* Small fish often used for bait: The stream is full of *minnows.*

mischievous [mis′chi·vəs] *adj.* Tending to be full of mischief; teasing: The *mischievous* boy pulled his sister's hair. *syn.* playful

miserable [miz′ər·ə·bəl] *adj.* Very unhappy: Katie felt *miserable* when she found that her boat had disappeared. *syns.* disturbed, wretched

mission [mish′ən] *n.* Job, goal: Alan took part in a space *mission. syns.* task, duty

mock [mok] *v.* **mocked, mocking** To imitate or copy: The boys were *mocking* the baby's way of talking. *syn.* mimic

monastery [mon′əs·ter′ē] *n.* A place at which religious men live as a group: The monk lived at the *monastery* for many years.

monitor [mon′ə·tər] *v.* To watch carefully; to pay attention to: The teacher will *monitor* her class during the exam. *syn.* observe

monk [mungk] *n.* A man who belongs to a religious group and lives with the group in their own community: The *monk* wore a long brown robe and sandals.

a	add	o	odd	oi	oil
ā	ace	ō	open	ou	pout
â	care	ô	order	ng	ring
ä	palm	ŏŏ	took	th	thin
e	end	ōō	pool	th	this
ē	equal	u	up	zh	vision
i	it	û	burn		
ī	ice	yōō	fuse		

ə = { a in *above*   e in *sicken*   i in *possible*
 o in *melon*   u in *circus* }

mood [mōōd] *n.* A feeling or state of mind: Cliff changes *moods* very quickly. *syn.* emotion

muffle [muf′əl] *v.* **muffled, muffling** Lessen: He *muffled* the ticking sound by wrapping the clock in a blanket. *syns.* quiet, deaden

mumble [mum′bəl] *v.* **mumbled, mumbling** To talk in a low, hard-to-understand voice: When he didn't know the answer, Neal *mumbled. syn.* mutter

N

narrative [nar′ə·tiv] *n.* An account or tale: She would rather read a *narrative* than an informational article. *syn.* story

nudge [nuj] *v.* **nudged, nudging** To touch gently, usually with the elbow: Maria *nudged* her brother when the light turned green. *syn.* push

nuisance [n(y)ōō′səns] *n.* Something that annoys or is bothersome: The banging shutter is a *nuisance. syns.* annoyance, bother

numb [num] *adj.* Without feeling: The loud noise made him *numb* with fear.

O

obedient [ō·bē′dē·ənt] *adj.* Following the rules or laws: The *obedient* dog did all of its tricks on command.

object [ob′jekt] *n.* Something that can be seen or handled: We found many interesting *objects* in Grandma's trunk. *syns.* matter, article

obvious [ob′vē·əs] *adj.* Clear: It is *obvious* that the ballplayer is a good athlete. *syn.* evident

odor [ō′dər] *n.* Smell: The *odor* of horses filled the stable. *syns.* scent, smell

opinion [ə·pin′yən] *n.* An idea a person thinks to be true but is not absolutely sure about: An *opinion* cannot be proved the way a fact can. *syn.* belief

orbit [ôr′bit] *n.* The route a planet, spaceship, or other heavenly body takes through space: The space capsule went into *orbit* around Saturn. *syn.* path ■

orchestra [ôr′kəs·trə] *n.* A large group of musicians playing many different instruments together: My brother plays the violin in the city *orchestra.*

outpost [out′pōst′] *n.* A settlement at a distance from the main population: There were many *outposts* when the West was being settled. *syn.* camp

overlook [ō′vər·look′] *v.* To omit; not notice: It is easy to *overlook* small things. *syn.* miss

---

P

---

package [pak′ij] *v.* To put into a box or a bundle: We have to *package* the bread before we sell it. *syn.* wrap

panic [pan′ik] *n.* Unexpected fear: She felt *panic* when the boat began to sink. *syn.* fright

patriot [pā′trē·ət] *n.* Someone who is very loyal to his or her country: George Washington was a great *patriot.*

peer [pir] *v.* To look carefully, to try to see better: He eagerly *peered* through the window. *syn.* peek

performance [pər·for′məns] *n.* A public presentation or exhibition before an audience: The bad play closed after three *performances. syn.* recital

permanent [pûr′mən·ənt] *adj.* Lasting; continuing in the same state: Father has a *permanent* job with the government. *syn.* enduring

persuade [pər·swād′] *v.* To influence someone to believe, do, or not do something: An advertisement will try to *persuade* you to buy a certain product. *syn.* convince

phenomenon [fi·nom′ə·non′] *n.* Something of interest that can be described or explained scientifically: Halley's comet is a *phenomenon* that occurs about every seventy-five years.

photo-cell [fō′tō·sel] *n.* A device used to change energy from the sun into electricity: We use the energy from *photo-cells* for all our electrical needs.

physical [fiz′i·kəl] *adj.* Having to do with size, shape, or the body: There was a *physical* change in the boy's face as he grew older.

piccolo [pik′ə·lō] *n.* A little flute whose sounds are one octave higher than a regular flute: The *piccolo* sounds like a bird singing. ■

piercing [pir′sing] *adj.* Sharp, penetrating: He gave the girl a *piercing* look. *syn.* intense

pike [pīk] *n.* A slender fish with a long snout and spiny fins that is found in fresh water: Dad caught a *pike* and we cooked it for dinner.

a	add	o	odd	oi	oil
ā	ace	ō	open	ou	pout
â	care	ô	order	ng	ring
ä	palm	o͝o	took	th	thin
e	end	o͞o	pool	th	this
ē	equal	u	up	zh	vision
i	it	û	burn		
ī	ice	yo͞o	fuse		

ə = { a in *above* e in *sicken* i in *possible*
      o in *melon* u in *circus* }

planetarium [plan′ə·târ′ē·əm] *n.* A building in which the stars and other celestial bodies are shown on a domed ceiling: We took a trip to the *planetarium* for our astronomy class.

plate¹ [plāt] *n.* In baseball, home base: Dave came up to the *plate.*

plate² [plāt] *n.* A flat dish used to hold food to eat: We each had a *plate* of spaghetti. *syn.* dish

pluck [pluk] *v.* **plucked, plucking** To pick or pull at; to quickly pull and release the strings of a musical instrument: She *plucked* the strings of the guitar.

plunge [plunj] *v.* **plunged, plunging** To push or force quickly: He *plunged* his hand into the water. *syn.* immerse

pneumonia [n(y)o͞o·mōn′yə] *n.* An inflammation of the lungs, caused by infection: The girl caught *pneumonia* after being out in the rain too long.

polio [pō′lē·ō] *n.* An infectious, serious virus most likely to occur in young people and be followed by paralysis: *Polio* is a very serious illness.

pollen [pol′ən] *n.* A fine powder found in flowers: I am allergic to the *pollen* from roses.

pollution [pə·lo͞o′shən] *n.* Impurities in the atmosphere and on the earth, usually from waste: *Pollution* in the air can be a health hazard. *syn.* contamination

potbellied stove [pot′bel·ēd stōv] *n.*

A freestanding cooking apparatus with a rounded or bulging body: The old house has a *potbellied stove* in the kitchen. ■

present [prez′ənt] *n.* The most recent time; current time: I will continue to sing with the chorus for the *present.*

procession [prə·sesh′ən] *n.* Many people or things arranged in a line that is advancing in a precise manner: The four bands marched in a *procession* down the street. *syn.* march

prodigy [prod′ə·jē] *n.* A young person with an extraordinary talent: The *prodigy* played a difficult piano piece perfectly. *syn.* genius

profit [prof′it] *n.* Any income over the cost of an investment: My parents made a *profit* when they sold our house. *syns.* gain, benefit

progress [prog′res] *n.* An advancing forward: The boys peddled faster to improve their *progress. syn.* headway

project [prə·jekt′] *v.* To make an image visible on a surface: Dad likes to *project* his picture slides on the screen.

projector [prə·jek'tər] *n.* A machine used to cause an image from a slide or movie to appear on a screen: There are many *projectors* in the audiovisual room. ■

promptly [prompt'lē] *adv.* At once: My sister came *promptly* when I called. *syn.* quickly

proportion [prə·pôr'shən] *n.* Size in relation to something: The *proportions* of the chair fit the room.

prose [prōz] *n.* Writing that is not poetry: We had to write *prose* for an assignment in creative writing class.

protest [prə·test'] *v.* **protested, protesting** To take exception to: Our team is *protesting* the umpire's call. *syn.* object

purpose [pûr'pəs] *n.* What a person wants to accomplish or plans to do: The author's *purpose* was to inform you about the world. *syn.* aim

---

Q

quality [kwol'ə·tē] *n.* The extent of worth or excellence of something: My stereo system is of high *quality*.

quarter [kwôr'tər] *n.* One-fourth of something: The picture takes up a *quarter* of the page. *syn.* one-fourth

quay [kē] *n. pl.* **quays** Wharfs or other structures where boats may dock: You may dock your boat at one of the *quays*.

quiver [kwiv'ər] *n.* A case to hold arrows: The archer keeps bows in a *quiver*. ■

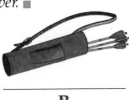

R

radiator [rā'dē·ā'tər] *n.* A series of pipes through which steam or hot water can run to provide heat: The *radiator* in my bedroom doesn't work.

rally [ral'ē] *v.* **rallied, rallying** To encourage a group to unite: After Jay *rallied* his team, they won the game. *syn.* cheer

ransack [ran'sak'] *v.* **ransacked, ransacking** To search thoroughly; to tear apart to find something: Jessie *ransacked* her room to find her other blue shoe.

a	add	o	odd	oi	oil
ā	ace	ō	open	ou	pout
â	care	ô	order	ng	ring
ä	palm	o͝o	took	th	thin
e	end	o͞o	pool	th	this
ē	equal	u	up	zh	vision
i	it	û	burn		
ī	ice	yo͞o	fuse		

ə = { a in *above*   e in *sicken*   i in *possible*
{ o in *melon*   u in *circus*

rapids [rap′idz] *n. pl.* A very rough part of a stream or river where the water moves very fast due to steep drops and curves: My parents rode the *rapids* in a raft.

ravine [rə·vēn′] *n.* A deep, lengthy, narrow area hollowed out of the earth by running water: We followed the river to a long *ravine*. *syn.* gorge ■

react [rē·akt′] *v.* To respond to someone or something: A comedian wants the audience to *react* with laughter. *syn.* answer

realistic fiction [rē′əl·is′tik fik′shən] *n.* A form of literature in which imaginary characters and events seem real and true-to-life: *The Midnight Fox* is an example of *realistic fiction*.

record [ri·kôrd′] *v.* **recorded, recording** To set down in writing for future reference: The secretary *recorded* the minutes of the meeting. *syn.* chronicle

recruit [ri·krōōt′] *v.* To draw new members for a group: The army will *recruit* many people this year.

reflector [ri·flek′tər] *n.* A telescope that gathers light through a curved mirror at the bottom of a tube: I got a *reflector* for my birthday.

refractor [ri·frak′tər] *n.* A telescope that gathers light though a glass lens at the front end of the tube: The observatory has a big *refractor* for viewing the stars.

reject [ri·jekt′] *v.* **rejected, rejecting** To not accept or use for the purpose intended: The committee *rejected* my ideas for the new monument. *syns.* refuse, dismiss

relationship [ri·lā′shən·ship′] *n.* The state of being connected or related: I have a close *relationship* with my best friend. *syn.* association

relief [ri·lēf′] *n.* Easing of something troublesome: It was a *relief* to finally get home. *syn.* comfort

reluctant [ri·luk′tənt] *adj.* **reluctantly** *adv.* Not willing: Benjamin entered the cave *reluctantly*. *syn.* unwilling

reputation [rep′yə·tā′shən] *n.* Renown or fame; the esteem with which a person or thing is held by others: Abraham Lincoln had the *reputation* of being an honest man.

require [ri·kwīr′] *v.* **required, requiring** To insist upon: Every student is *required* to have a pen and pencil for the test. *syn.* order

reserved [re·zûrvd′] *adj.* Set aside for a special purpose: The hotel room was *reserved* for our stay.

resound [ri·zound′] *v.* **resounded, resounding** To produce a loud sound: The boys' voices made a *resounding* noise in the hallway.

reserved [ri·zûrvd′] *adj.* Set aside for a special purpose: The hotel room was *reserved* for our stay.

resplendent [ri·splen′dənt] *adj.* Gorgeous: We admired the green *resplendent* trees in the countryside. *syn.* splendid

response [ri·spons′] *n.* An answer or reply: I have two more *responses* to my party invitations. *syns.* answer, reaction

rheumatism [rōō′mə·tiz′əm] *n.* An inflammation of muscles or joints that causes pain and stiffness: My grandmother suffers from *rheumatism.*

rotate [rō′tāt′] *v.* To revolve or move around a center: The earth *rotates* once every 24 hours. *syns.* turn, spin

rouse [rouz] *v.* **roused, rousing** To excite; awaken: It is hard to *rouse* my sister in the morning.

routine [rōō·tēn′] *n.* A set way of doing something: My dad has a *routine* for cleaning the house. *syn.* order

ruffled [ruf′əld] *adj.* Having a decorative trimming that has been drawn into folds: The salesperson said the *ruffled* curtains were the most popular.

rustling [rus′ling] *n.* The quick, short sounds of things moving together: We made a *rustling* in the woods as we stepped on the leaves.

S

sample [sam′pəl] *n.* A small piece that shows what a whole thing is like: The teacher showed us questions that were *samples* of tomorrow's test. *syn.* example

satchel [sach′əl] *n.* A case or knapsack: Maria keeps her books in a small *satchel. syn.* bag ■

schedule [skej′ōōl] *n.* List of the times when certain things are to take place: *Schedules* showing the times for races were posted on the bulletin board. *syn.* timetable

science fiction [sī′əns fik′shən] *n.* A contrived, often way-out, adventure tale in which the plot is centered around either real or imaginary scientific things: Ray Bradbury is a writer of *science fiction.*

scorched [skôrcht] *adj.* Burned slightly on the surface: Dwight couldn't eat the *scorched* toast. *syn.* singed

a	add	o	odd	oi	oil
ā	ace	ō	open	ou	pout
â	care	ô	order	ng	ring
ä	palm	ŏŏ	took	th	thin
e	end	ōō	pool	th	this
ē	equal	u	up	zh	vision
i	it	û	burn		
ī	ice	yōō	fuse		

ə = { a in *above*   e in *sicken*   i in *possible*
 o in *melon*   u in *circus* }

script [skript] *n.* A written copy of a play or movie: It took the actress two weeks to learn the whole *script.*

seal [sēl] *v.* **sealed, sealing** To make secure or close: The winner's name was *sealed* in an envelope. *syn.* fasten

seamstress [sēm'stris] *n.* A woman who is trained to sew: The *seamstress* made a beautiful shirt for me.

securely [si·kyoor'lē] *adv.* Fastened or fixed firmly: Tom held his bookbag *securely* during the bumpy ride. *syn.* tightly

sensation [sen·sā'shən] *n.* The stimulation of any of the five senses: The burning *sensation* in my mouth told me the food was too hot. *syns.* feeling, impression

sensible [sen'sə·bəl] *adj.* Displaying or having good judgment: My mother is a *sensible* woman. *syn.* rational, reasonable

sensitive [sen'sə·tiv] *adj.* Quick to react to what is happening: My brother is a *sensitive* baby and cries often. *syns.* touchy, susceptible

sentry [sen'trē] *n.* A soldier standing guard to look out for danger: The *sentries* stood outside the fort all night. *syns.* guard, watchman ■

sequence [sē'kwəns] *n.* The order in which one thing comes after another: The months of the year follow a certain *sequence. syn.* series

sewer [soo'ər] *n.* A pipe to carry off dirty water and waste. It is usually found underground: The *sewer* for our house is brand new. *syns.* canal, drain

sham [sham] *n.* A decorative fabric made to look like an article of linen and used in place of or over it: Mother placed *shams* over the pillows to protect the original fabric. *syn.* pillow case

sheltered workshop [shel'tərd wûrk'shop'] *n.* A place where some handicapped people are taught to do special jobs: My mother works at a *sheltered workshop* on the weekends.

shift [shift] *v.* **shifted, shifting** To adjust position from one place to another: Barbara *shifted* the food to the other side of her plate. *syn.* move

shrill [shril] *adj.* High in sound: The telephone has a *shrill* ring.

shudder [shud'ər] *v.* To shake: I *shudder* when I hear the squeal of brakes. *syn.* vibrate

shuttle [shut'(ə)l] *n.* A car or ship that goes back and forth on a regular basis: The airplane *shuttle* goes between Boston and New York.

silicon [sil'ə·kən] *n.* A carbon-related element with many uses:

Silicon is used to make computer chips.

sixteen [siks'tēn'] *n., adj.* One more than fifteen: Her birthday cake had *sixteen* candles on it.

slacken [slak'ən] *v.* To let up; lessen: When Jim let go, the rope began to *slacken. syn.* loosen

slate [slāt] *n.* A rock that can be split easily into thin layers; a piece of this type of rock used in roofing or chalkboards: The teacher wrote on the *slate* with chalk.

sleek [slēk] *adj.* **sleekly** *adv.* Smooth: The horse ran *sleekly* across the field. *syn.* elegant

slide trombone [slīd trom·bōn'] *n.* A brass instrument in which a slide is moved to change the tone: Willie plays the *slide trombone* in the school band. ■

slot [slot] *n.* A thin opening: He put a letter through the mail *slot* in the door. *syn.* opening

smother [smuth'ər] *v.* To muffle: I tried to *smother* the sounds of my cough, but I couldn't.

smuggle [smug'əl] *v.* To secretly take items or people over a border, or to and from somewhere: He *smuggled* a great deal of jewelry past the security guard.

sneer [snir] *v.* **sneered, sneering** To display contempt or scorn by raising the upper lip: The man *sneered* at the burglar.

social worker [sō'·shəl wûr'kər] *n.* A person who works to improve conditions in the community: The *social worker* helped the orphans find new homes.

solder [sod'ər] *v.* **soldered, soldering** To join or mend with a melted metal or alloy: John is *soldering* these pipes. *syns.* connect, attach

sparkling [spär'kling] *adj.* Bubbly: The *sparkling* soda quenched my thirst. *syns.* effervescent, bubbly

species [spē'sēz] *n.* A group of similar living things: You and I are members of the human *species. syn.* kind

spectacle [spek'tə·kəl] *n.* A showy and impressive public display: The half-time show is a real *spectacle. syn.* exhibition

splendid [splen'did] *adj.* Great: The fireworks were *splendid* this year. *syns.* fantastic, terrific

sputter [sput'ər] *v.* **sputtered, sputtering** To say in a confused or angry way: He was so angry he just stood there and *sputtered.*

a	add	o	odd	oi	oil
ā	ace	ō	open	ou	pout
â	care	ô	order	ng	ring
ä	palm	o͝o	took	th	thin
e	end	o͞o	pool	th	this
ē	equal	u	up	zh	vision
i	it	û	burn		
ī	ice	yo͞o	fuse		

ə = { a in *above* e in *sicken* i in *possible*
{ o in *melon* u in *circus*

SQ3R [es′kyoo′thre′är′] *n.* A five-step study plan that helps students organize their study time and remember more of what they study: The steps in *SQ3R* are survey, question, read, recite, and review.

stalk [stôk] *n.* The main stem of a plant, or a connecting or supporting part: The *stalk* of the flower broke when the baseball landed in the garden. ■

stallion [stal′yən] *n.* A male horse that can be bred: A *stallion* is running gracefully in the field.

starched [stärcht] *adj.* Stiffened by the use of starch: My father likes the collars on his shirts *starched*.

startle [stär′təl] *v.* **startled, startling** To surprise or frighten suddenly: That loud noise *startled* me.

steeple [ste′pəl] *n.* A tall structure coming to a point at the top of a church tower: My kite was stuck on the *steeple*. *syn.* spire ■

stilt [stilt] *n.* One of two long, thin poles that are used for walking some distance above the ground: The clown at the circus walked on *stilts*.

stocking [stok′ing] *n.* A tight-fitting woven or knitted covering for the legs and feet: Andrea wore red *stockings* today.

stoop¹ [stoop] *n.* A porch or platform at the entrance to a house: We sat on the *stoop* in the evening and played checkers. *syn.* stairway

stoop² [stoop] *v.* To bend over: We had to *stoop* to get under the fence. *syn.* squat

stride [strīd] *n.* An extended step while walking: The lion moves fast with its long *strides*.

stub [stub] *n.* The small piece that remains after something is removed or used up: All that is left in my raffle book are the ticket *stubs*.

stubble [stub′əl] *n.* The low stalks of a crop that are left after harvesting: The wheat field was full of *stubble* after the farmer finished the harvest.

subject [sub′jikt] *n.* The person or thing written about: The writer's favorite *subjects* are tigers and lions. *syn.* topic

submit [səb·mit′] *v.* **submitted, submitting** To present for judging, testing, or approval: Connie hoped the article she *submitted* would be accepted for the school paper. *syn.* present

substance [sub′stəns] *n.* The matter of which a thing is made or consists; a definite portion or matter:

Unknown *substances* were found mixed in with the food. *syn.* material

subtopic [sub'top·ik] *n.* A subject that is second in importance to the main topic being considered, discussed, studied, or written about: An outline tells the *subtopics* in an informational article.

succession [sək·sesh'ən] *n.* A number of things or persons that follow one after another: A *succession* of teenagers came to apply for the job. *syn.* line

suitor [so͞o'tər] *n.* A man who courts or seeks to marry a woman: My older sister has a new *suitor. syn.* beau

sundial [sun'dī·əl] *n.* An outdoor instrument that shows the time of day by means of a shadow cast by a pointer onto a horizontal surface: The *sundial* at the zoo helped us keep track of the time.

supply [sə·plī'] *v.* **supplied, supplying** To provide something that is needed: The carpenter *supplied* us with all the tools for the job. *syn.* furnish

surface [sûr'fis] *n.* The exterior part of an object: The *surfaces* of the outside of our house are wood and brick. *syn.* face

suspicious [sə·spish'əs] *adj.* Doubtful; unbelieving: The student's excuse seemed *suspicious.*

symbol [sim'bəl] *n.* Something that stands for another thing: This

feather is a *symbol* of courage. *syn.* sign

symphony [sim'fə·nē] *n.* A piece of music, usually with four movements, written for a symphony orchestra: The last *symphony* by Beethoven is my favorite.

T

tapestry [tap'is·trē] *n.* A heavy cloth woven with designs and pictures, usually displayed on a wall: We saw a beautiful old *tapestry* at the castle. ■

technique [tek·nēk'] *n.* The manner in which something is done: The chef has a special *technique* for slicing vegetables. *syn.* method

tend [tend] *v.* To favor a view; to lean toward: I *tend* to wear a lot of blue.

a	add	o	odd	oi	oil
ā	ace	ō	open	ou	pout
â	care	ô	order	ng	ring
ä	palm	o͝o	took	th	thin
e	end	o͞o	pool	th	this
ē	equal	u	up	zh	vision
i	it	û	burn		
ī	ice	yo͞o	fuse		

ə = { a in *above*, e in *sicken*, i in *possible*, o in *melon*, u in *circus* }

terminal [tûr′mə·nəl] *n.* A device used to enter and receive information from a computer: Kathy's office has eight computer *terminals.*

texture [teks′chər] *n.* The order of threads on a woven fabric: John's new jacket has an interesting *texture.*

thatch [thach] *n.* A covering of straw or other material used on a roof; something that resembles this type of covering: The spaceman had a blond *thatch* of hair on his head.

thicket [thik′it] *n.* A dense growth of bushes or trees: We lost our baseball in the *thicket.*

tilt [tilt] *v.* **tilted, tilting** To lean: The tower was *tilted* even further after the storm. *syns.* slant, incline

topic [top′ik] *n.* Something that is being considered, discussed, studied, or written about: The *topic* of my article is polar bears. *syn.* subject

topple [top′əl] *v.* **toppled, toppling** To tip over or fall forward: The baby *toppled* the building blocks.

transfer [trans′fər] *v.* To move from one place to another: My father was *transferred* from Chicago to Minneapolis. *syn.* move

translate [trans·lāt′] *v.* **translated, translating** To explain the meaning of something in another language: My mother *translated* the menu in the Mexican restaurant for me. *syn.* interpret

treacherous [trech′ər·əs] *adj.* Dangerous: Mountain climbing is a *treacherous* sport.

tricorne [trī′kôrn] *adj.* Having three corners: The children in the play wore *tricorne* hats.

tripod [trī′pod′] *n.* A three-legged stand for a telescope or camera: The TV camera sat on a *tripod.* *syn.* stool ■

triumphant [trī·um′fənt] *adj.* Victorious: We attended the parade for the *triumphant* war heroes. *syn.* successful

tympanist [tim′pə·nist] *n.* A musician who plays a set of kettle drums in an orchestra: My cousin is a *tympanist* in the city-wide orchestra.

U

unconscious [un·kon′shəs] *adj.* Unable to think or feel: My brother was hit on the head and became *unconscious.*

upward [up′wərd] *adv.* Toward a higher place or point: The airplane flew *upward* after takeoff.

urgent [ûr′jənt] *adj.* Requiring prompt attention: The patient is in *urgent* need of blood. *syns.* pressing, insistent

V

variety [və·rī'ə·tē] *n.* Different things: There are a *variety* of flowers in this vase. *syn.* assortment

varnish [vär'nish] *n.* A hard covering for a surface: We covered our new table with *varnish*.

venture [ven'chər] *v.* **ventured, venturing** To expose to risk: The girl *ventured* into the building alone. *syn.* hazard

vibration [vī·brā'shən] *n.* A series of rapid motions from side to side: Rona felt the *vibration* of the motor while sitting in the car. *syn.* shaking

victory [vik'tər·ē] *n.* A triumph: The win was a great *victory* for our team. *syn.* success

viewpoint [vyōō'point'] *n.* A position from which a person thinks about something: The author's *viewpoint* is that solar energy is useful. *syn.* attitude

viol [vī'əl] *n.* A six-stringed instrument from the 16th and 17th centuries that was played with a bow: The *viol* is an ancestor of the violin. ■

visualize [vizh'ōō·əl·īz'] *v.* To see in the mind: The children could *visualize* the scene as it was described to them. *syn.* picture

volley [vol'ē] *n.* A burst of many things shot off at the same time: The students asked the teacher a *volley* of questions.

vow [vou] *n.* A declaration or promise: The couple exchanged their marriage *vows*. *syn.* pledge

W

warehouse [wâr'hous'] *n.* A building in which goods are stored: The department store keeps its extra merchandise in a large *warehouse*.

waste [wāst] *n.* Something that can't be used and will be disposed of: A nuclear plant produces many *wastes*. *syn.* garbage

whittle [(h)wit'(ə)l] *v.* To chip away at wood with a knife: Grandpa likes to *whittle* toys out of wood.

whopping [(h)wop'ing] *adj.* Very large: The winner of the fishing contest had reeled in a *whopping* trout. *syn.* huge

wince [wins] *v.* **winced, wincing** To shrink back, as from pain: The boy *winced* when he fell and cut his knee. *syn.* flinch

Z

zwieback [zwī'bak' *or* zwē'bäk'] *n.* A type of bread or biscuit that is baked in a loaf and then sliced and toasted until crisp: My baby brother likes to eat *zwieback*.

Photographs

Key: (1) - Left; (r) - Right; (c) - Center; (t) - Top; (b) - Bottom.

Illustrators